MW00608983

# 365 DAYS OF PRACTICE

## by Rick Margitza

Graphic Design - Matt Heister
Artwork - Silvia Kleyff
Cover Design - Attila Nagy & Hetty Kate

# Table of Contents

Rick Margitza—photo by Carl Strømer

# Standing On the Shoulders of Giants

To all the people in my life who been my mentors, teachers, guides, supporters and inspirations. Starting with my parents, grandparents and the rest of my wildly talented family. Too many names to name, but continuing with my first piano teacher in Dearborn, Michigan through my junior high and high school band directors, then on to my private saxophone teachers in Detroit, college professors at Wayne State University, Berklee College of Music, University of Miami and Loyola in New Orleans, all my colleagues during our student days in every city along the way, jamming, discussing, living and breathing music together, all the people who trusted me enough to hire me and let me share the bandstand with them, and all the people who have played in my various bands over the years. Then of course all the masters whose recordings and live concerts changed and continue to change my life every time I listen to them. And lastly to the younger generation of musicians who continue to keep this music alive. This book is humbly dedicated to you.

Special thanks for Jeff Ellwood who painstakingly entered each day's example and its description into Finale, so when the year was finished, I had a template to work from. He saved me an enormous amount of time and for that I'm forever grateful. Besides being a great musician, he is also a dear friend.

# About This Book

## GENESIS

The seed for this project was planted when I watched a YouTube video on December 31st, 2019. I don't remember the specific title or author, but it was done by a Buddhist teacher who talked about 1. Setting personal goals and 2. The importance of following through/finishing them. I had been aware of and followed several people who were posting a 100 days of practice and had thought of doing something like that but the notion never came to fruition. After that, all I remember was waking up on New Years day 2020 and in a flash, the idea of posting an idea a day for a year came to me. I had no idea of what form the project would take, which in a way made it seem more manageable. So, I started with post #1 and had no intention of turning the material into this current book or awareness of the upcoming Covid pandemic that would hit the world in March 2020. In the course of the next several months, numerous people who had been following my posts suggested that this material would make a great book and also said that they looked forward to my daily postings because it took their minds off of being locked down if only for a little while.

## STRUCTURE/FORMAT

As mentioned above, the ideas/examples don't follow any specific/logical order. I just went into my practice notebook, found an idea that I thought was interesting and posted it with a description that illustrated the concept(s) associated with it. There are many however, who's main concept was explored/examined/expanded over the course of several days. Also, there are numerous ideas that appear early in the book, for example: open triads or half whole diminished shapes, who's concepts re-appear later on in the work.

## BACKING TRACKS

I've recorded all the examples and created backing tracks in my home studio. Most of them repeat three times. The first with me playing, the second without me and the third with me back in. Several of them just repeat and fade. In the course of creating some of these tracks, some of the original posts turned into mini compositions or small forms. This happened organically. If an idea felt like it wanted to be expanded, I let it happen. Also, in the process of recording these tracks, some of the keys and content were changed from the original posts. Finally, since all of this material was conceived on the Bb tenor saxophone, the problem of creating a version of this book for concert instruments presented a problem. It would have been impossible to transpose everything in the book and then re-record all the examples because of range issues on the horn. So, the best compromise was to transpose all the recorded material using Logic. The result is that the saxophone sounds a bit strange because the audio file was moved up a whole step. Since this was done for the purpose of making this book available to guitarists, pianists, flutists etc…I assume/hope that the somewhat odd sounding saxophone won't be that big of an issue.

## PRACTICE METHOD

I added an introductory chapter that explains my method of practicing which yielded most of the material in this book. It serves as a point of reference as there are numerous daily posts that mention the practice routine. Early in the project, I briefly explained how it works, but this in depth look at what it is and how is works will greatly enhance the understanding of how I came up with this stuff and how you can use it to develop your own ideas.

# Practice Method

This method of practice is something I learned from the great Gary Campbell when I studied with him at the University of Miami in 1983. It is referred to throughout this book as "the routine" and a thorough understanding of how it works will greatly enhance not only your experience of the material presented here, but will enrich and inform your own musical explorations. There are two main components of this method. The first being the Practice Sequence/Grid or Matrix which deals with directional combinations and second, the Intervallic Families, which is based on the division of the octave. The Practice Sequence is designed to make sure that you work through whatever material you are practicing in all directional combinations. Below, you are given the basic layout. **The four directions are: 1. up 2. down 3. up-down and 4. down-up. And the two global directions are: A. Ascending and B. Descending. When we combine these elements, we end up with: 1A through 4B.** This is a very effective way to work on basic material. The example given here illustrates how to implement this technique while working on diatonic 3rds. As you can see, 1A has the 3rds going up as you ascend the scale and 1B has the 3rds going up as you descend. 2A has the 3rds going down as you ascend and then 2B has them going down as you descend. 3A through 4B follow the same scheme except the 3rds are now alternating directions. The next step is to substitute diatonic 4ths for 3rds and then 5ths, 6ths, 7ths etc…This should be done of course, in all keys. The next step is to do the same thing…3rds through 7ths in all directional combinations but working through melodic minor scales. So, diatonic 3rds in C major might not be a challenge but 6ths in Ab melodic minor might take a little more time. You can then pick any other type of scale and work it through this matrix. The goal here is to have a rock solid foundation and control of these basic elements in all keys…

## DIATONIC INTERVALS

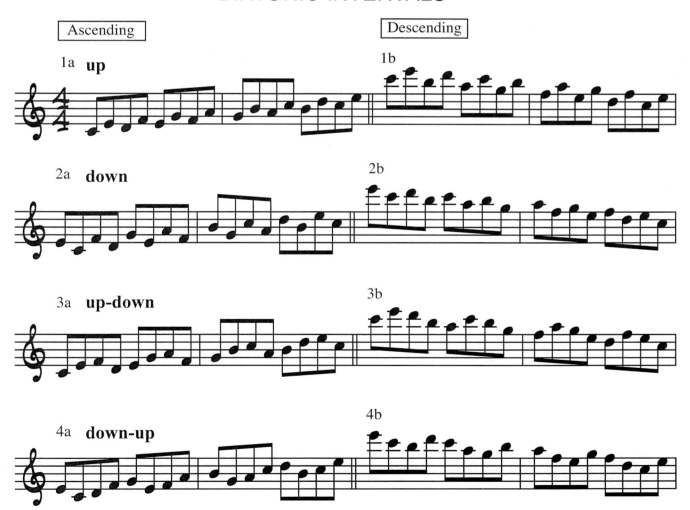

iv

The next step after diatonic intervals is diatonic triads and then diatonic 7th chords. These next steps follow the exact same scheme, i.e., 1A-4B but instead of diatonic intervals, we are substituting diatonic triads and then diatonic 7th chords. Once again, nothing creative here, just basic but necessary work to develop fluidity and control. Now, on to the Intervallic Families.

# DIATONIC TRIADS

# DIATONIC 7th CHORDS

3a        3b

4a        4b

The Intervallic Families concept is based on the division of the octave, not unlike a lot of the material in *The Thesaurus of Scales and Melodic Patterns* by Nicolas Slonimsky. Each division of the octave yields a specific intervallic family and each family represents a specific relationship. Below, you can see the first division divides the octave into 12 parts and gives us the chromatic family. The second one division is one of whole steps which gives us the whole tone family. Note that in order to include all 12 tones, there are two groups of whole tones, or two whole tone families. The next two groups are minor 3rds-the diminished family and major 3rds-the augmented family. When we say diminished and augmented family we are not talking about diminished or augmented scales or chords, but just the groups of minor or major thirds and the sounds/relationships they represent. The next group of intervals is 4ths. This group doesn't divide the octave but is the next type of interval. I call this the cyclic group. The last two groups are tri-tones and 5ths. After that, every other type of interval is related to one of the previous groups through inversion: min 6ths=maj 3rds, maj 6ths=min 3rds, min 7ths=whole steps and maj 7ths=half steps. These groups/families should be memorized, as visualization while practicing is an important component of this type of work. Another indispensable aspect of this method is having the ability to hear what these groups sounds like. Think of developing a catalog of these sounds in your mind's ear. The next step is where things become more interesting and challenging. We will now look at how to combine the directional combinations with the intervallic families.

## INTERVALLIC FAMILIES

INTERVAL                                             RELATIONSHIP

Half Step                                             Chromatic

Whole Step                                          Whole Tone

1.                                 2.

**Minor Third**

Diminished

**Major Third**

Augmented

**Fourths**

Cyclic

**Tri-Tone**

Tri-Tone

**Fifths**

Cyclic

The first step in combining the combinations and families is working with scales. The example shown here is one octave major scales in half steps. As you can see, the directional combinations stay the same (1a-4b). What changes is that instead of ascending or descending diatonically, we are now moving up or down in half steps, i.e., the first intervallic family. Step two is major scales in whole steps, i.e., the second intervallic family. When we work the material in whole steps, we have to do it twice because there are two groups of whole steps.

The next steps would then be minor 3rds through 5ths. In total, there are 18 intervallic combinations to practice, (half steps through fifths) meaning that after going through all these steps, you will have worked major scales in every combination of direction and intervallic group. Admittedly, it is a little tedious at first, but I have found that as the interval becomes wider, the sounds become more interesting. Also, any type of scale can be plugged into the routine. Some are redundant, for example whole tone scales in whole steps, or diminished scales in minor thirds. After working scales through the routine, it is time to move on to triads.

# SCALES

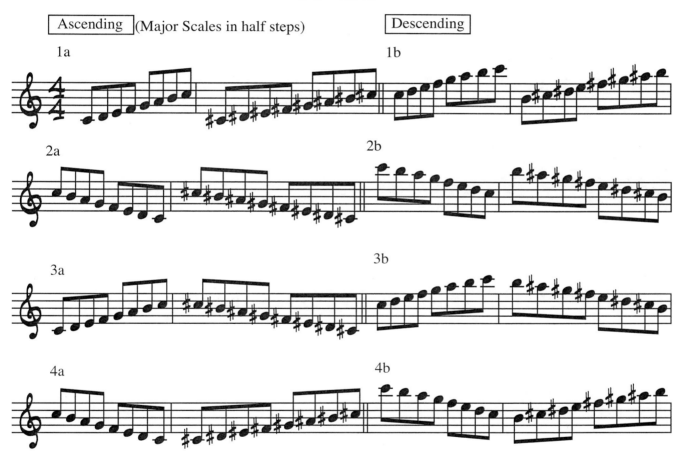

viii

Triads are the bedrock foundation for an enormous amount of the material that follows, so slow, dedicated and concentrated work needs to be devoted to working on them. When I say triads, I'm talking about major and minor in their three inversions. So, there are six in total that have to be mastered. The method described in the previous description is exactly the same but instead of working major scales through the routine, we now plug in and work triads. In the example below, the subject to work through the routine is a major triad in second inversion. This assumes that we've already worked major triads in root position and first inversion. We can also see that the example is moving in whole steps, so this also assumes that we've already done them in half steps. The next step would then be this same triad but with the other group of whole steps, then on to minor 3rds through 5ths. After working the six triads types, its time to move onto 7th chords.

## TRIADS

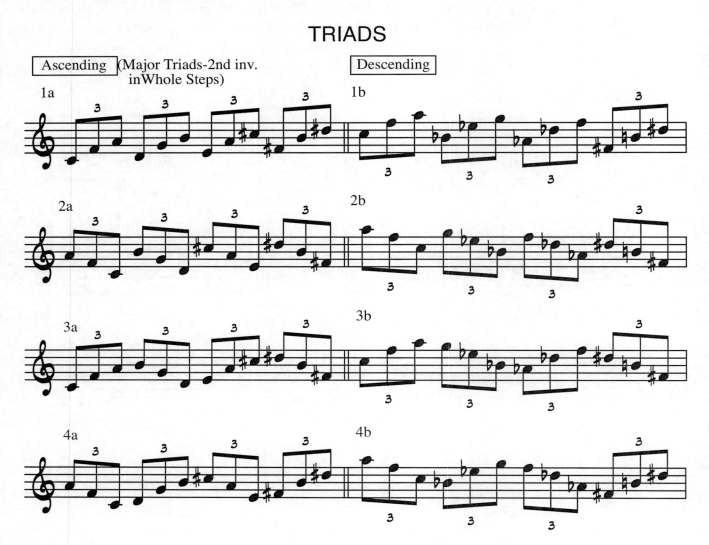

Once again, the method stays exactly the same. The only thing that changes is the subject, i.e, the material that we are putting through the routine. We are now at the point where the subject is a 7th chord. The example here is a major 7th chord in half steps. I think by now, you get the drill, you would then work the same major 7th chord in the remaining 17 combinations. You could/should take any/every chord type: minor 7th, dominant 7th, major 7th (#5) etc…as well as their inversions and work them through this process. The next step is to take 7th chords and change their note order. You will have already done some of this when practicing their inversions, but this step unlocks some other very cool shapes and sounds.

# 7th CHORDS

Ascending | (Major 7ths in half steps)          Descending

There are 24 ways to combine 4 notes. Here we are taking a minor 7th chord and changing the note order to 1537, which means that the down version is 7351. This example is already at step 7 (first group of major 3rds). You can see that by taking any 7th chord and any of the 24 possible shapes and then working it through the routine will result is a tremendous amount of melodic material. Of course, everything I laid out up to this point represents an extreme amount of work. I strongly suggest keeping a practice journal/notebook with you as you work through all this stuff. It is very important to work slowly and progressively. For example when working with the diatonic intervals, (the first step in all of this stuff) there is no rule or deadline. Its okay to just practice a couple of keys a day. It's much better and will pay off in the long run if you can control two keys a day instead of going through six but with sloppy results. Not to get too philosophical, but it's definitely about the journey and not the destination.

## 7th CHORDS-CHANGING NOTE ORDER

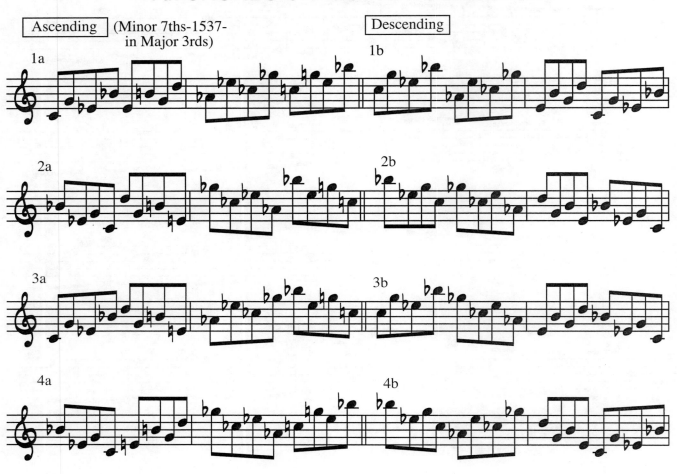

At this point, if I am presenting this method at a master class, a couple of questions usually pop up…"why?" and/or "how do you use this stuff?" Obviously, this way of practicing is very mechanical and pattern based and doesn't seem to be very musical. This is true, but it is just a means to and end. What we're trying to do here is develop a personal language and vocabulary. After all, isn't that why we are drawn to this music? Because it allows us to express our individuality? I've found that this method has opened doors for me to do exactly that. You might not, or it might lead you to find another avenue. Before any of us start to develop something personal there has to be an intense study of what's come before us. There is a lot of literature talking about all the styles of jazz that have led us to this moment, so I'm not going to take the time to do that here. Suffice to say that we stand on the shoulders of giants and I cannot stress enough that a thorough study of their music through listening, transcribing and playing along with recordings is a completely necessary step.

In my playing, I've worked on combining things that I've come up using the practice method with material that I've taken from the traditional language that as I said, must be absorbed before moving on. Think of John Coltrane's progression from the Prestige through Impulse recordings. A clear line can be heard from his absorption of the be-bop/hard-bop language to what eventually became his personal voice. In this book, there are examples that range from basic language to advanced superimposition of harmony. I started developing a more complex harmonic language by using a technique that I call transforming be-bop. Here is an example of how I started coming up with material that eventually found its way into my playing in a way that is organic and has become a big part of my personal sound.

The way I started transforming be-bop was to take a very basic idea, i.e., the 2-5 in C and then find something before it to use as an approach. In this example, I approach the Dm7 in major 3rds from below while changing directions (3a). I show the chords below because they are being superimposed. The chord in the measure before can be anything. Whatever the "wrong notes" are become justified when we hit the Dm7 and the symmetry behind the idea alleviates any confusion the listener might have felt up to that point. Mind you, the approach chords can be anything…half steps from above, whole steps from below etc… In the second example, instead of messing with the 2 chord, I extend the resolution by superimposing descending major 7ths in major 3rds. This is a more familiar sound because of the Giant Steps three tonic system. So there you have it, a basic explanation of how I use things that I've discovered as a result of practicing with the method outlined above.

# TRANSFORMING BE-BOP

This hopefully provides a contextual framework for how I came up with a lot of the material in this book and how to take ideas from the book and implement them in your own improvisations. I highly recommend creating your own backing tracks or using different play-along tracks…IrealPro, Aebersold etc…and then forcing yourself to "plug in" things that you are working on. They will feel forced at first but they will eventually become part of your personal language and will find their way into your playing organically. Another very useful exercise is writing etudes/solos over tunes or isolated chord progressions. This allows you to make choices that you normally would not be able to during a live playing situation. Once again, by doing this, these ideas become part of how you hear and intuit things. What follows is an etude written over the chords of All The Things You Are that uses specific ideas in the book. The ideas that are not referenced with an idea number are things that came out as a result of using my ear to naturally complete or continue an idea.

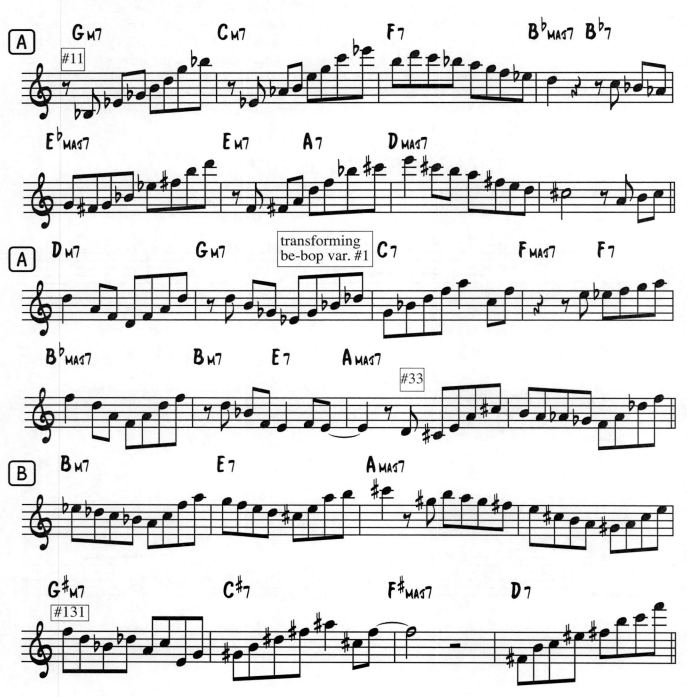

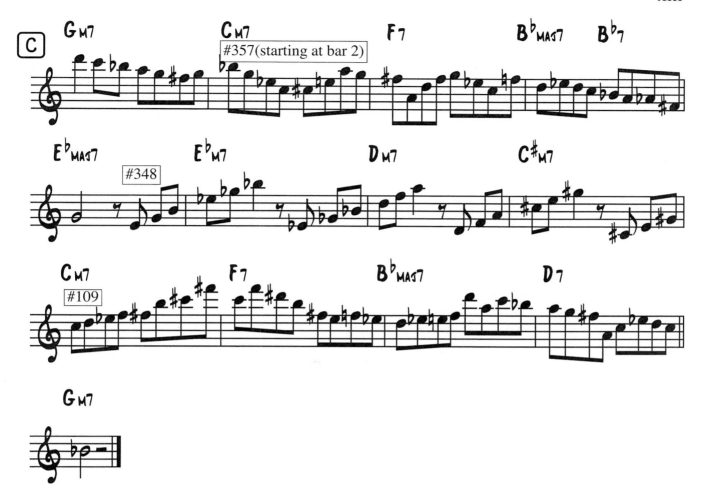

# 365 Days

#1 This is a shape that is extracted from the D, F#, Bb augmented scale which works over a minor 9th chord if you start the idea on the 6th, or a minor major 7th chord when you start on the b5.

(tacet last x)

#2 Today's example takes the shape from yesterday and places it in two different 2-5-1 situations.

(tacet last x)

#3 Here is more material based on #1. As you can see, I've dissected it into three smaller units (1, 2 and 3 with 4 being the original shape) Each example moves either up or down in different intervallic relationships as per the routine outlined in the chapter on the practice method.

#4 Back to basics. The first line is pretty obvious…just 2-5-1 guide tones but relatively challenging when you move them up and down through all the intervallic families. The next exercise in 3/4 is great for developing flexibility because of the wide leaps. Depending on your instrument and key, you will have to adjust the octave/range. Notice that the guide tones above the bass notes change directions as per the directional combination section in the practice method chapter.

#5 Today is diminished day. One of the challenges of using this scale is trying to not have it sound like a pattern. So, in this example, I've extracted three different shapes and strung them together in different orders and directions. I suggest working each shape separately through the routine.

#6 Nothing terribly exciting, just a melodic minor exercise that helps with technique and fluidity within each key. The next few days will deal with more involved exercises and uses of the melodic minor.

#7 Here's a longish C melodic minor idea that can be broken down into smaller components. This could be used over any of the modes but the three I have listed are the strongest for this example. In the case of the two dominant chords, the resolution to the 5th of the tonic minor or major is implied. I suggest you come up with your own resolution ideas.

#8 Here are three of the infinite number of possible resolutions of yesterday's idea. The ideas are obviously in different keys, but they all start on the 5th.

#9 Today's example is a diatonic line that moves up in major thirds. At first we hear it over the tonic keys. The second example takes the same material but places it in a 2-5-1 situation. Obviously there a lot of avoid tones, but the tension they create is resolved when we reach our destination.

#10 This one uses the same principle as #9. This time in 3/4 and the line goes down instead of up. The bracketed notes belong to both keys and serve as a link between the two.

#11 This example is based on a structure that is built by using the common tones between minor triads that are related by major thirds. The minor third of F#m becomes the fifth of Dm etc…As in the two previous examples, there are several avoid-tones which the ear justifies by the parallel structure and resolution/target.

#12 Here we use C as a common/pivot tone, making the 7th of Dm7 the 3rd of an Ab triad which resolves down to the G triad on beats 3 and 4.

#13 Here we are thinking down in whole steps while alternating between minor 7th and major 7th chords. I've found this way of thinking to be helpful when playing over Giant Steps. (If you listen to the recording, in the first four bars, Paul Chambers is playing a descending whole tone scale.)

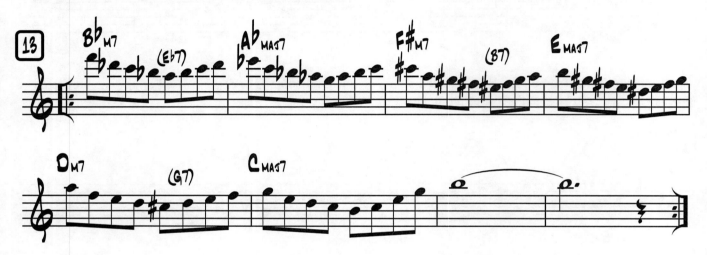

#14 This one uses the same principal as #13, here over the first four bars of Giant Steps.

#15 Today's example is another one based on major triads that are linked by common tones. Here, the lead up to the tonic is pretty self-explanatory. The twist/surprise happens when we get to the descending resolution.

#16 This is an extended version of the resolution from yesterday's post. Good for working on flexibility (the major 7th jumps) and useful in the context of cadenzas or rubato playing.

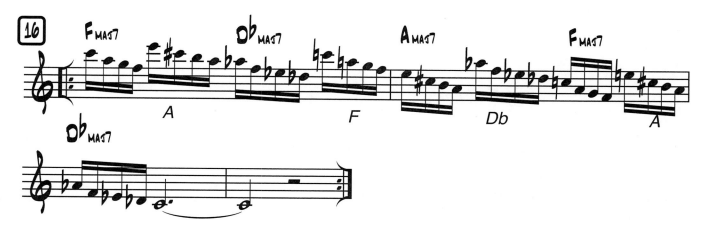

#17 Today's example is a 2-5-1 in E major that uses the tri-tone sub over the V chord. Here, I'm not thinking about the F7…just F#m7-Cm7-Emaj7.

(tacet last x)

#18 Here's a 2-5 in Eb. Over the Fm7, I'm using the C, E, Ab augmented scale which I've spread out into 5ths. Over the Bb7alt, I'm thinking Bm6, and over the Ebmaj7, I'm using the Eb, B, G augmented scale which I'm thinking about as Gm, Bm, Ebm with the last Gm being the link to Eb major.

#19 The first measure of this example is a chromatic shape that targets the C in bar two. That C functions as a pivot note and turns the Ab7 into a D7 (tri-tone sub.) Remember that any of these components can be isolated and practiced separately through the routine.

(tacet last x)

#20 Here's a line that you can use over either a ii-V7alt or just a V7alt. A lot of chromatics here, but the target is the b13 on beat three of measure two. I always think about/hear the b13 as the fifth of the melodic minor I am using. (When I see A7alt, I am thinking and hearing Bb minor) Since this example resolves to the fifth of the tonic, it could be used in either a major or minor key.

#21 Here's a five-note shape that works over F#7(#9) as well as A, C and Eb7(#9) (resulting in different tensions as the root of the chord changes). I'll be giving different examples of this over the next few days. But for now, just look at the different ways the 3-2 or 2-3 versions of these work when you change directions of each 3 or 2 note grouping.

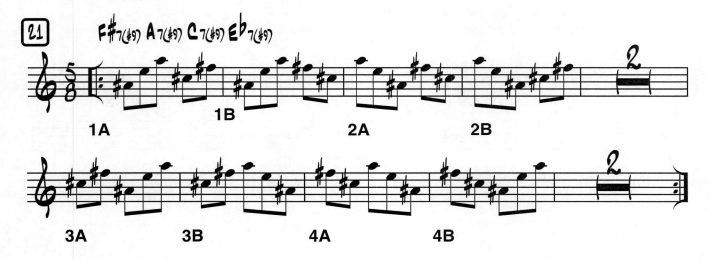

#22 Today's material is based on yesterday's ideas. The first example is shape 2A moving up in minor thirds. The second one alternates between shapes 3A and 4B and moves up in whole steps.

#23 More material generated from post #21. The first idea is a mirror image of the second idea from yesterday. The second one combines 3-2 and 2-3 shapes going down in major thirds and then that intervallic unit (C7-Ab7) moves down in whole steps (Bb7-F#7)

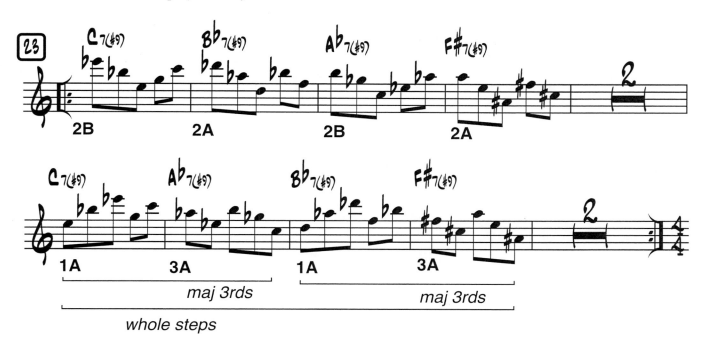

#24 Today it's time to do an about face from the somewhat complicated material of the last couple of posts. The idea is to play a 2-5-1 using only diatonic notes, starting on every note of the diatonic scale. The objective is to convey the feeling, sense of question/tension (2-5) and answer/resolution (1). After you master this, the next step is to introduce the use of chromatic passing tones, chromatic approach tones, wrap arounds etc…more on that in the next couple of days.

#25 Today I took the examples from yesterday and added one or more chromatic passing tones. Some of the resolutions here are not earth shattering but the discipline was to end on the same note as yesterday. Tomorrow I will extend the resolutions which will hopefully make things a little bit more interesting.

#26 As promised, extended resolutions of yesterday's examples. The chromatic passing tones add color and motion/momentum.

#27 Today's exercise is a continuation of #24 where the objective was to start a 2-5 on every note of the diatonic scale. Here I start every 2-5 on every non-diatonic tone. Seeing these "avoid tones" as being valid melodic choices adds freedom, motion and color to your playing.

#28 Here are a couple of diatonic exercises that are pretty self-explanatory. The objective in the first one is to help you not shy away from the avoid tones. The second one uses the 1, 4 and 5 triads and their inversions. Notice that the 2nd note of the 3rd, 7th and 8th group's second notes "interrupt" the triads.

#29 All these examples deal with shapes from yesterday's post. Example 1 takes the shapes built off of the 1st, 2nd and 4th (descending) degree and places them in a 2-5-1 context. Example 2 is the shape off of the 4th and 1st degree (also descending). Example 3 is more of an exercise...play each shape over every degree of the diatonic scale...this generates many beautiful Aaron Copland type colors. Example 4 utilizes an inversion that I didn't include in yesterday's example...this is another possible shape off of the 7th degree. It starts off diatonically but on beat 1 of the second measure, the F acts as a link to the same shape, but in the key of Db (this triad is extracted from the G half/whole or Ab melodic minor scales). Example 5 takes the shape off of the third degree and moves it up in minor thirds (with extra diatonic notes that are used as connectors. Example 6 takes the shapes built on 5 and 6 and treats them as a unit. (A,B,C and D are the different possible combinations of directions). Example 7 takes direction B (down/up) and moves the unit upwards in major thirds (or whole steps is you look at every component) with a slight variation for the resolution.

#30 This one is the first example from yesterday but with two different resolutions that stay within the same mood as the beginning of the idea.

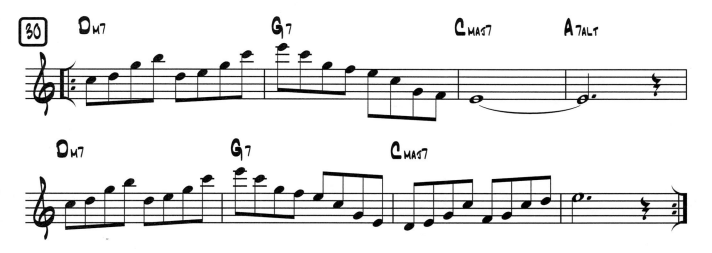

#31 Here are two ideas that are based on the concept that I talked about in post #11, which was how minor triads in major thirds are linked by common tones. So today's ideas show how to ascend or descend using these common tones as pivots.

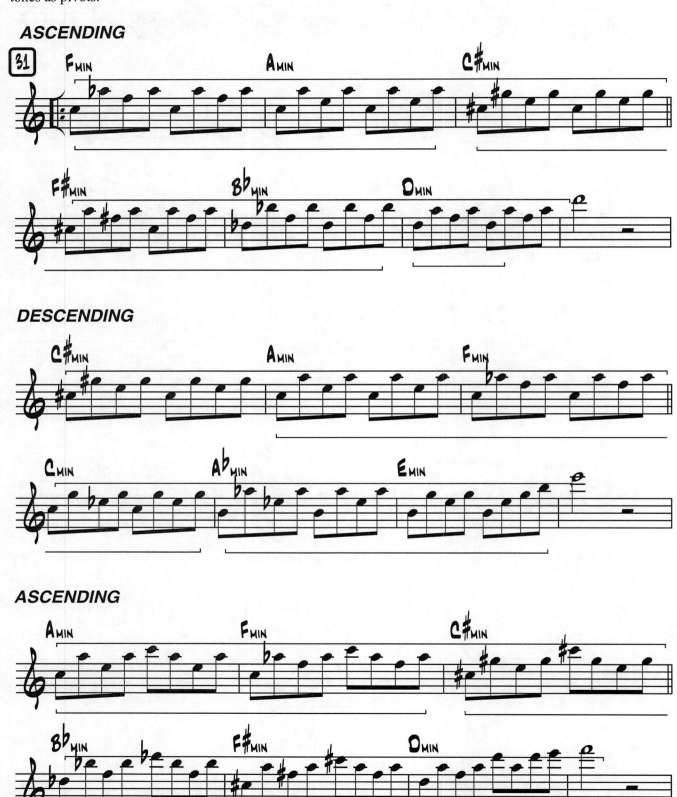

**DESCENDING**

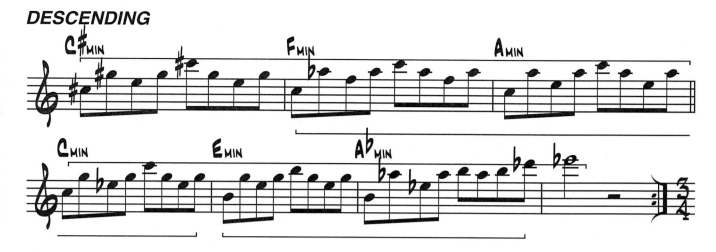

**ASCENDING**

**DESCENDING**

#32 The last couple posts have been dealing with common tones between minor triads, whose relationship is based on major thirds. Today's is the opposite. When you link major triads together by common tones, the relationship between them becomes one of minor thirds. So, the structure on the left is basically the four major triads contained in the diminished scale but spread out and linked by common tones. The example based on this is a 2-5 in Bb major. These four triads are the triads contained in the diminished scale that you would play over F7, (basically ignoring the 2 chord). And the strength and motion of the D# (major 3rd of B) being the last triad you hear resolving to Bb gives it its direction.

#33 These two extend the idea of common tones between triads to common tones between scales. The brackets above the notes show the links between the three major (line 1) and melodic minor scales (line 2) that are related by major thirds. Once again, any "wrong notes" are justified when the line resolves on the tonic chord.

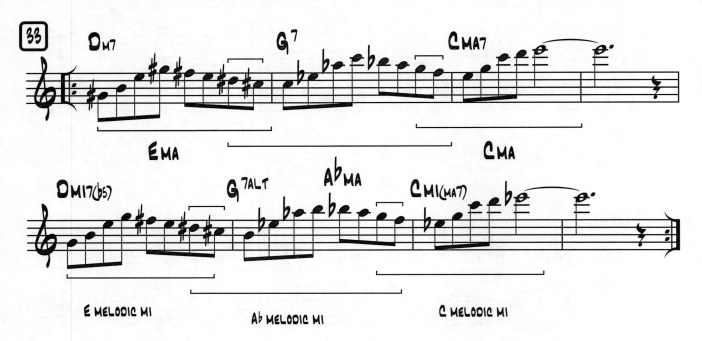

#34 Today's material utilizes the same concept as yesterday. This one however, does not use common tones to move from one scale to the next.

#35 Today's examples take a slightly different look at #33. The first one, instead of targeting the tonic by major thirds from below, targets the upper extension G/C by major thirds from below. The second one targets the upper extension of Am11 (G/C) which also functions as a link to the final Fmaj7(#11).

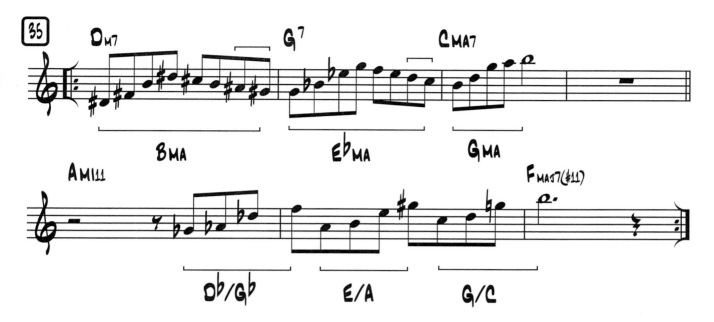

#36 These examples deal with altering the dominant chord in a 2-5-1 progression through the use of the melodic minor scale.
Idea #1 is unaltered and serves as the basis for the other examples.
Idea #2 replaces the descending major scale with the Ab melodic minor scale.
Idea #3 anticipates the V chord by switching to the mm scale two beats early.
Idea #4 is a variation of number three.
Idea #5 delays the alteration by two beats.
Idea #6 delays it until beat three. While it is necessary to understand on an intellectual level which tensions are created through the use of the melodic minor, in essence what you are doing is playing Ab minor over G7. Learn the rules and then forget them...let your ears be the guide.

#37 These examples look at how to add direction/momentum to the tonic by using a diminished major 7th as a passing chord. Both ideas use the same material over first measure of the tonic. The only difference is the second one has a longer set up and an extended resolution.

#38 Here is a 2-5-1 in Ab with a super delayed resolution. The 2-5 targets Eb, so, it is surprising/upsetting when you resolve to the E natural instead. The E acts as a link to C major (Abmaj7(#5)) which leads up to the F# which implies an Eb7(#9b9) which eventually leads you to the Eb that your ear was expecting.

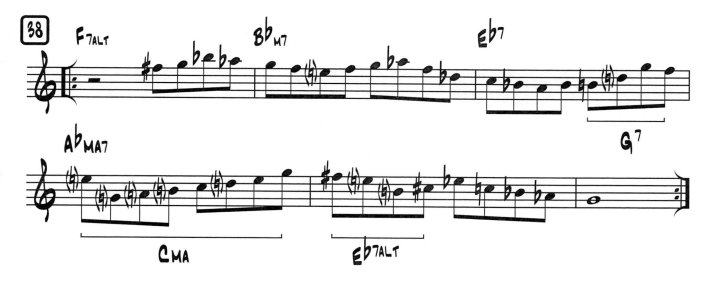

#39 The next couple of days are going to explore the implied i-V7(b9) interchange in the harmonic minor scale. The first two examples illustrate this relationship and sound. The third example takes advantage of the fact that Dm, Fm, Abm and Bm share the same diminished chord (The upper extension of each of their respective V7(b9) chords). So, if we look at the third of Dm also being the root of Fm and so on, we could use their shared diminished chords as pivots between the different tonalities. Example 3 illustrates this concept.

#40 Here is more harmonic minor material. The first example uses the same concept as the 3rd line of #39, but instead descends. The second example replaces the diminished chords with C/C# for A7(b9), Eb/E for C7(b9) etc...these chords are extracted from the diminished scale.

#41 Here we have Db/D, Bb/B etc... which are extracted from the diminished scale and function as E7(b9) since we are in the key of A minor. We then modulate to D minor where we use the corresponding dominant substitutes.

#42 The opening phrase to the masterpiece "Close To Home". R.I.P Lyle Mays

#43 Last-day of harmonic minor for now. Today's examples show the possible resolutions of B/C if we impose the condition that says the last note of the chord must resolve by a half step. On line 1, the chord is going up which result in three possibilities, and line 2 shows the resolutions when the chords are going down.

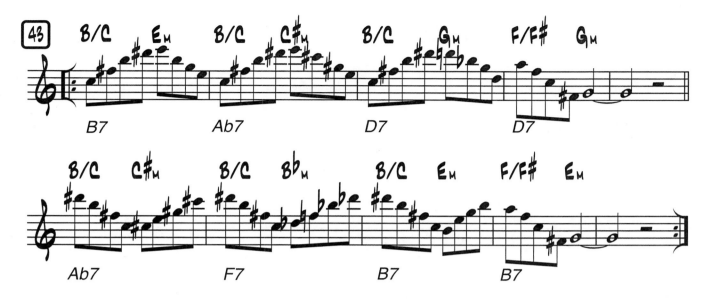

#44 This example is based on the minor 6/9 pentatonic. It is extracted from the melodic minor scale and used in the same way. You can see, the E only appears once at the top of the line. You can also take smaller portions of this line and combine them.

**Numbers Below the line represent the Shape Number.**
**These numbers will be seen in exercises #45 and #46.**

#45 Today we will be examining example #44. The first thing we can do is break it down into its various components. Example 1 takes the first two four note groups from yesterday and combines them, resulting in a new one measure unit. I then move that up in whole steps. Example 2 takes the same one measure unit and moves it up in major thirds. Example 3 is a 2-5-1 in E minor. It starts with the same one measure grouping and then moves to a new one measure unit which is a combination of the 7th and 8th four note groups from yesterday. The resolution utilizes the same principle of taking and combining shapes from #44.

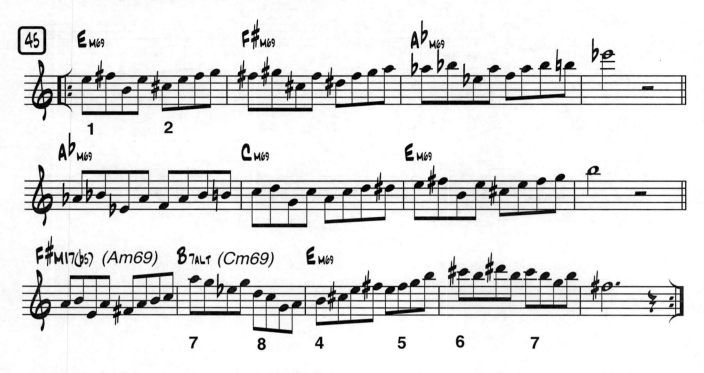

#46 Today we will continue the concept that was looked at in example 3 of yesterday's post, which is shifting around the m6/9 pentatonic over minor 2-5. As I mentioned before, this pentatonic is extracted from the melodic minor scale, so it is used in the same exact way. The first example combines groups 3 and 4 which results in a one measure unit that is moved accordingly over the chords. The second example does the same thing only it combines groups 9 and 10 and treats them as a unit. The next two examples are a little more interesting because they switch between the two bigger phrases so you are not playing the same shape over every chord.

#47 This example takes minor 6/9 chords and moves them down in minor thirds with Ebmin6/9 being the target. Ebmin6/9 over D7=D7(alt). Each minor 6/9 is a different shape and all of these should be practiced separately through the routine. By using a different shape for each superimposed chord, the idea doesn't sound like a pattern. And since it resolves to the 5th, this idea can be used in either a major or minor context.

#48 Here's a pentatonic that is extracted from the Ionian scale (5th mode). The Mixolydian pentatonic has a beautiful bright sound and works over F7 or Fsus. It also works well over Dorian chords...in this case Cm7.

#49 Here we continue to look at the Mixolydian pentatonic. A lot of times when people deal with pentatonic scales, they feel like they are limited to just the five notes in the scale. In today's example, I've come up with six twelve note shapes, one for each degree of the scale and one extra for the first degree in order to finish the idea. As you can see, each line incorporates chromatic passing tones. These non-scale tones add a lot of color and can make using pentatonics feel less restrictive.

#50 Here's one more pentatonic scale that I use a lot. I'm sure there are other names for this one. I call it minor major 6/9. I have also heard it referred to as the Phrygian natural six which is the second mode of melodic minor. To me it's much easier to think of as being based on the root of the related melodic minor because it is used the same way you use the melodic minor scale. For example, if I see an E7(alt) I think and hear Fminmaj6/9 (even though the F is not in the scale) instead of G Phrygian natural 6. So, today's examples are pretty straight forward. We have a 2-5-1 in C minor and use the appropriate minmaj 6/9 pentatonic for each chord. What I like about this scale is that I doesn't contain the root, which gives it an ethereal quality.

#51 Today's example takes a major pentatonic and superimposes it over a dominant 7th chord. I look at the F as being a common tone between G7 and Db major pentatonic. It's not that far from an altered scale because the pentatonic gives you the same tensions. What makes it sound more outside than it is, is the lack of the third.

#52 Here's more pentatonic based material. Today we are superimposing an F minor pentatonic over Bm7 which leads to the #9 of the E7. That whole measure seems to want to go to an E natural when we get to the Amaj7. So instead, it resolves to the F natural which is the third of the D flat triad which makes the chord Amaj7(#5) for two beats until we finally hear the E natural on beat three.

#53 This post deals with adding chromatic passing tones to the whole tone scale. As I talked about in post #49, when people deal with pentatonic scales they sometimes feel limited to just the five notes. The same holds true for the whole tone scale. Adding these chromatic passing tones adds a lot of fluidity and color to the scale that could sometimes sound/feel one dimensional.

#54 This one is a fun challenge. We take four chord types...maj7(#5), maj7(#11), min7(b5) and minmaj7 and move them up in whole steps. This is symmetrical at the major 3rd (when you get to the F#, the four-chord cycle starts again). As you can see, line two and three change directions as per the routine.

#55 This is a shape that connects two open triads by their common tones. The first one is major triads in major 3rds. The 2nd is minor triads in minor 3rds.

#56 Developing the idea from yesterday, here we put it in a 2-5-1 context by starting with the minor version. (yesterday's second example). So, in D minor, the two triads are Dm and Fm. When we get the top, the Ab/G# becomes the common tone of the descending version of yesterday's first example which gives us E and C which is the target resolution. The descending E triad in the second measure serves three purposes.
(1) its common tone between Fm and Cmaj7(#5)
(2) Over G7, it is one of the 4 major triads that can be extracted from the half
whole scale, which gives us G13(b9)
(3) It's the link to C major by major thirds. (Ab-E-C)

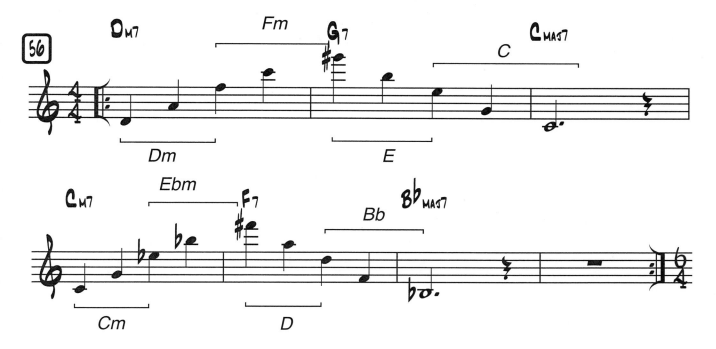

#57 This is an ascending line over Fm7. The B and E naturals are the only two non-chord tones and are also the only two notes that descend, give it it's slightly twisted character. Tomorrow's post will finish the line with a resolution.

#58 As promised, an answer to yesterday's question. Over the Bb7, the intervals descend until beat 4 when they change direction...the opposite of what happens over the Fm7. Also, the "outness" of the B and E naturals in the first measure is continued by the E and A naturals in the second measure. I don't think of the last four notes in the second measure as being outside because they are legal alterations, Bb7(alt). The last measure wraps things in a more traditional way, although the appoggiaturas and switching directions echo the material in the first two bars.

#59 The next couple examples break down #58 example into smaller components. So, if we look at the first four notes, we can see that it is an Fm7 in a different order, (one of the 24 ways you could arrange 4 notes) next to it, is it's mirror image. So, the first example on line two takes it and its mirror image and moves them up in major thirds. The second example moves the third and fourth notes up a half step turning it into an Fmaj7. After that, we move the first and second notes up a half step resulting in an F#m7 which then turns into a F#maj7 by repeating the same process. You can also go down in half steps by reversing the process. I find that having control over the smaller units of a long line really helps to internalize the bigger structure.

#60 Today, we are continuing to look at post #58. Here I am isolating the second group of four notes. On its own, it is a Cmaj7. The first example on line two takes it and its mirror image and moves it up in whole steps. The second example does what I did to the first four notes yesterday. When I lower the B and E naturals a half step, it turns it into a Cm7. Then I lower the C and G by a half step which results in a Bmaj7 etc... once again, the objective of these exercise is to gain control over all components of the bigger structure. On the last line we can see that if we play the first two chords in root position, we have Fm7 and Cmaj7. When we lower the last two notes by a half-step, we end up with Fm7 and Cm7 which is basically Fm11. As we saw in example #58, the B and E naturals eventually get resolved to C and Eb, so we could look at the first eight notes as being a fragmented Fm11.

#61 Continuing to look at post #58. Here I am isolating the first 3 beats of measure 2. In this example, I'm using them over Fm7 instead of Bb7. This results in us approaching the b7 and b3 by a half step above (beat 2 to beat 3). This slight change/interruption in what the ear was expecting results in a surprisingly fresh sound.

#62 More material from #58. Here we are isolating beats 3 and 4 from bar two and placing them over Fm7 instead of Bb7 and also changing the note order of the last two notes. The first example takes the second shape and while moving down in half steps, switches direction. The 2nd example takes that second shape and places a two note pick up a half step below the target note (b7). Finally, example 3 targets that same note from a half step above which once again results in that rub of the major 7th and major 3rd moving down to the b7 and b3.

#63 Continuing to examine the smaller components of #58, today we look at the last 4 notes of measure two. On line 2, I've taken the Fm9 in its modified form that we looked at yesterday which approaches the B natural by a half step. The third line shows what the B, F# and C# represent, which is a Bminmaj9, i.e., B melodic minor... Bb7(alt).

#64 Today we look at the concept behind the last four notes of measure two in #58, i.e., stacked perfect 5ths. In that example they are used over Bb7(alt). Here we are in D major and we see how they can be used over every chord in a 2-5-1. Over the next days, we will be looking at these in more detail.

#65 Today we are looking at the same set of open perfect fifths from yesterday. As you can see, I've changed the note order and/or direction. The other difference is that I have omitted the B natural (the top note of the third group).

#66 Here's some more material based on stacked perfect 5ths. If we stack two off of the root, go up a half step and stack two more, we end up with a minor 11th chord. Two off of the root, up a whole step and then two more results in a maj7(#11).

#67 Here are two variations on yesterday's post. The first one omits the top note.... helpful when you get higher on the horn. And the second one changes the note order and octave displacement.

#68 Today we continue to look at stacked perfect 5ths. The last couple of days we have been looking at them from the root going up. Today the target is the 9th going down. All the two note groupings are approaches to the 9th. The examples on the first line are single approaches. The first is a half-step below then a half step above. Bars 4 and 5 reverse the order. The second example in 7/8 are double wraparounds. The next two examples are the same as the first two except the approaches move up instead of down.

#69 Following #68, today we change the directions of the double wraparound.

#70 Today we are looking at more stacked perfect fifths. The last couple of days have been dealing with perfect fifths off of the root (Ascending) or 9th (descending) The 1st example shows the other sets of fifths that can be played over Dm7. The 2nd example approaches the top notes of each set of 5ths from a half step below. And the 3rd example approaches them from a half step above.

#71 This one looks at the same sets of stacked fifths over Dm7 that we looked at yesterday. These examples approach the 9th, 11th and 13th by different combinations of half steps above and below. As you can see the first repeat stays in the key of Dm and the second reharmonizes the material.

#72 This example is based on the same structure/chord progression that you can see in post #66. The obvious difference is the melodic shape and octave displacement. Also, since the progression is moving down in half steps, the chord order is reversed (maj7(#11) to m11).

(tacet last x)

#73 One more post based on open fifths. Today we're taking major 7th (#11) chords (lines 1 and 2) and moving them down in half steps. And m11th (lines 3 and 4) and moving them up in half steps.

#74 This is a long E major approach to C major. Even though it does not move through Ab major, it sounds like a Giant Steps progression. This example has the line moving over a 6-2-5-1 but will work over anything moving to C major.

#75 Talked about this in one of the earlier posts. A way to navigate Giant Steps progressions is to think down in whole steps and alternate between major7th and minor7th chords. More on this in the upcoming days.

#76 More material based on #75.

#77 More Giant Steps based material. This one is a more extended version but uses the same principal of thinking down in whole steps while alternating between major and minor.

#78 More material based on the concepts we've been talking about for the last couple of days. This one is a little more ornamented with chromatic passing and neighbour tones.

#79 One more day of material based on the concepts we've been talking about for the last several days. Examples over the last couple days have been getting a little bit more complicated. This one simplifies things a bit.

#80 Here's a 2-5-1 in Bb major with moving inner voices.

#81 Same material as #80 but with a different note order.

#82 Over the next several days, we'll be looking at material that I call arpeggiated piano voicings.

(tacet last x)

#83 I call this one Night Indonesia.

#84 Day three of piano voicings. As always, practice this progression (the bracketed material) through all the intervallic families.

#85 More arpeggiated piano voicings. This-one works really well moving down in whole steps. You can also just move around the 2 and 5 without the resolution.

(tacet last x)

#86 This one is loosely based on the piano voicing-based concept. This one has a film noir quality to it.

#87 This one is an extension of #83.

#88 The first idea is another 5-1 example that is based on a piano type ostinato. The idea continues in measure 5 with a variation where the bass line is more active giving you the feeling of the ostinato and bass line happening at the same time.

#89 More piano voicing stuff. The 5 chord is an upper extension triad on top of the root, third and seventh. And the tonic chord is a shape that I posted earlier based on stacked perfect 5ths.

*(repeat and fade)*

#90 Here we're looking at the two ways of constructing/voicing a dominant seventh chord. Either the root 3rd and 7th, or root 7th and 3rd with an upper extension triad on top. The triads are extracted from either the melodic minor or half/whole diminished scales. Below is a list of available triads (the ones in bold type are common to both scales). Half/whole diminished: C Cm Eb Ebm F# F#m A Am Melodic minor: C#m D Ebm F# Ab

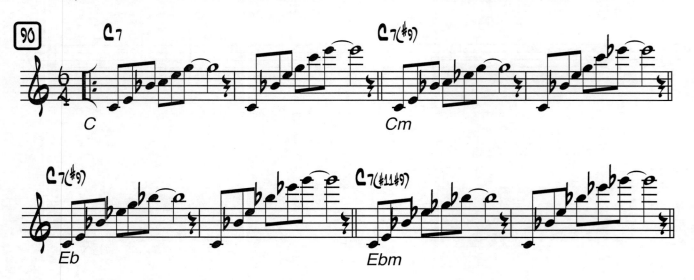

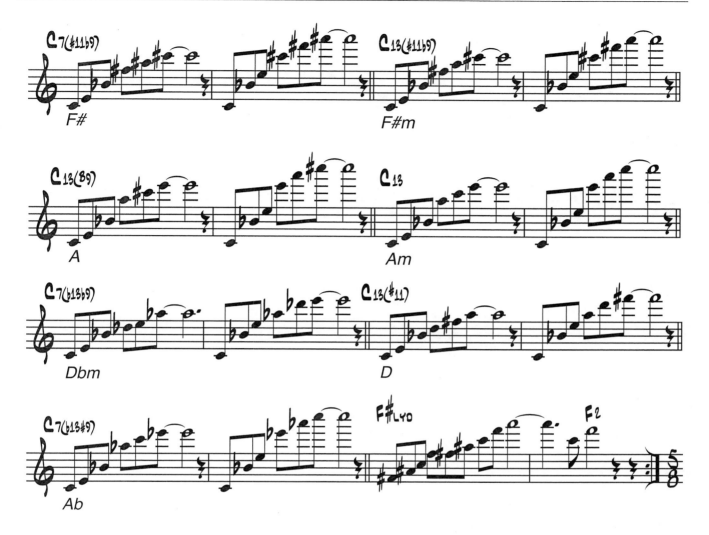

#91 Post #90 gave the basic principles of playing piano voicings on a single note instrument. This one illustrates how moving inner voices, based on example #90, creates motion, color and interest.

#92 This one is a variation/extension of #91.

#93 This one started out as a line over Fsus that turned into this 12-bar progression. It's helpful to take each four-note group and run it through the routine. You can also isolate two groups of four notes (first two, middle two or last two) and work them as a unit. Note that each phrase ends with a slight variation and the line over the last four bars stays the same but is used over an altered dominant chord.

#94 Here's a 2-5-1 in Bb. The first measure implies a G minor tonality (vi in Bb). Remind you a certain standard? This creates motion and direction over the 2 chord that continues over the 5 until the 3rd measure when we finally reach the F in measure 4 where the line switches direction and moves up to the tonic. The 2nd version of the phrase shows how this line works over a 3-6-2-5 even though the melodic material doesn't change. And finally, the 3rd version uses half step approaches while again, not changing the line except for the use of the diminished major 7th for the resolution.

#95 Here's a 2-5-1 in C that has two different resolutions. The first one sets up the turnaround and the second finishes the idea. The Gb and Ab moving up to the F natural implies an Ebm11 (the Db is heard even though it's not played). So, although the rest of the notes are completely diatonic, (except for the second resolution that uses a diminished major seventh) the two non-chord tones create a twist that creates interest/movement.

#96 This one is a shape over Bbm7 that's starts with three "wrong notes". Who was it that said there are no wrong notes, only wrong resolutions? Anyway, I think of the first five notes as a Bbmaj7(#5) with the F being the link to Bbm7 (or Bbm9 in this case). The material in bars 9 and 10 is a variation of the main subject and functions as a turnaround.

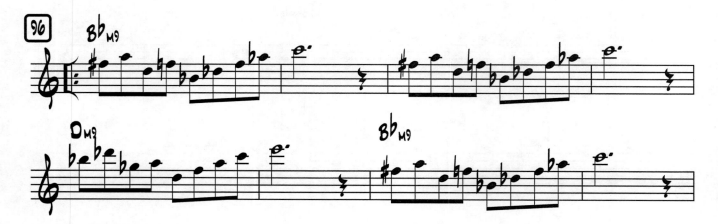

*(repeat and fade)*

#97 I think of this as an F#min triad moving to a Gm7 with the A#/Bb being a link between the two shapes. This one turned into a 6 bar minor blues when I created the backing track, so the 3rd shape (over D7alt) is a variation based on the original material.

*(repeat and fade)*

#98 This idea combines examples #96 and 97. Even though the backing track is a turnaround that uses different chord changes, this example works over a straight 2-5-1.

*(repeat and fade)*

*(backing track)*

#99 Here's a Db melodic minor shape used over a C7alt. Once again, it's a good idea to take the different components of this line and practice them separately. For example, the first eight notes going down in minor third sounds really nice. Also, since this line resolves to the 5th, this line can be used going to F minor.

#100 This is a diatonic melody that creates movement by taking the first shape and moving it up a fifth.

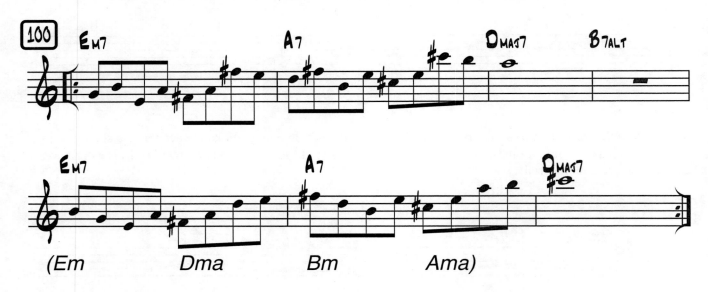

#101 Taking the material from #100 (first 8 notes) and moving it down in major thirds. What's interesting about this, is that even though we are moving down in major thirds, the line moves upwards. We start in Bb, go through F# and end up in D. The first 2-5 is in G so the resolution/target is D/G. The second is a 2-5 in D, so we end up in the tonic key as opposed to an upper extension triad.

#102 Here's a 2-5-1 in Eb. Over the five-chord, the B minor (makes Bb7alt) shape moves up in major thirds. What's cool about this is that the G minor which is a part of the major third pattern (Bm, Ebm and Gm) functions as a link between the major third group and the tonic. (vi minor)

#103 A G melodic minor shape over F#7(alt) or C7(#11) that can resolve to either Bmaj or Bmin.

#104 Here's a 2-5 in Bb with four different Lydian/m6/9 shapes moving up in minor 3rds. The last group (Alyd/F#m6/9) results in F7alt. Once again, take each 4-note shape through the routine, then each 8 and 12 note group.

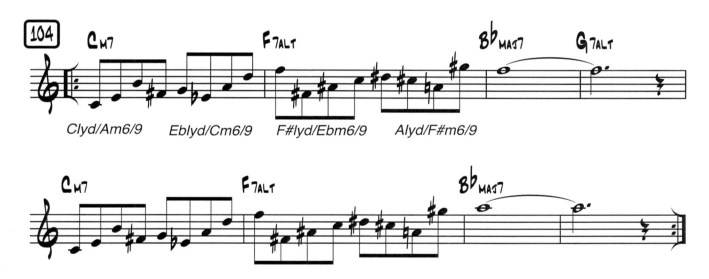

#105 Here's a wide shape for minor 11th chords...sorry brass players. The first line moves up in minor 3rds and the second goes up in major 3rds.

\# 106 Here's a 2-5-1 in Bb with a twist. The A in measure two is a common tone and thus functions as a link between Cm7/F7 and Bm7/E7.

#107 Here's a V7(alt)/im6 resolution. The essence of this exercise is to isolate the m6 chord of the 7(alt) moving to the m6 chord of the tonic. You can add variety by omitting the roots on beat one and changing the directions of the m6 chords.

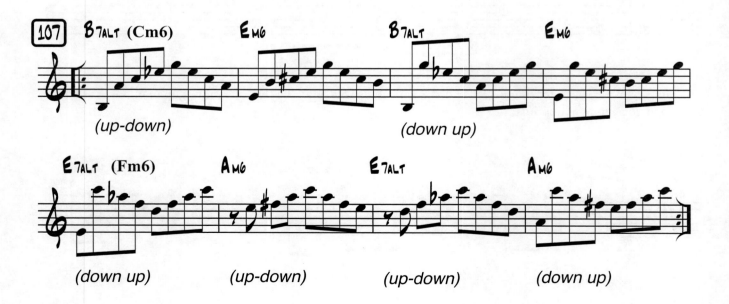

#108 Nothing terribly adventurous harmonically today. I like this one because of the way the directions change and the accents shift. The resolution also adds a little twist by using the #5 as a passing tone.

#109 A 2-5 whose color comes from the Bmaj triad over F7. What's nice about this one is that the alteration comes early, so it ends up feeling less boxy.

#110 This is an example of how I expand/extend the be-bop vocabulary. This concept assumes that a strong foundational knowledge of the traditional language has been developed through transcription, listening to and playing along with recordings. The line in the first 4 bars is the subject that will be expanded. The next 4 bars are the extended/expanded version. In measure 5 (with the pick-up from bar 4), I outline a descending Bminmaj9(b6). The A# and F resolve to the A and F# of the line which is then interrupted/extended by inserting a Cm7 shape that links back to the original subject by using the A natural as a common tone.

#111 Here is an extended version of #110 that's used over a 3-6-2-5.

#112 This is an extended wraparound moving down in major 3rds. I like this one because you get the color of the #4 and #5 resolving to the 5th.

#113 I call this one Debussy. This material sounds good in all intervallic relationships. Certain relationships require subtle adjustments and there are several variations that help to make it sound like less of an exercise. We will look at those over the next couple of days.

#114 Today we are taking a look at yesterday's example and what we need to do when we practice it in different intervallic relationships. The first line goes up in ½ steps and second down in ½ steps. From there we continue down through major 3rds. When practicing it going down, you can see that you will need to add two notes in every case in order to make a smooth transition. Tomorrow we will start looking at some variations.

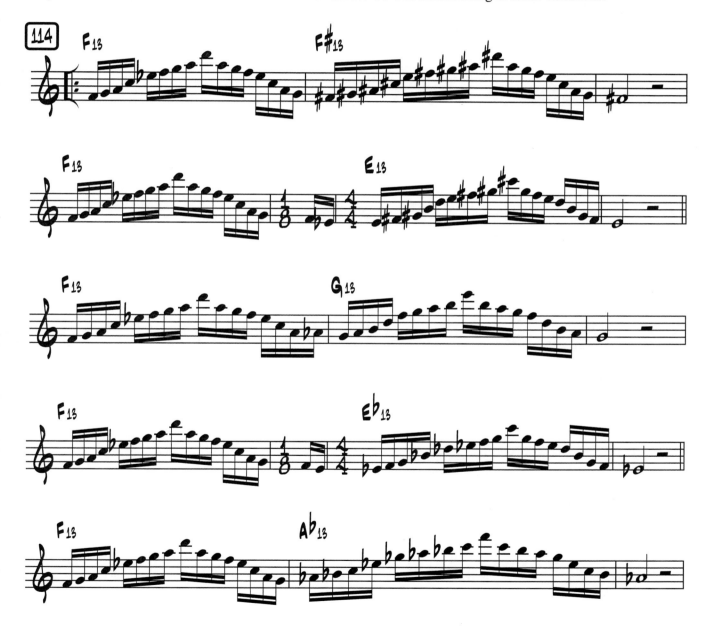

#115 Here are three variations on #113. The first one adds the little turn around at the top of the line and ascends in ½ steps. The second one just isolates the last eight descending notes and descends in ½ steps. And the third one adds a two note pick up and descends in whole steps, goes up in ½ steps and descends again in whole steps. All of them sound good when taken through the different intervallic families.

#116 Here's what I call a hyper-extended wraparound, or a super elaborate pick up, to the minor third of F#m7. The resolution is a sequence of the first line.

#117 Here's a 2-5 in D major. I'm thinking Bbm7-Eb7, so it is basically a long tri-tone substitution.

#118 Today's example is a turnaround in Bb where the line over the Cm7 is transposed down a tri-tone over the F7. So, in essence, it is a tri-tone sub except I'm just thinking C minor to F# minor instead of C minor to F#m7-B7. The resolution uses notes from the augmented scale as passing tones. I'm not thinking Bbmaj7(#5#9).

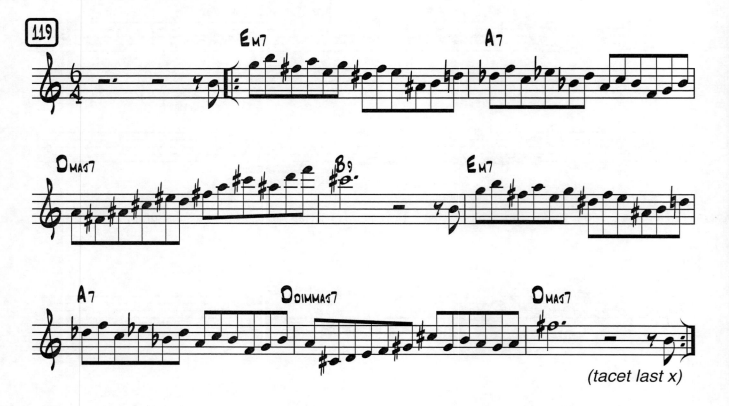

#119 Here is an extended version of #118.

#120 Here is an ostinato-ish minor 6/9 shape that works over all the modes of the Ionian scale.

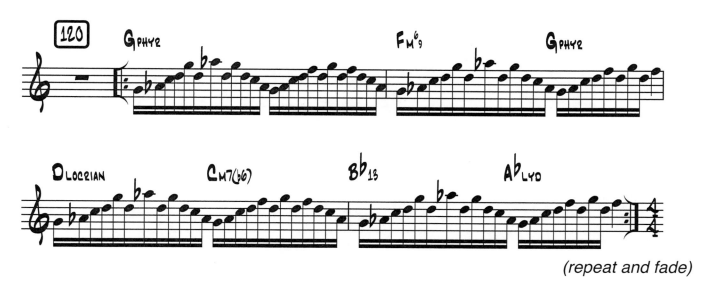

*(repeat and fade)*

#121 Today's example is a turnaround that uses C minor over both the 2 and the 5. Technically, you are shifting between the 6th and 2nd modes of melodic minor, which results in using the same scale over both chords. Also notice that the first two phrases resolve to G major even though the chords are Bm7-E7. Leaving this space and not feeling like you have to play over every chord is very freeing. It gives you time to think/hear what your next phrase will/could be and also gives the rhythm section the opportunity to be involved in the conversation.

#122 This is a long pentatonic line that could be broken down into several smaller combinations.

(repeat and fade)

#123 Here is bar three of yesterday's example going down in major thirds. The downbeat of each bar is a common tone, so when one group cadences another one starts. Starting at measure 9, each four-bar phrase modulates, so after the last phrase, you will have gone through the four groups of major thirds, which gives you Giant Steps relationships in every key.

*(repeat and fade)*

#124 This is a three bar 2-5 in E major that starts a half step above F#m7 and then uses the same two notes to start the line over B7. It then modulates down in major 3rds.

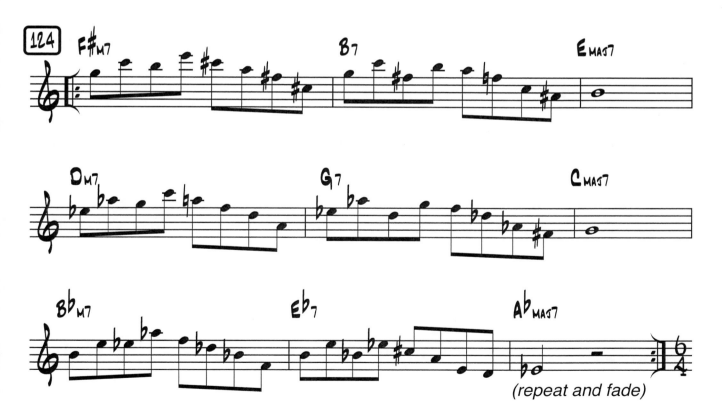

*(repeat and fade)*

#125 Here's something I use as a warm up. It's basic be-bop language but uses common tones to modulate in major 3rds.

#126 Here's the descending version of example #125.

#127 Here are three variations on #125 that keep progressively more complex/ornate. Note that for examples 1 and 3, the resolution note is a common tone that acts as a link to the next key.

#128 Here's a 2-5 that moves down in minor 3rds where the resolution note (the tonic in this case) becomes the starting point for the idea in the new key.

#129 Today's example is an altered shape that resolves in minor. What I like about this one is the natural 13 moving to the b13.

*(repeat and fade)*

#130 Here is what I call a set up...basically the 2 chord in a 2-5-1...the part of the idea that asks the question. Instead of practicing/writing a complete idea, these set-ups voice lead you to a chord tone (in this case, the 3rd of the dominant chord) that can then be resolved (or not, sometimes just asking the question and letting the rhythm section finish the cadence is the best option) in an infinite number of ways. The first part of this one asks the question and leaves it unanswered. The second part of it shows a possible resolution.

#131 A little while ago I started experimenting with 12 tone rows and came up with some that work over 2-5-1 progressions. The principle is to organize them into three groups of four notes with the last four notes being something related to the key that you are in.

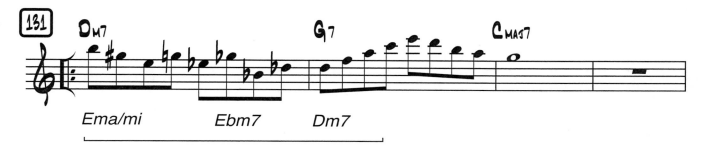

#132 Another 12-tone example that was organized using the same principle as yesterday's material.

#133 Another 12 tone 2-5.

#134 Here's the last 12 tone example. This one is a little different. Instead of dividing the 12 notes into three groups of four, I divided them into two groups of six. The first group is an F augmented scale and the second is a G augmented scale. Augmented scales a whole step apart gives you all 12 notes. Also note that the second 12 tone row is the mirror image of the first.

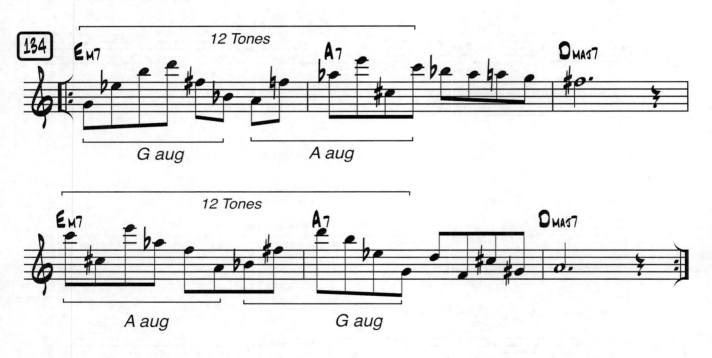

# 135 Here's something completely different from the last several posts. Just a descending diatonic line with chromatic passing tones. This is a good warm-up and a very useful way to feel comfortable and gain control of the harder keys. This one also works ascending.

#136 Another descending diatonic tongue twister.

#137 One more diatonic tongue twister. This one also works descending.

#138 Here is a cool way to practice diatonic 7th chords. There are two versions to ensure that you play each chord in both directions. The first is shown here (Cminma7-Dm7). The second version starts on the second degree, so the diatonic chords would be Dm7-Ebmaj7(#5). The range shown here in the descending versions might be a little extreme... make the necessary adjustments according to your individual level.

### C melodic minor

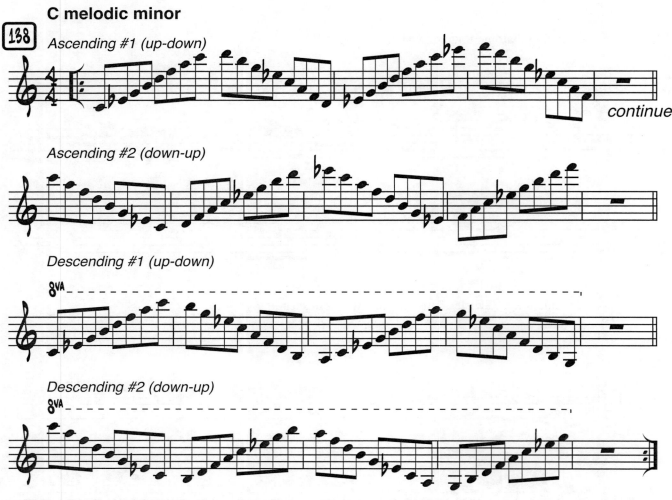

continue

#139 Another way to practice diatonic 7ths. The range is a little tighter on this one and applies the same principles as #138.

### C melodic minor

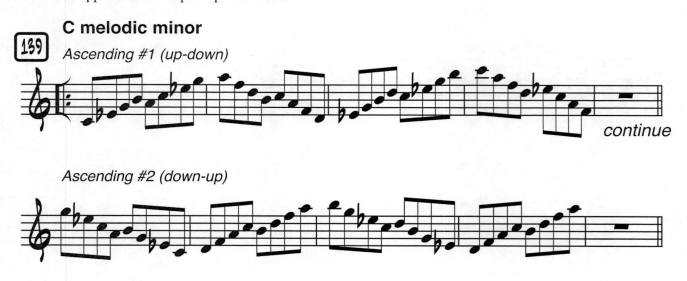

continue

*Descending #1 (down-up)*

*Descending #2 (up-down)*

#140 This example takes the same shape but starts on a different degree of a minor 6 pentatonic scale in each measure. So, the idea becomes a melodic sequence instead of a pattern.

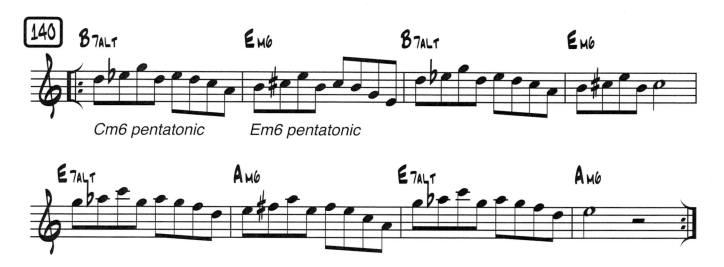

#141 Here's a line in A harmonic minor that implies a 5-1 movement.

*(tacet last x)*

#142 This one is a line over an altered 5 chord. What I like about it, is that it incorporates the natural 13th until beat three.

#143 Here's a simple 5-1 melody. We'll be looking at different ways to develop this over the next couple of days.

#144 We're going to start looking at different ways to develop yesterday's idea. The first line modulates up a half step by using the first note in each measure as a common tone. The second one moves down in half steps. The third line adds an extra two notes, turning it into a 4/4 example and moves up in whole steps. And the fourth line does the same thing but moves down in whole steps.

#145 Here we change the direction of the last 3 notes in the first measure. From there the resolution is extended turning it into a two-measure line that repeats a fourth higher which then continues through the cycle.

#146 Here are two more variations based on #143.

#147 This is a line over a 1-2-5-1 progression on minor. The shape on the first two beats of the 2nd measure (used throughout this example) is one that I talked about in post #40.

#148 Here are five examples that use upper extension triads that are extracted from either the melodic minor or half-whole scale. Shown below are the triads that I am thinking/hearing. For me, it is much easier than thinking about the actual alterations that these triads represent.

#149 This is an etude that explores triads that change direction over a moving/descending bass line. This fits into the wide interval/piano voicing category that we looked at starting with #82.

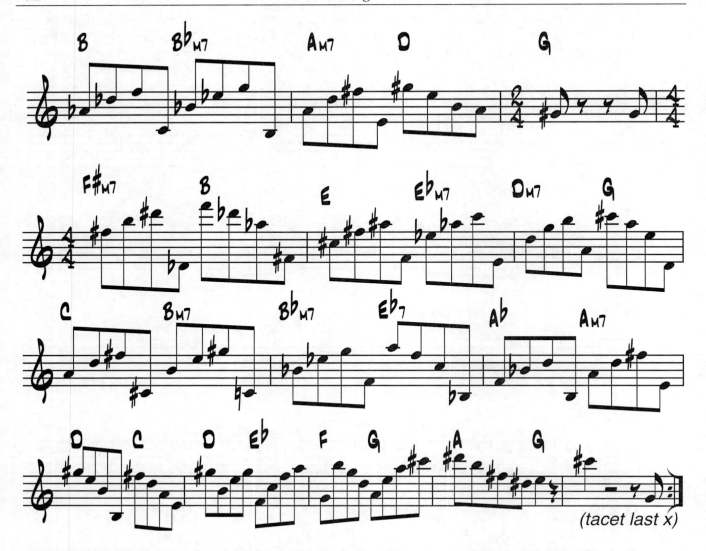

(tacet last x)

#150 On line one is a two-octave descending be-bop scale in F. On the second line is the same idea but transformed/adjusted to conform to the first three measures of Giant Steps. And on line three, we take the transformed material and superimpose it over the original 2-5 in F.

#151 Here's another transformation of some be-bop language. This one is a little more radical yet still keeps the character of the original line.

#152 Today's exercise is generated by combining two different be-bop phrases. Although the first two lines are pretty basic, they are important foundational elements of the be-bop language and should be practiced in all intervallic relationships. Also, seeing/hearing how you can get to two different keys from the same common note is very useful. Line 3 links E7 and C7, turning it into a unit the moves up in half steps by using the resolution note as a link to the next dominant chord.

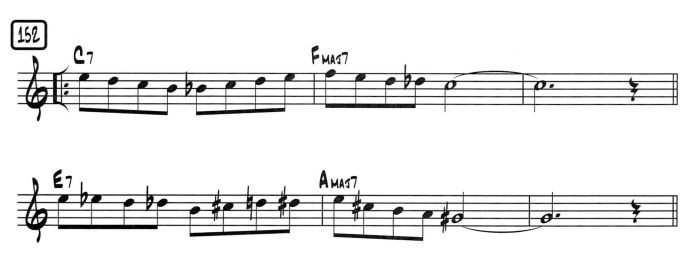

#153 Here's a cool sus chord workout that has them switching directions while moving down and up in major thirds.

#154 This is a 2-5 in C. Even though it does not move through Ab first, it has a Giant Steps sound/feel.

#155 Here's a shape/chord that should be taken through the routine. On the second line the example moves/transposes that shape over a 2-5-1 which results in really nice upper extension harmonies.

#156 Here's a variation based on the concept discussed in #155.

#157 Here is a concept that I really like and use a lot...the idea of using the major 3rd and major 7th moving up or down to the b3 and b7 over a minor 7th/9th chord.

#158 This is a descending shape based on the Ebm6/9 pentatonic. This can be used in any context where you would use the Eb melodic minor scale. And since every six-note group contains a different combination of intervals, they could all be practiced separately. Also note that each bar starts on a different degree of the scale.

#159 Here's a line in D minor (then C minor in this example) that also works, as seen here, in a 2-5 situation.

#160 Here is a 2-5 in D major whos main focus is the movement from an F#min to F#maj triad. (beats 2 and 3 of measures 1 and 2) The resolution utilizes the diminished major 7 sound which we've talked about in earlier examples.

#161 This one is a 2-5-1 in C that approaches the Dm7 in major 3rds from below. All the "wrong notes" are justified when we finally get to the Dm7 (below) in measure two.

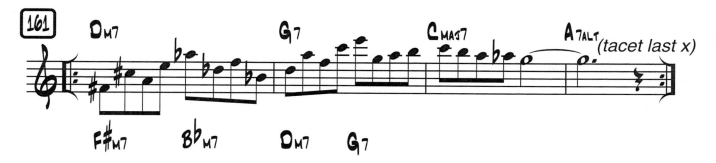

#162 Here's a 2-5 in A, whose resolution mirrors the shape used over the 5 chord.

#163 For the next couple of days we will be talking about triad stacking. In this case, minor triads descending in half steps. The first two measures show the stacked triads. Measures 3-6 show an example based on this concept with A minor being the target both ascending and descending.

**#164** This example is based on stacking augmented triads descending in half steps. The first two bars show the basic shape and bars 3-6 is the example where the 1st triad is the root and the 3rd is the target upper extension.

**#165** Here's a 2-5 in D that reminds me of one of my favorite tunes by the great Don Grolnick called *The Four Sleepers*. This one should be practiced up and down in all intervallic relationships.

*(repeat and fade)*

#166 This is a line that alternates between a major and minor 6/9 pentatonic. By shifting the root under the minor 6/9 pentatonic, the character/mood of the line is completely changed.

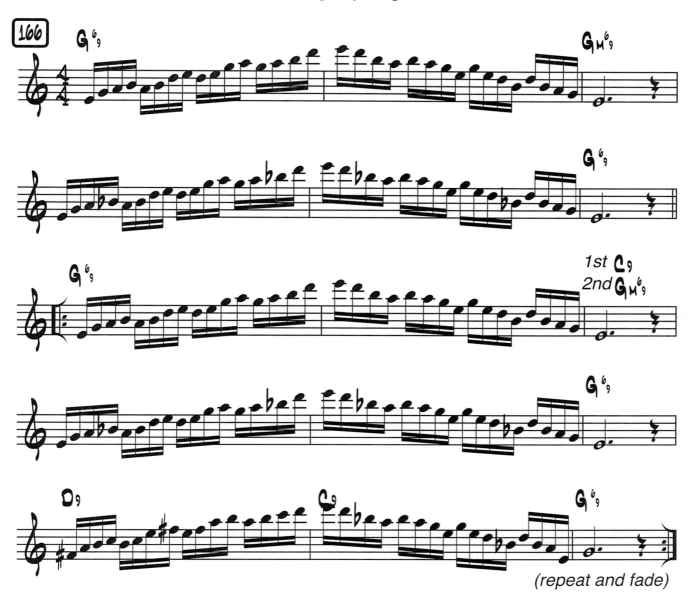

*(repeat and fade)*

#167 Here's a progression of 2-5's that uses wide intervals (4ths and 5ths) that spell out piano voicings, which is a concept that we've looked at several times earlier.

#168 This one is a turnaround in D. In the first half, I'm not thinking about the Em7, just three different colors over A7. The C is the link between the Ab/A and A7alt. In the pick-up to the second half, the D triad over the passing C7(#11) functions as a link as I treat the B7 with the half-whole scale which includes the F, Ab, B and D triads. I make use of the D/Eb chord/shape (which is derived from that scale) that we've discussed in earlier posts. This shape is shifted around and takes us to the 2 chord where the lines leads us to the A# on beat 3 of bar 6 which becomes the same F#/G shape that we used/heard earlier, which resolves down to the 5th of the tonic.

#169 Here's a shape that works over either Em7, A7 or as in this example, Em7-A7. This one started with the second measure first. I played the Bb/B and heard it resolving down to the G natural in bar 3. I found the first measure separately and it felt/sounded like it functioned as an elaborate pickup to the B on beat one of measure two. Looking at it afterwards, I realized that the first note in each measure, when combined, spells out a G, B, or Eb augmented triad, meaning that the idea could be repeated/continued a major 3rd higher by starting on the G on which it ends.

#170 Here is another shape that can be used over a 2-5 or just or just a 5 chord. The beginning of it is loosely based on a whole tone scale. The target is the F natural on beat three of measure two which implies Bbmin (A7alt) resolving to D major.

#171 Here's a 2-5 in D major that combines #169 (set up) and #170 (resolution).

**#172** This is the same shape as yesterday but starting a whole step lower on the 2 chord, which gets you to the target note (b13) on beat one instead of beat four. The line is then slightly modified in order get you back to the b13 on beat four which results in the same resolution as yesterday.

**#173** Here is a simple interchange between 1 and 5, but with a small twist. We treat the 5 chord as a maj7(#5) resulting in an interchange between an Am and Abmaj triad which opens up the sound in a fresh way. The material used over the Dm modulation starting in bar 7 is loosely based on this sound which adds some variety before we return to the original material for the last 4 measures.

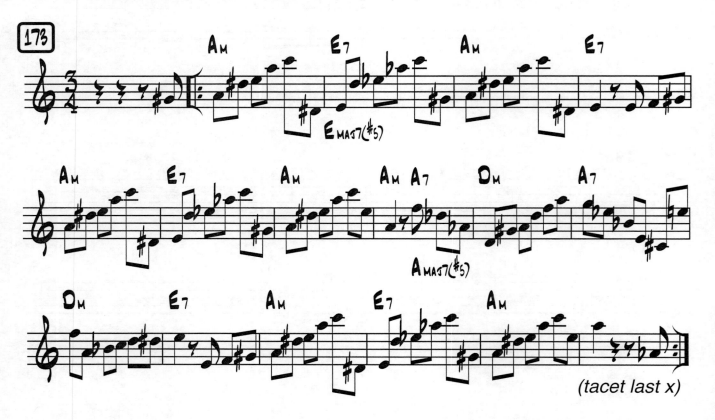

(tacet last x)

#174 This example deals with a simple melodic minor phrase that moves up in major 3rds. In the first 4 measures, the melodic line is based on the tonic of each chord. In the second phrase, the line stays the same while the harmony moves down a half step and are replaced by altered dominant chords thus changing the function of the melodic material.

#175 Here's an example that combines the harmonic movements from yesterday's post.

#176 This idea is in response to a question asked in our corona practice Facebook group by the great Jeff Ellwood. It is the beginning of something I played on one of my earlier recordings. It started out as just the first four notes which I remember discovering because I was looking for something that felt different on the horn in order to get away from finger habits and the low C to B to side D is what I came up with. I wasn't thinking about anything harmonic. I later added the Ab to G as a continuation. The first two measures show the resulting 6 note shape. I then found that adding an F# to the end of it turned it into something I could use over a Bm6/9 chord. To put this idea into context, I came up with a quasi-B minor blues, which you can see in the rest of the example.

#177 This is the next stage in the evolution of this material and are shown here marked A B and C. Example A is an extension of the 6-note shape shown in the first 2 bars of #176. The four notes I added are a sequence of the proceeding four notes (down a major 3rd) resulting in a 10-note shape. Example B is a further extension of the idea by adding the last F and F#. The resulting 12 note shape (which I discovered after the fact…thanks Florian Loebermann…is a 12-tone row) is shown in brackets. This example illustrates how the shape functions as a loop (with the first two notes transposed up an octave). Example C places the idea once again in the context of a quasi-B minor blues. (8 bars in this case)

#178 Here is a re-ordering of the notes from yesterday's 12 tone row. The 1st line is descending and the 2nd is its mirror image. As you can see, the three groups of four are symmetrical groups moving down (or up) in major 3rds. And to clarify, when I say G, Eb and B, I'm not thinking major or minor…just the root and fifth with chromatic neighbours.

#179 Okay, so today we are going to break down the 12-tone row from yesterday and look at one of the four note groups. i.e., the second group in Eb. Here, we take those four notes and show the four possible directional combinations and their mirror images. (marked 1a-4b)

#180 Today's material is based on yesterday's four note group and it's directional combinations. Here we take those four directional combinations and modulate every four notes.

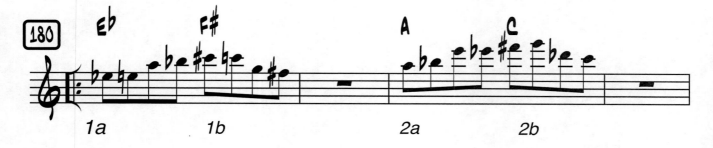

#181 Today's example takes mirror images 2b and 1b from #179 and moves them down in major thirds. Line 2 is the same material but shifted over by an 8th note. I heard the last phrase as a way to finish the material with something that is slightly different.

#182 Today we are taking shape 1a from post #179 and stacking it in major 3rds. Even though there are a lot of avoid tones, it works over E13 because of where it ends.

#183 Since this is a leap year, today's post marks our half way point (should have called it 366 days of practice). So, in that spirit, here's a shape taken from rearranging the notes in the F augmented scale into two augmented triads (F+ and Ab+) and then it's mirror image.

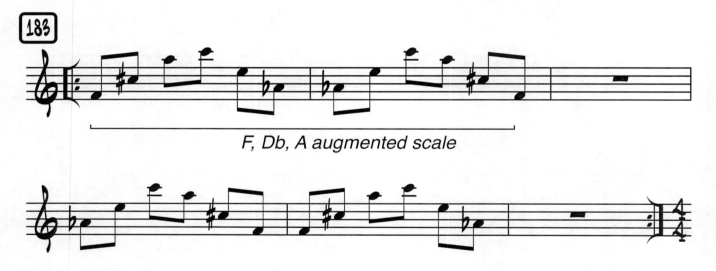

#184 Today's example combines two elements. First a 12 tone row from which I use the first 7 notes in bar 2 and second, to start the line I use the first 6 notes of yesterday's augmented scale shape. The D and D# on beat 4 of bar 1 function as a link. I then use the combined elements over a 2-5-1 in G.

#185 Here is another 2-5-1 in F that utilizes the shape from post #183. This time it starts on beat 3 of bar 1.

#186 This is a shape that I don't necessarily think of/use only when I'm playing in 5/4.... just notated it this way for the sake of seeing-feeling how to phrase it correctly. This one works well in a rubato/cadenza situation.

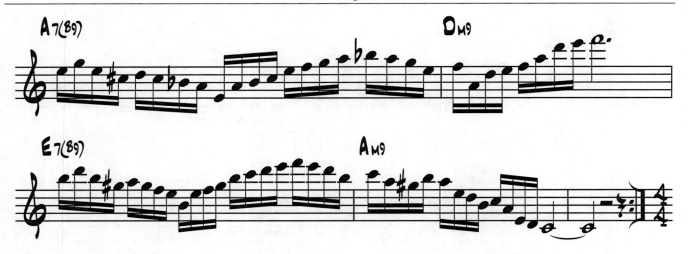

#187 Here's a 5-1 in F minor that utilizes fragments of the altered and harmonic minor scales over the 5 chord.

#188 This is a 2-5 in E that uses the tri-tone sub in both measures.

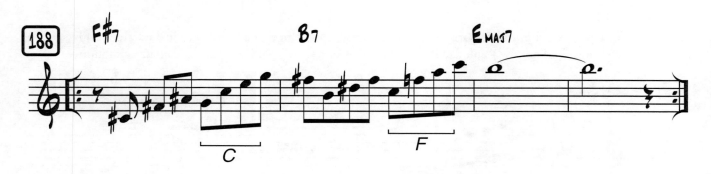

#189 Here's a 2-5 in Eb that uses the tritone sub in bar 1 and the melodic minor in bar 2.

#190 Here's a 2-5 in G, who's color/surprise comes from descending guide tone line that leads to the F# which quickly modulates to Bbm in the first measure. The 2nd measure is diatonic with some chromatic passing tones which leads you to the Bb on beat four which becomes the 5th of Eb melodic minor making the chord D7alt for one beat.

#191 I realize I've been posting a lot of 2-5-1 ideas that stop when we get to the tonic chord. So, we're going to spend a few days looking at what to play when you finally get there. Here is a possible resolution of yesterday's idea, shown here in a different key.

#192 As mentioned yesterday, we're going to spend a few days on material to use over the tonic chord. For this one, I've included two options for the resolution that incorporate the movement from the #5 to the natural 5.

#193 More material to play over the tonic chord. Beats 2 and 3 function as a long embellishment/interrupter as the line would work if you jumped from beat 1 to 4. Also, beat three is a nice wraparound as it includes the #4 and #5.

#194 Another tonic line with chromatic passing tones that add motion and color.

#195 Here is a line that incorporates some superimposed harmony. The tonic acts as a link between C and Db major.

#196 Here's one that modulates to Db in the middle. Of course, you don't have to play the whole line. This one, sounds good if you stop on beat three of measure two.

#197 Today we are taking the first 12 notes of yesterday's example and moves it up and down in major thirds. The common/transitional notes are bracketed.

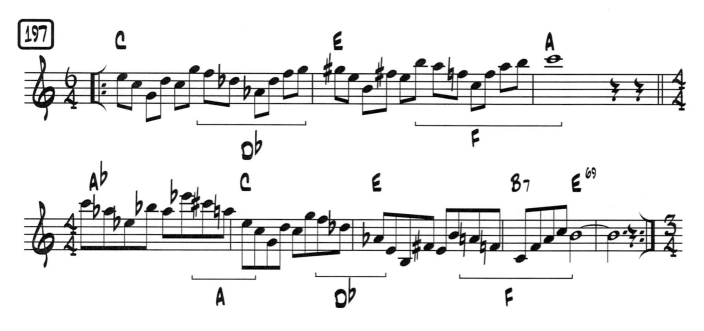

#198 Here's another shape to play over the tonic chord. No superimpositions here, just chromatic neighbour and passing tones. The second line over the 5 chord is a sequence of the first line, with a slight variation of the first.

#199 Switching gears away from things to play over the tonic chord. Here's something to use over the 2 chord. This example plays around with moving the 5th, 7th and 9th up and down in half steps.

#200 Here's a continuation of yesterday's idea. Over the five chord I am extracting a B and Ab triad from the half-whole scale. And over the tonic I'm using a passing chord that is very close to the diminished major. The D# replaces the C# making it Gminmaj9(b6) instead of Gdimmaj9. I suggest playing it both ways...with a C# and then as written...to hear and feel the subtle difference.

#201 Here's a pretty basic 2-5 in C. I like this one because the line leads you to the third of the tonic and instead takes you to the #4 which starts the wraparound which includes the #5 that finally resolves to the 5th.

#202 This is a variation on the resolution from #201 moving down in major 3rds.

#203 Today's example is a 2-5 in Eb. It's pretty simple, the first two beats are a half step above the root, but quite effective. This also functions as a sequence because the shape in bar two resolves the shape in the first measure.

#204 Here's another one that's similar to yesterday's post in that it starts a half step up. After that, it moves up in whole steps with the Eb and F being kind of a double approach to the G on beat 1 of bar 2. For all of these examples with simple resolutions, we could go back to the earlier posts and try to incorporate some of the more involved cadences.

#205 Don't think I've covered this yet. Developing the ability to hear and clearly outline the 6 chord setting up the 2 chord is extremely important. In the example above, even if changes were Cmaj7 for 2 measures, you could still imply the A7. The C# (leading tone in D minor) is powerful, as it conveys a lot of forward motion.

#206 Here is another example that shows how to get to the 6 chord. In this one, the C# is slightly delayed and comes on beat three. Except for the Db major7 on beat 3 of bar 4, everything else is diatonic but uses chromatic passing and approach notes.

#207 More 6 chord-based material. Today we are putting it at the end of the four-bar cycle as opposed to the second measure. Also, a big difference in today's example is that we are getting the feeling of the 6 chord setting up the 2 chord in bar 5 without the use of the leading tone. (no C#) Here the Bb and F takes its place. The rest of the example is a sequence with the A-E to Ab-Eb in bar 6 echoing what happened in bar 4.

#208 Here's a line over the first four bars of rhythm changes.

#209 Here's another turnaround. This one utilizes ascending scales and sequences.

#210 Today's turnaround is closely related to yesterdays. We get to the 6 chord two beats earlier (C and D natural in bar 1, and when we do, the sound is a little bit more modern. Again, a shape in bar 2 is extracted from the half/whole scale. Beats three and four of measure two brings it back to more traditional language, which is the tone this example uses in its resolution.

#211 Here's a 3-6-2-5 where the 3 and 2 chords are half-diminished...think of the last six measures of Stella. Over the Em7(b5), I'm thinking and hearing G Dorian which for me, is much easier than thinking/hearing A Locrian. For the 2-5 in C, I am using the appropriate melodic minor scales. The Db triad on beats 3 and 4 can be extracted from either of the melodic minor scale or the half/whole scale.

#212 R.I.P. Steve Grossman

#213 Here's a 2-5 in C that is based on Giant Steps/Countdown (major 3rd) based movements but not the exact Coltrane progression. This could also be played over just a vamp in C Major.

#214 Coltrane changes in A major.

#215 Here's a line in F major that can be used in several situations. Each repeat uses a different set of chord changes. It can be broken down into several smaller components.

#216 Here's a line in D minor that briefly moves up to Eb minor. The line is then repeated in G minor.

#217 Today's examples use the 2nd (Phyrgian natural 6) and 7th (Altered) modes of D melodic minor. They use the same material for the pick-up and first measure. After that, the line changes but uses the same shape to resolve to the major 7th of their respective target keys. The third ending is a freely associated line that uses the F# augmented scale.

#218 Here's a 2-5 in C that uses chromaticism on the 2 chord to give it motion and direction into the 5 chord, where basic language is used to lead us to the altered resolution/ending of the phrase.

#219 This is a line over Esus/Bm7 that slips down a half step before the resolution. The line then modulates down a tri-tone.

#220 Here's a line over Cm7/F7 that starts a half step above and uses A#/Bb as the common tone/link between the two keys. The line then repeats a minor third lower.

(Repeat and fade)

#221 Here's a simple phrase that moves from the tonic through the subdominant and dominant. This one is fun when you move it up and down through the different intervallic families. This example moves down in major 3rds.

#222 Here's a long melodic minor line that moves from 5-1. When we get to the tonic chord the first two bars of the line are transposed to the tonic key. As always, these long lines can be broken down to smaller components and practiced separately.

#223 We talked about breaking yesterday's example down into smaller components and working them. Here is an example of that. The first two bars take measure two from yesterday and moves it up in minor thirds. Then bars 3 and 4 takes measure three and moves it down in major thirds.

#224 Here's another 2-5 that starts a half step away. The first two beats imply a pick-up of Em7. The second measure is a sequence of the first measure's shape and utilizes an E triad over Bb7. I'm giving you two different endings that both start in the same place.

# 225 This is a 5-1 example that uses the major 7th over the dominant chord which adds a really nice unexpected color.

#226 Here's a simple two measure progression. The line isolates the root and seventh (except the last chord of the progression) of each chord. Because the line changes direction in each key, you have to practice this one twice. First time as written, then the second time starting down.

(continue)

#227 Here's an extended diminished line. The challenge with this scale is to get away from playing patterns. So here, every four notes are a different shape. As usual, each shape can be isolated and worked separately. There are also some nice 8 and 12 note combinations that could be extracted and worked on. This one also works if you play it backwards.

#228 This is a line that alternates between Lydian and Dorian while moving down in half steps.

#229 Same concept/progression as yesterday. To me, these lines/progressions have a film score quality to them.

#230 Another variation on the posts that started a couple days ago. This one goes from Lydian to Dorian as well, but goes through both modes before modulating down a half step. This is kind of a neat trick, you could switch modes by switching triad pairs. For Fmaj7(#11) they are F and G. And for Fm13 they are Fm and Gm.

#231 Here are two examples that use both the major and b7 over the dominant chord.

#232 Here's a 5-1 resolution in F that uses diminished shapes from prior posts.

#233 Today's example is another one that uses both the major 7th and the b7th on the dominant chord.

(repeat and fade)

#234 Here's an example over a 2-5 in G. The melodic material is based on the movement of the 9th-b13th-9th (the first note of every bar) Underneath in parentheses are the chords you're actually playing/thinking.

#235 There are 24 ways to combine 4 notes. So here is an example that uses the same principle as #234 but uses a different combination/shape over each chord.

#236 Here's another variation on #234 that uses different shapes.

#237 Here's a shape over Cm11 that kind of has a Steve Reich vibe to it. This is another idea that can be broken down into smaller components and put through the routine. Will post some examples over the next couple of days.

#238 Here are two variations on post #237. As you can see, in the first variation I use the D as a link to extend the idea and modulate to Em9. In the second variation I replace the D with a Db which moves it to Ebm9.

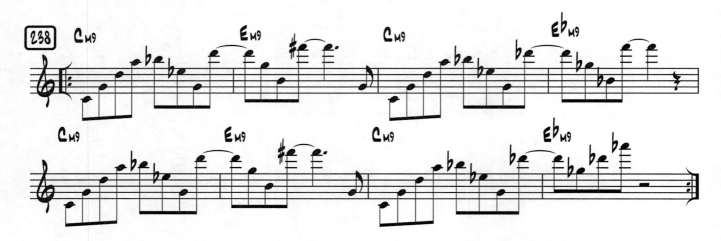

#239 Here are three more variations on #237. They all change the octave and/or direction of the first four notes. Also, the G sharps are replaced by G naturals in order to accommodate the chord progression.

#240 Here's the last variation on post #237. As you can see, this one moves further away from the original shape while still maintaining the basic feel and color.

#241 Here's the shape/progression that we will be looking at over the next couple of days.

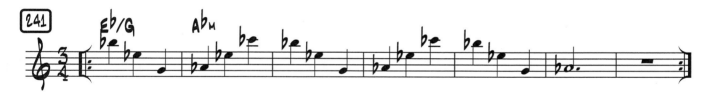

#242 Starting to look at yesterday's post, here are the four possible directional combinations. This example moves up in minor 3rds and down for the last one.

#243 Here's the first variation on #242. Instead of 5-1, this example goes from 1 to 5. And here the tonic is major instead of minor. We now have 16 versions to work with i.e., 5-1, 1-5 in major and minor with 4 directional combinations each.

#244 Here are four variations on posts #242 and 243. The first two are 5-1 in minor, going up in whole steps and then 5-1 major, going up in major thirds. The next two are 1-5 in minor, going up in minor thirds and 1-5 in major, going down in whole steps.

#245 More variations on material we've been looking at since #241 but now with added notes (bracketed) for more melodic flow and variety.

#246 Here are two more variations. For these two, the extra notes come after the two open triads. Remember, these also work going up and down in all intervallic groups.

#247 More variations with added notes.

#248 Further adventures with 5-1 open triads. The shape used in these examples is a little different. As you can see, the root of the 5 chord and the 5th of the 1 chord function as pivot notes.

#249 Here are some more variations on the open triad concept. These use wraparounds for both the 5 and 1 chords.

#250 Here are some more elaborate variations on the open triad concept.

#251 Another variation on the open triad 5-1 concept. This one moves up in 4ths.

#252 Last one in the open triad series for now. This one is a little different because the 5 chord includes the (b9) and it resolves to the 1 chord with a (b6). I like this one because the middle two notes stay the same while the first and fourth notes move up in half steps. Here I've given you the four different directional combinations. These examples move down in whole steps (lines 1 and 3) and up in whole steps (lines 2 and 4). But should be practiced in the other intervallic combinations.

#253 Today's example is a complete shifting of gears away from the open triads that we've been looking at for the last several days. This one is a close knit, kind of snaky chromatic line that is shown here over a II7-V7 in D minor but will also work over a minor 2-5, or just D minor.

#254 Here's a complete about face from yesterday's dark chromatic line. This melody uses only notes from the major scale and is influenced by Aaron Copland. I call this mood Americana (when it was bright and optimistic). The first time through, the melody is played without any chords. After that, I've given two of the many possible reharmonizations.

#255 Here are two lines that utilize what I call extended chromatic wrap arounds. They work over C minor or as shown, over a minor 2-5.

#256 Here's a 2-5 in Eb where the shape at the beginning of the line is sequenced at the end.

#257 Here is a 2-5 in C major where the underlying concept is one of switching between Dm7 and Dm7(b5). This one has two examples. The first uses 8th notes which results in the line ascending on the 2 and descending on the 5. The second uses 16th notes so the line ascends and descends over both chords.

**#258** Here's a 5-1 in Bb that creates tension by using the D7(#9) and B triad from the half whole scale. The tension gets resolved when we get to the D on beat 5 which sets up the syncopated release of the tonic.

**#259** One of my favorite sounds is minor triads in major thirds. I call this my Danny Elfman sound. The notes with circles above/below them are common tones between the different triads. The Bb min triad in the 5th measure starts the cycle again.

**#260** Another example of minor triads, this time adding the major 7th, in major thirds. Another layer of interest is added by adding the V7alt chord before moving to the next triad a major 3rd higher. Note that the triad over the 5 chord stays the same. So, Gm moving to Gm/F# which results in F#7alt which then resolves to Bm moving to Bm/Bb (Bb7alt) etc…

#261 Here's the descending version of yesterday's example. This one adds the 2nd as a passing tone into the next key.

#262 Another example of how minor tonalities moving up in major thirds also function as altered dominants.

#263 This is a variation on #262.

#264 Another variation of the material we've been talking about the last couple days. Adding the lower neighbor b5 adds a nice dark color. And as you can see, the descending versions shape is a little different.

#265 RIP Sean Connery

#266 More material based on minor keys moving in major thirds.

#267 For the next several days we are going to move away from minor keys in major 3rds to major keys in major 3rds. This material is based on Coltrane's three tonic system.

#268 Day two of major keys moving in major thirds. This is where I stray from strict Coltrane changes because I don't include the 5 chord. Here we just move major 7th chords up in major 3rds. Also note the use of the first four note wraparounds in each key, they add a lot of color and motion.

#269 This is a continuation of the material based on major thirds. The first one descends and the second descends.

#270 This one is based on a concept that I call major tone rows. The idea is to use all seven notes of the scale before repeating one. The result is another example of the mood that I call Aaron Coplandish-Americana. See #254, which is not a major tone row because some notes are repeated before all are 7 notes are used.

#271 Developing yesterday's concept, the 7 note row can be derived from any type of scale. Here are two 7 note tone rows. The first in A harmonic minor, with the tonic being the link to its relative C major.

#272 Moving back to major 3rd based material. Each line starts the same and ends with a variation of the resolution. Also, this one goes back to adding the 5 chord before the 1.

#273 Large Leaps

#274 More large leaps. Technically the minor chords could be major because of the absence of the third. It's just that in my mind's ear, I am hearing minor tonalities moving in major thirds. In the fourth measure, the tonic becomes the 5 chord.

#275 This one uses the Abm6/9 (subset of Ab melodic minor) over G7alt. Since it resolves to the 5th, the chord could be major or minor.

#276 Here's a fun line that is made up mostly of 2nds, 4ths, and 5ths. The 2-5-1 or just the 5-1 can be played separately depending on the context.

#277 Here's a simple pentatonic based 2-5 in C.

#278 Here's a figure that feels like it could be a starting motor rhythm figure for a tune. The minor 3rd and 2nd alternate directions (3rd-2nd in measure one and 2nd-3rd in measure two.)

*(repeat and fade)*

#279 This is 5-1 diatonic line with chromatic embellishments that sequences itself.

#280 This 2-5 in Bb uses a pick up a half step below the 2 chord.

#281 Autumn Leaves changes with half step approaches. I condensed the resolution resulting in a 7 bar phrase. The high descending melody works as a counterpoint against the root movement. With this one, you have to adjust the octaves depending on what key you are in. On the backing track, I used one of my favorite tunes by the great Don Grolnick, The Four Sleepers, as a counterpoint.

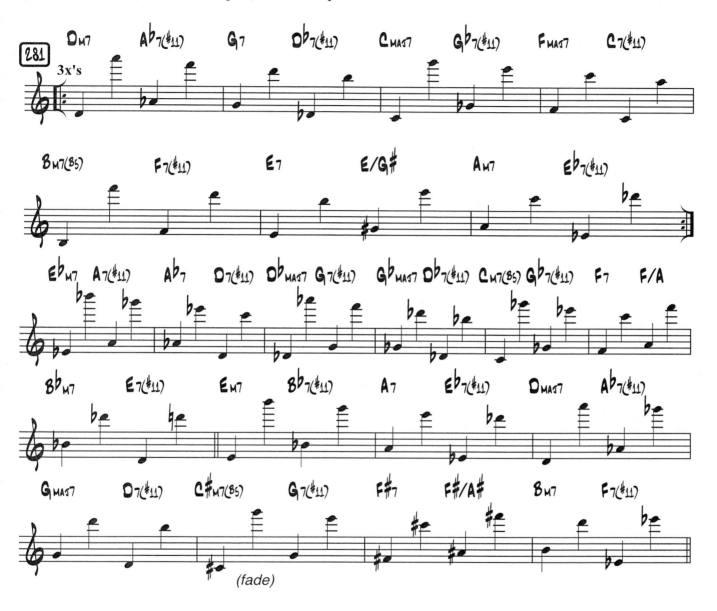

(fade)

#282 Here's a line that descends in major 3rds. You can also take just the 2nd, 4th and 6th measures and when you do that, you get Giant Steps changes.

#283 A variation on #282.

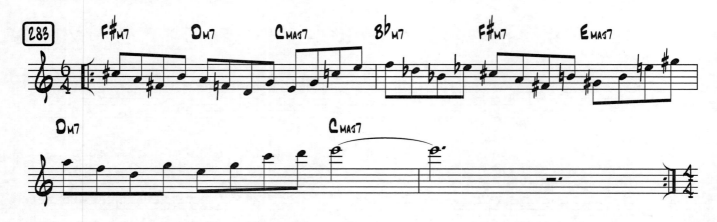

#284 Here's a 5-1 that uses wider piano based voicings.

*(repeat and fade)*

#285 This is another one that's based on piano voicings; it reminds me of Bill Evans' type voicings with moving inner/outer voices. This example also draws heavily on the mood of Ravel's masterpiece La Valse.

#286 This example explores descending upper voices over pedal point ostinatos.

*(repeat and fade)*

#287 Here's a 2-5-1 that uses three shapes that are extracted from the half-whole scale. This line works both Ab and F major since they share the same half-whole scale. In F the line resolves to the 3rd and in Ab, to the 5th.

#288 Here's a 2-5 in C. The second measure can be used on its own over a two measure 2-5.

#289 Here's a 2-5 in C that uses mainly 4th and 5ths. The beaming on the second line reflects the inherent grouping of the eighth notes.

#290 Here's a 2-5-1 which gives the feeling of two things happening at once i.e., the bass notes and an ostinato on top.

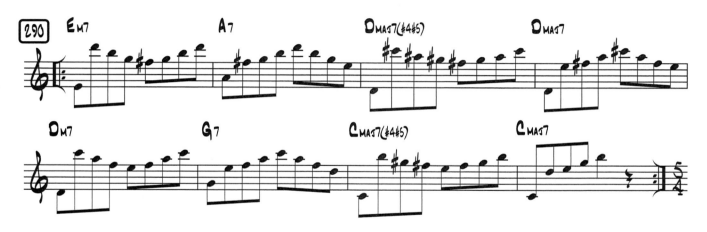

#291 Here's a 7(#9) shape that moves between 2-3 and 3-3 groupings that moves down and up in major 3rds.

#292 Today's idea is more of an etude...but works really well in a cadenza situation. Minor sixth chords...with an alternate fingering at the top...moving down in major thirds. The F sharp that ends the idea in Eb minor becomes the root of F# minor, which would continue the cycle.

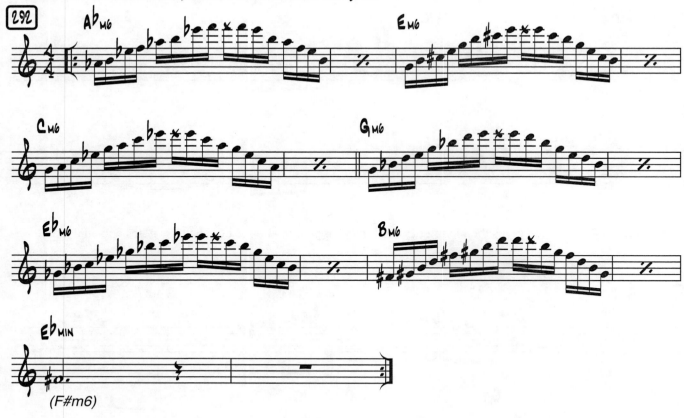

#293 Here's are two 2-5's in G. The first one utilizes the three major triads related by major thirds relative to G major (G,Eb,B). The second one uses Coltrane changes which as you can see uses the same three triads as in the first example but with their Vsus chords before them and with each triad being tonicized instead of being superimposed.

#294 Here's a turnaround in A major that starts with an F triad over Bm9. These three notes alternate with the natural 5th (F-F#), major 7th (A-A#) and natural 9th (C-C#) of the chord. The same thing happens with the G triad over C#m7.

#295 Here is an altered 5-1 in D minor. This idea can be started at different points, so it works in other meters as well. More on this tomorrow.

#296 Here are two variations based on yesterday's post.

#297 Here's a descending shape that starts with a 12 tone row that was inspired by a line from one of several masterpiece cadenzas by John Coltrane on "I Want To Talk About You." This one is from "Live In Stockholm"

#298 Today's example is a turnaround in A major. There are 6 different examples that all start with the same material and then branch off with each one having its own resolution.

#299 The next couple of posts are going to deal with wide intervals. On this one, after playing the root of each chord, the next three notes are stacked fifths but in a different order. So in the first measure the original note order would be F-Ab-Eb-Bb which is changed to F-Eb-Ab-Bb. That same pattern continues for the entire example.

#300 This one is a "classical" sounding progression composed mainly of descending 1st inversion triads.

#301 More material based on stacked 5ths. (See #299) I really like the movement from G9 to G7alt that results by moving the 5ths down a half step.

#302 Here's a descending line who's three main components are ascending. This one is definitely influenced by Chopin.

#303 Another one influenced my Chopin...lots of chromatic passing tones and wraparounds.

#304 Here's a nice ascending line over sus chords that uses half step approaches to start each three-note group.

#305 The next three examples will be melodic minor lines over different roots to illustrate how the same line changes color depending on the mode. This one uses the C# melodic minor shape over C7alt and then Ebsus(b9).

#306 This one uses an F# melodic minor shape over F7alt and B7(#11).

**#307** This last one uses a G melodic minor shape over C9(#11) and Asus(b9).

**#308** Here's a turnaround in Bb who's main material is derived from the augmented scale. The concept is to spread out the scale into three groups of 5ths that are extracted from the scale. So, C-Eb-E-G-Ab-B-C becomes C-G, E-B, Ab-E. I look at this grouping as the root and fifth of C, E and Ab major triads. In this example I start with E-B then Eb-Ab (reverses the order) and C-G, which are the root and fifth of the chord we are playing, giving it a strong sense of resolution and direction.

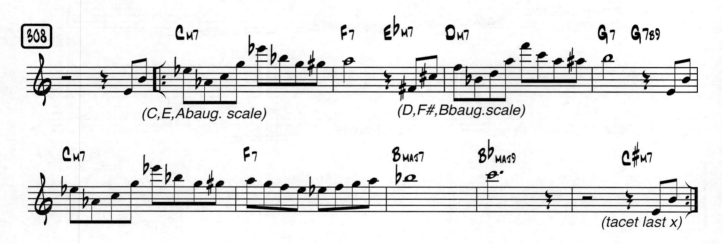

**#309** This is a simple tonic, sub-dominant, dominant exchange that moves from D to F# major and then back down.

#310 This line is based on material that we covered starting in post #262. i.e., minor chords moving up in major thirds.

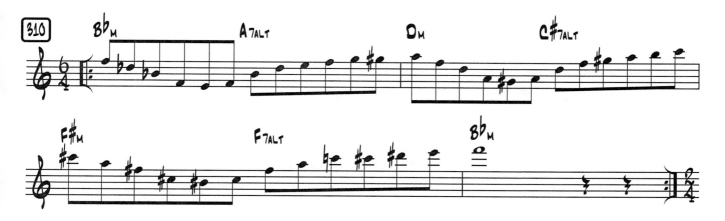

#311 Minor triads moving down in major thirds. Note the wrap around to the fifth of each triad where the b6 and b5 add a dark color.

(tacet last x)

#312 This one is major triads moving up in major thirds. Here, the passing tones are chromatic between the 3rd and 5th.

#313 Today's example started as the first four measure descending ornamented line. While making the backing track to this one, I heard the four measure answer which appeared organically. No theory behind it, just connecting be-bopish language. I like this answer because it balances the more mechanical feeling of the first four bars.

#314 This is a pretty simple 2-5 line with the exception of two notes. On beat 5, the F# and B approach the 9th and 5th of the chord from a half step below, these notes are unexpected and create tension and surprise if only for one beat. But that one beat is enough to make this line feel and sound fresh.

#315 Here's a simple chord progression with the bass note and moving upper voice. This is a nice workout in every key and good for flexibility and intonation.

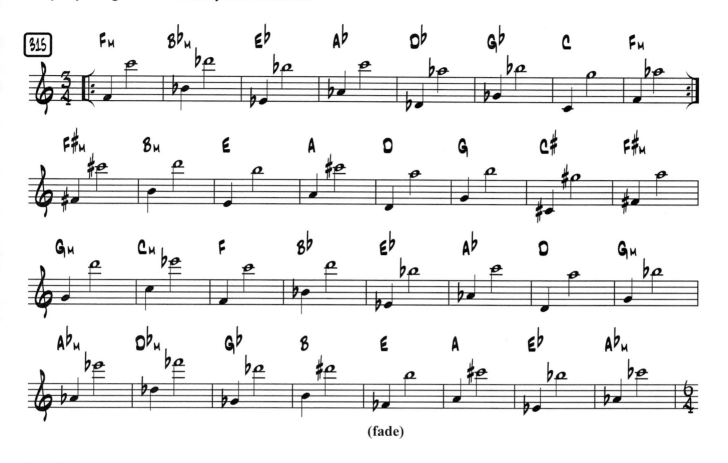

(fade)

#316 This example explores the use of open 5ths.

#317 This one looks at the 5-1 open triads that we examined starting in post #241 resolving to major then minor with a pivot note (the root of the 5 chord becomes the 5th of the tonic).

#318 Here's another example of wide intervals. This one is a bass line with high register answers. The chord progression is something we've looked at before. i.e., minor keys moving in major thirds. In bar three, the tonic becomes a V7 which takes us into another group of minor keys in major thirds.

#319 Here's a fairly simple 2-5 in D. The two note wrap around pick up gives it a slightly twisted character.

#320 Here's another example based on Coltrane's three tonic system. This one is major keys moving up in major thirds. The use of the #5 as a passing tone adds a nice color and also foreshadows the next key (the #5 becomes the 3rd of the next tonality). Also, the use of the sus(b9) chord in place of the usual V7 or Vsus adds a darker color to the progression.

#321 More Giant Steps based material. This one is cool because the line over the tonic incorporates the #5 triad.

#322 Here's an arpeggiated piano voicing that utilizes upper structure triads over the roots. The progression is 2-5's descending by half steps. The element that gives it its character is the use of the #5 triad over the tonic chord which then becomes the triad based on the minor third of the 2 chord. (Cmaj7(#5)=E/C, C#m7=E/C#).

#323 Here's another fun way of working on diatonic 7th chords. It's important to think of the quality of every degree of the scale (shown under the chords of the vamp). Sometimes in some of the easier keys, it's easy to let your fingers do their thing without thinking about what you're playing.

#324 This one is another piano based ostinato that in the process of creating the backing track turned into this little tune.

*(repeat and fade)*

#325 This example uses triad pairs that are displaced by an octave, i.e., the 2nd triad is an octave higher than the 1st which results in a beautiful, open sound. Over Fm7, the triad pair of A-B is used, which is actually the wrong one. The correct one would be Ab-Bb but for this example, we're using A-B because the top D# functions as a link to the 7th of Fm7 (D#/Eb). At this point, the triad is still not resolved until the third beat with leads us to the 5 chord and its be-bop scale. The descending pair of E-F# are then used giving us Bb7alt and Eb-F are used over the tonic resulting in Ebmaj7(#11). The progression then moves down in whole steps.

*(repeat and fade)*

#326 The next few days we will be looking at more shapes that are extracted from the half-whole diminished scale.

#327 Day two of half-whole shapes. Yesterday's example moved up in minor 3rds with the roots of the chords, so the tensions stayed the same. Today's line moves down in minor 3rds with the chords moving up in minor 3rds, so the quality of the chords change slightly.

#328 This is another one that got away from me while I was creating the backing track. This example started with just the first 8 notes but felt like it wanted to be expanded, so I followed my ear and turned it into the 8 bar blues.

*(repeat and fade)*

#329 The last days of half-whole shapes. Like yesterday's example, this one started with just the first 8 notes but then turned itself into this 4 bar blues.

(repeat and fade)

#330 This is a minor figure that include both the natural and flat 5; another one that has a spooky, cinematic quality.

(repeat and fade)

#331 Major 7th chords followed by their relative minor 7ths, descending in major 3rds.

#332 This one is min7th chords moving down in major thirds. This movement and the sound/feeling it creates reminds me of Prokofiev.

(tacet last x)

#333 This is another one that got away from me when creating the backing track. It started with just the first 5 beat ostinato. I then started fooling around with the idea of what that line would sound like over every degree of the Eb melodic minor scale. The first 7 measures are a result of that idea. I changed the idea slightly in order to leave some space to breathe. When the line cadenced on the Gm7, I heard it continuing, now in a slightly different configuration, over the modes of the Bb major scale with the Gm7 functioning as the iv minor. When those 7 measures cadence on the Bb7(b6), I heard it moving back to the Eb melodic minor scale with the Bb7(b6) functioning as the 5th mode, mixolydian b6. Once again, the figure is transformed for the last 7 bars. This is a really helpful exercise. By taking any figure that clearly spells out the sound of the tonic chord and then changing the root, you will start to develop a catalog of sounds/emotions for each mode of that particular scale. I find this skill to be very helpful when composing.

#334 Here are 4 ascending major scales with chromatic neighbor tones. Each one uses a different harmonization.

(tacet last x)

#335 Here is the same melodic minor shape harmonized in four different ways.

1. C7ALT                                                    Fм9
2. F#7(#11)                                                 FMAJ7
3. Eᵇsus(♭9)                                               FMAJ7
4. C#м⁶9                                                    Fм9

#336 This one deals with material based on a concept that we've seen several times already, i.e., minor tonalities that become altered chords by shifting the root down a half step. This example moves up in major 3rds and is slightly changed in the second 4 bars.

#337 Minor 7th chords moving up and down in major 3rds with the last one changing to its relative dominant which resolves to its tonic chord.

#338 This one has major 6th chords moving up in minor 3rds.

*(tacet last x)*

#339 More material based on the concept mentioned in #336

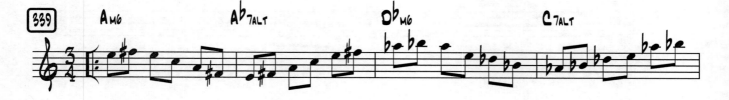

#340 This one is kind of cool. It is Giant Steps changes but substituting maj7(#11) chords for V7 chords, i.e., Db/B for B7 going to E major.

#341 Here's a 2-5 in Ab that goes from a shape in Dbmaj7 over Bbm7 (legal) which then moves the same shape up a minor 3rd to Emaj7 over Eb7alt (illegal) but the symmetry justifies the wrong notes. The two shapes over the tonic chord go from Ab to C which results in the tonic chord going from Ionian to Lydian Augmented.

**#342** This one is a descending version of #338. Notice that the movement from major to minor is reversed.

(tacet last x)

**#343** Here's a descending version of #339 but set over a V713 instead of a V7alt chord.

**#344** This one started out as a line over a minor 2-5 (bars 2 and 3) that turned into a minor blues during the making of the backing track.

#345 Here's an eight note shape that was extracted from the half-whole scale. What's kind of interesting about this progression is that we're used to hearing diminished based material moving in minor thirds. This one, moves down in major thirds giving it a somewhat fresher sound.

#346 I cheated on this one because I took the material over the V chord from one of John Coltrane's masterpiece cadenzas on I Want To Talk About You. This one is from Live At Birdland. The line over the tonic is based on Coltrane's language.

#347 This one is related to #345, i.e., diminished material moving in major 3rds.

#348 Here's a 2-5 line that approaches the 2 chord from a half step above. Very simple but is a very effective way to create tension and motion.

#349 This is a fun way to work on sus chords. The root functions as a pedal point while the upper voice moves up and down.

#350 Here's some more open triad based material. This one is a 2-5 that is approached by its 6 chord that has a Bach cello suite vibe.

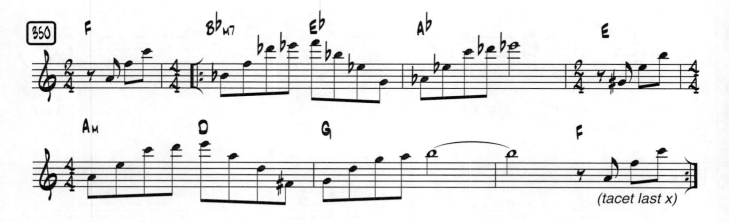

#351 This is a 2-5 in F and then another in G. Both start with a fragment over the 2 chord taken from another masterpiece cadenza by John Coltrane on I Want To Talk About You. This material is from Live in Stockholm. After that, I followed my ear and used different resolutions for each key. The first uses the F augmented scale and the second treats the tonic with a passing chord, i.e., Gminmaj9(#5) – Gmaj9.

#352 Here's a classical sounding/inspired ascending harmonic minor line that uses chromatic neighbor and wrap around tones. This is another one that started out with the first phrase that extended itself when I created the backing track.

#353 This one is a 2-5 in B that takes the material (in brackets) from the 2 chord and moves it up a minor 3rd over the 5.

#354 Here's a progression that we've looked at several times earlier in the book. It moves from Lydian to Dorian, then down in half steps using the last note in Dorian as the first note in Lydian.

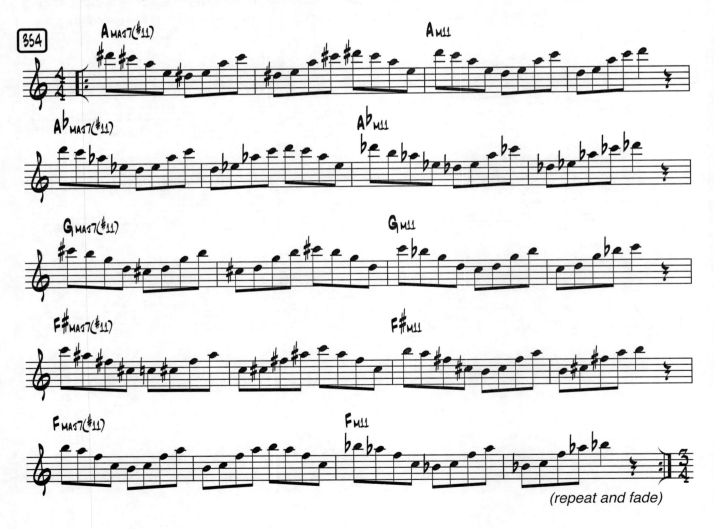

#355 This one uses the same progression as the previous example but with different harmonic rhythms.

(repeat and fade)

#356 This one is what I like to call a dressed up 5-1. The 5 chord is treated as a sus (b9) chord and the tonic uses the passing diminished major seventh sound.

#357 Here's a turnaround in Bb that shows the superimposed triads and seventh chords underneath.

#358 Here's a major 2-5 where the 2 chord is half diminished. Since the resolution note is the 5th, the tonic chord could also be minor.

#359 This one is a variation of #353.

#360 This one is an etude on minor 6th chords descending in major 3rds.

#361 This is an exercise utilizing the interval of a major seventh extracted from the diminished scale.

*(repeat and fade)*

#362 Here's a be-bop line that moves down in major thirds where the resolution tone becomes the starting point for the next key.

#363 This is a 12 tone row that resolves to D and then it's mirror image which resolves to G.

#364 Here's a 4th based example that started with the first phrase and then became what is it while I was creating the backing track.

(tacet last x)

#365 Here's some material based on descending diatonic 3rds moving down in major 3rds. First over major 7th chords and then their corresponding dominant sus chords.

#366 The last one goes through the four families of major 3rds with a different shape for every key.

# Example From Original Notebook

# About the Author

Born in Detroit, Rick Margitza has studied classical saxophone with Donald Sinta at the university of Michigan, and jazz with Sonny Stitt, Gerry Niewood, Michael Brecker, Gary Campbell and David Liebman. He studied at Wayne State University in Detroit, the Berklee School of Music in Boston, the University of Miami, and graduated with a bachelors of music from the Loyola University in New Orleans. After living in New Orleans, Margitza moved to New York in 1989. He has performed and/or recorded with McCoy Tyner, Bobby Hutcherson, Tony Williams, Eddie Gomez, Chick Corea, Maria Schneider, Dave Douglas and Miles Davis. He has led his own band and performed in clubs, concert halls and festivals around the world. His 10 albums as a leader document the evolution of his playing as well as his growth as a composer. Margitza has also composed music for orchestra including two symphonies and a saxophone concerto. He currently lives in Paris since moving there in 2003. He is of Eastern European Gypsy decent and is part of the new band called Gypsy Tenors with fellow countrymen Gabor Bolla and Tony Lakatos. His two new recordings-Cheap Thrills-The South Florida Jazz Orchestra plays the music of Rick Margitza and Sacred Hearts, recorded with his French quartet, were released in 2020 and 2021.

As well as performing and recording around the world, Rick Margitza has committed himself to the evolving field of jazz education. His master classes in everything from improvisation to composition to practice techniques are geared towards helping students find and cultivate their individual voices.

- PRINCETON UNIVERSITY
- PHILADELPHIA COLLEGE FOR THE ARTS
- THE NEW SCHOOL (NEW YORK CITY)
- UNIVERSITY OF MIAMI
- INTERLOCHEN ACADEMY FOR THE ARTS
- LOYOLA UNIVERSITY (NEW ORLEANS)
- NEW ORLEANS CENTER FOR THE CREATIVE ARTS
- OLD DOMINION UNIVERSITY (ARTIST IN RESIDENCE)
- UNIVERSITY OF WHITEWATER, WISCONSIN
- WAYNE STATE UNIVERSITY
- WESTERN MICHIGAN UNIVERSTIY
- SIBELIUS ACADEMY, HELSINKI FINLAND
- ROYAL CONSERVATORY THE HAGUE
- CITE DE LA MUSIQUE, PARIS

# The Sher Music Co. Catalog

visit **SherMusic.com** for more information and to order online.

## BEST-SELLING BOOKS BY MARK LEVINE
The Jazz Theory Book
The Jazz Piano Book
Jazz Piano Masterclass: The Drop 2 Book
How To Voice Standards at the Piano

## THE WORLD'S BEST FAKE BOOKS
The New Real Book - Vol. 1 - C, Bb and Eb
The New Real Book - Vol. 2 - C, Bb and Eb
The New Real Book - Vol. 3 - C, Bb, Eb & Bass Clef

The Real Easy Book - Vol. 1 - C, Bb, Eb & Bass Clef
The Real Easy Book - Vol. 2 - C, Bb, Eb & Bass Clef
The Real Easy Book - Vol. 3 - C, Bb, Eb & Bass Clef
The Latin Real Easy Book - C, Bb, Eb & Bass Clef
Drum Supplement for Real Easy Book - Vol. 1

The Standards Real Book - C, Bb and Eb
The Latin Real Book - C, Bb and Eb
The Real Cool Book - Octet charts from the 1950s
The All-Jazz Real Book - with selected audio
The European Real Book - with selected audio
The Best of Sher Music Real Books - C, Bb & Eb
The World's Greatest Fake Book - C only
Jazz Arrangements of Public Domain Songs
The Yellowjackets Songbook - separate parts

## LATIN MUSIC BOOKS
Contemporary Latin Jazz Guitar - by Neff Irizarry
Decoding Afro-Cuban Jazz - by Mauleon & Valdes
The Salsa Guidebook - by Rebeca Mauleõn
101 Montunos - by Rebeca Mauleõn
The Latin Bass Book - by Oscar Stagnaro & Chuck Sher
The Latin Real Book - C, Bb, & Eb
The True Cuban Bass - by Carlos del Puerto
The Brazilian Guitar Book - by Nelson Faria
Inside the Brazilian Rhythm Section - Faria/Korman
Conga Drummer's Guidebook - by Michael Spiro
Language of the Masters - by Michael Spiro
Introduction to the Conga Drum DVD - by M. Spiro
Afro-Caribbean Grooves for Drumset - JPhi Fanfant
Afro-Peruvian Percussion Ensemble - H. Morales
Flamenco Improvisation - Vol.1-3 by Enrique Vargas
Muy Caliente! - Afro-Cuban Book & Play-Aong audio
Music of the Arará Savalú Cabildo - Galvin & Spiro

## DIGITAL FAKE BOOKS
The New Real Book - Vol.1 - C, Bb & Eb
The Digital Standards Songbook - individual songs
with lyrics, plus C, Bb, Eb, High Voice & Low Voice
The Digital Real Book (650 songs from all our books)

## THE DIGITAL SONGBOOK SERIES
The Kenny Barron Songbook
The Carla Bley Songbook
The Tom Harrell Songbook
The Oscar Hernandez Songbook
The Alan Pasqua Songbook
The Horace Silver Songbook
The Steve Swallow Songbook
The Ralph Towner Songbook
The Wayne Wallace Songbook
The Kenner Werner Songbook
The Randy Brecker Songbook
The Larry Dunlap Songbook
The Barry Finnerty Songbook
The Benny Golson Songbook
The Steve Khan Songbook
The Doug Morton Songbook
The Andy Narell Songbook
The Enrico Pieranunzi Songbook
The Dave Tull Songbook
The Denny Zeitlin Songbook

## FOR STUDENT MUSICIANS
The Real Easy Book - Vol. 1 - C, Bb, Eb & Bass Clef
The Real Easy Book - Vol. 2 - C, Bb, Eb & Bass Clef
The Real Easy Book - Vol. 3 - C, Bb, Eb & Bass Clef
The Latin Real Easy Book - C, Bb, Eb & Bass Clef
Drum Supplement for Real Easy Book - Vol. 1
The Blues Scales - C, Bb, Eb, Bass Clef & Guitar
Rhythm First! - C, Bb, Eb & Bass Clef - by Tom Kamp
Guitarist's Introduction to Jazz - by Randy Vincent
Walking Bassics - by Ed Fuqua
Foundation Exercises for Bass - by Chuck Sher

## CDs
Poetry+Jazz: A Magical Marriage - by Chuck Sher
Play-Along CDs for The New Real Book - Vol.1
The Latin Real Book Sampler CD

*continued on next page*

# SHER MUSIC CO. JAZZ METHOD BOOKS
## available in both print & digital forms

## GUITAR
**Jazz Guitar Voicings: The Drop 2 Book**
   - Randy Vincent
**Three-Note Voicings and Beyond** - Randy Vincent
**Line Games** - Randy Vincent
**Jazz Guitar Soloing: The Cellular Approach**
   - Randy Vincent
**The Guitarist's Introduction to Jazz** - Randy Vincent
**Contemporary Latin Jazz Guitar** - Neff Irizarry

## PIANO
**The Jazz Piano Book** - Mark Levine
**Jazz Piano Masterclass: The Drop 2 Book -** M. Levine
**How To Voice Standards at the Piano** - Mark Levine
**An Approach to Comping - Vol. 1** - Jeb Patton
**An Approach to Comping - Vol. 2** - Jeb Patton
**Introduction to Jazz Piano: A Deep Dive** - Jeb Patton
**Playing for Singers** - Mike Greensill
**Wisdom of the Hand** - Marius Nordal
**The Jazz Solos of Chick Corea** - Peter Sprague

## SAXOPHONE
**The Practice Notebooks of Michael Brecker**
**The Jazz Saxophone Book** - Tim Armacost

## VOiCE
**The Digital Standards Songbook** - individual songs
with lyrics, plus C, Bb, Eb, High Voice & Low Voice
**The Jazz Singer's Guidebook** - David Berkman

## DRUMS
**Syncopation Companion** - Bryan Bowman
**Inner Drumming** - George Marsh
**Drum Supplement for Real Easy Book Vol.1** - Alan Hall
**Afro-Caribbean Grooves for Drumset** - JPhi Fanfant

## TRUMPET
**New Orleans Trumpet** - Jim Thornton
**Modern Etudes for Solo Trumpet** - Cameron Pearce

## BASS
**The Improvisor's Bass Method** - Chuck Sher
**Concepts for Bass Soloing** - Marc Johnson & C. Sher
**Walking Bassics** - Ed Fuqua
**Foundation Exercises for Bass** - Chuck Sher

## JAZZ THEORY AND HARMONY
**The Jazz Theory Book** - Mark Levine
**The Jazz Harmony Book** - David Berkman
**Forward Motion** - Hal Galper
**Metaphors for the Musician** - Randy Halberstadt
**Minor is Major!** - Dan Greenblatt
**Rhythm Changes Guide** - Lukas Gabric
**Jazz Scores and Analysis - Vol.1** - Richard Lawn
**Jazz Scores and Analysis - Vol. 2** - Richard Lawn
**The Blues Scales** - C, Bb, Eb, Bass Clef & Guitar
   - Dan Greenblatt

## PRACTICE GUIDES
**The Practice Notebooks of Michael Brecker**
**Jazz Musician's Guide to Creative Practicing**
   - David Berkman
**The Serious Jazz Practice Book** - Barry Finnerty
**The Serious Jazz Book II** - Barry Finnerty
**Building Solo Lines from Cells** - Randy Vincent

## EAR TRAINING
**The Real Easy Ear Training Book** - Roberta Radley
**Reading, Writing and Rhythmetic** - Roberta Radley

## RHYTHM SECTION GUIDES
**Essential Grooves** - Moretti, Stagnaro & Nicholl
**Inside the Brazilian Rhythm Section** - Nelson Faria
   & Cliff Korman
**The Salsa Guidebook** - Rebeca Mauleõn
**Decoding Afro-Cuban Jazz** - Mauleõn & Valdes

## BILINGUAL OR LIBROS EN ESPANOL
**101 Montunos** - Rebeca Mauleón
**Muy Caliente!** - Afro-Cuban Book & Play-Along
**El Libro del Jazz Piano** - Mark Levine
**The Latin Real Book** - C, Bb and Eb

## MISCELLANEOUS
**Method for Chromatic Harmonica** - Max de Aloe
**Jazz Songs for the Student Violinist**
   - Kevin Mitchell & Joanne Keefe

*Sign up for our monthly discount newsletter*
*by writing shermuse@sonic.net*

NATIONAL GEOGRAPHIC

# World Cultures and Geography
## SUB-SAHARAN AFRICA

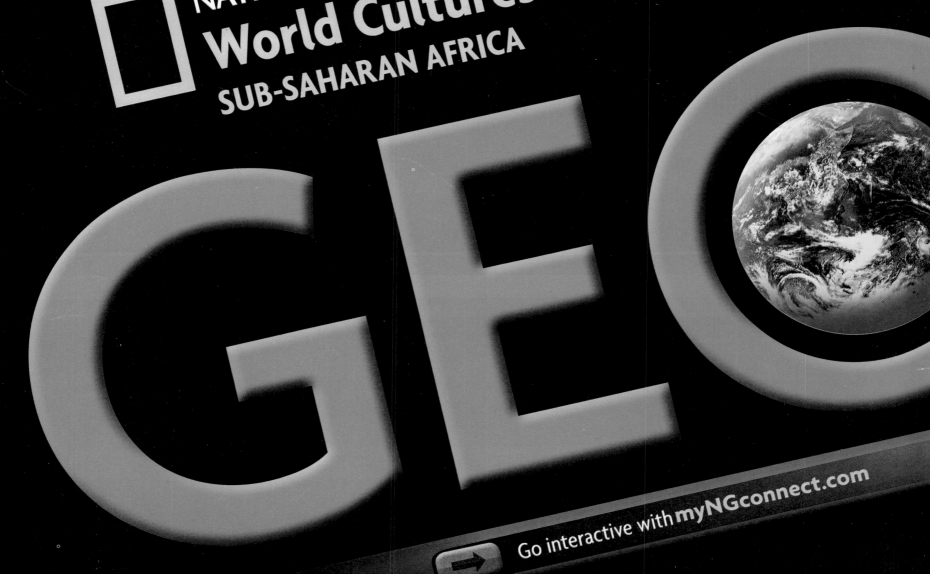

Go interactive with **myNGconnect.com**

## Acknowledgments

Grateful acknowledgment is given to the authors, artists, photographers, museums, publishers, and agents for permission to reprint copyrighted material. Every effort has been made to secure the appropriate permission. If any omissions have been made or if corrections are required, please contact the Publisher.

## Photographic Credits

Front Cover: © Denis-Huot/Hemis/Corbis

Acknowledgments and credits continued on page RB125.

Visit National Geographic Learning online at www.NGSP.com

Visit our corporate website at www.cengage.com

Printed in the USA
RR Donnelley
Menasha, WI

ISBN: 978-07362-9007-4

11 12 13 14 15 16 17 18 19 20

10 9 8 7 6 5 4 3 2 1

# World Cultures and Geography OVERVIEW

| STUDENT EDITION UNITS | COMPREHENSIVE (SURVEY) | EASTERN HEMISPHERE | WESTERN HEMISPHERE |
|---|:---:|:---:|:---:|
| THE ESSENTIALS OF GEOGRAPHY | ● | ● | ● |
| NORTH AMERICA | ● | | ● |
| Central America & the Caribbean | ● | | ● |
| South America | ● | | ● |
| Europe | ● | ● | ● |
| Russia & the Eurasian Republics | ● | ● | ● |
| Sub-Saharan Africa | ● | ● | |
| Southwest Asia & North Africa | ● | ● | |
| South Asia | ● | ● | |
| East Asia | ● | ● | |
| Southeast Asia | ● | ● | |
| Australia, the Pacific Realm & Antarctica | ● | ● | |

# UNIT 7

# SUB-SAHARAN AFRICA

## TEACHER'S EDITION

# CONSULTANTS AND REVIEWERS

## Program Consultants

**Peggy Altoff**
*District Coordinator*
*Past President, NCSS*

**Mark H. Bockenhauer**
*Professor of Geography,*
*St. Norbert College*

**Andrew J. Milson**
*Professor of Social Science Education*
*and Geography, University of Texas (Arlington)*

**David W. Moore**
*Professor of Education,*
*Arizona State University (Phoenix)*

**Janet Smith**
*Associate Professor of Geography,*
*Shippensburg University*

**Michael W. Smith**
*Professor, Department of Curriculum,*
*Instruction, and Technology in Education,*
*Temple University*

## Teacher Reviewers

**Kayce Forbes**
*Deerpark Middle School*
*Austin, Texas*

**Michael Koren**
*Maple Dale School*
*Fox Point, Wisconsin*

**Patricia Lewis**
*Humble Middle School*
*Humble, Texas*

**Julie Mitchell**
*Lake Forest Middle School*
*Cleveland, Tennessee*

**Linda O'Connor**
*Northeast Independent School District*
*San Antonio, Texas*

**Leah Perry**
*Exploris Middle School*
*Raleigh, North Carolina*

**Robert Poirier**
*North Andover Middle School*
*North Andover, Massachusetts*

**Heather Rountree**
*Bedford Heights Elementary*
*Bedford, Texas*

**Erin Stevens**
*Quabbin Regional Middle/High School*
*Barre, Massachusetts*

**Beth Tipper**
*Crofton Middle School*
*Crofton, Maryland*

**Mary Trichel**
*Atascocita Middle School*
*Humble, Texas*

**Andrea Wallenbeck**
*Exploris Middle School*
*Raleigh, North Carolina*

## Reviewers of Religious Content

**Charles Haynes**
*First Amendment Center*
*Washington, D.C.*

**Shabbir Mansuri**
*Institute on Religion and*
*Civic Values*
*Fountain Valley, California*

**Susan Mogull**
*Institute for Curriculum Reform*
*San Francisco, California*

**Raka Ray**
*Chair, Center for South Asia Studies*
*University of California*
*(Berkeley)*

# NATIONAL GEOGRAPHIC EXPLORERS, FELLOWS, AND GRANTEES

**Greg Anderson**
*National Geographic Fellow*

**Katey Walter Anthony**
*National Geographic Emerging Explorer*

**Ken Banks**
*National Geographic Emerging Explorer*

**Katy Croff Bell**
*National Geographic Emerging Explorer*

**Christina Conlee**
*National Geographic Grantee*

**Alexandra Cousteau**
*National Geographic Emerging Explorer*

**Thomas Taha Rassam (TH) Culhane**
*National Geographic Emerging Explorer*

**Jenny Daltry**
*National Geographic Emerging Explorer*

**Wade Davis**
*National Geographic Explorer-in-Residence*

**Sylvia Earle**
*National Geographic Explorer-in-Residence*

**Grace Gobbo**
*National Geographic Emerging Explorer*

**Beverly Goodman**
*National Geographic Emerging Explorer*

**David Harrison**
*National Geographic Fellow*

**Kristofer Helgen**
*National Geographic Emerging Explorer*

**Fredrik Hiebert**
*National Geographic Fellow*

**Zeb Hogan**
*National Geographic Fellow*

**Shafqat Hussain**
*National Geographic Emerging Explorer*

**Beverly Joubert**
*National Geographic Explorer-in-Residence*

**Dereck Joubert**
*National Geographic Explorer-in-Residence*

**Albert Lin**
*National Geographic Emerging Explorer*

**Elizabeth Kapu'uwailani Lindsey**
*National Geographic Fellow*

**Sam Meacham**
*National Geographic Grantee*

**Kakenya Ntaiya**
*National Geographic Emerging Explorer*

**Johan Reinhard**
*National Geographic Explorer-in-Residence*

**Enric Sala**
*National Geographic Explorer-in-Residence*

**Kira Salak**
*National Geographic Emerging Explorer*

**Katsufumi Sato**
*National Geographic Emerging Explorer*

**Paola Segura**
*National Geographic Emerging Explorer*

**Beth Shapiro**
*National Geographic Emerging Explorer*

**Cid Simoes**
*National Geographic Emerging Explorer*

**José Urteaga**
*National Geographic Emerging Explorer*

**Spencer Wells**
*National Geographic Explorer-in-Residence*

# Best Practices
## For ACTIVE Teaching

**To bring best practices into your classroom, choose from the following technology components and instructional routines and make them part of your daily instruction. Many of these practices are also built directly into the instruction in your Teacher's Edition.**

## PROGRAM TECHNOLOGY

*World Cultures and Geography* provides a variety of technology to make your job easier and to help students become motivated, independent learners. Use the online components listed below to supplement print resources or to create an entirely digital learning environment.

| STUDENT COMPONENTS | TEACHER COMPONENTS |
|---|---|
| Student eEdition | Teacher's eEdition |
| Interactive Map Tool | Core Content Presentations |
| Digital Library | Online Lesson Planner |
| Magazine Maker | Assessment |
| Connect to NG | Interactive Whiteboard GeoActivities |
| Maps and Graphs | Guided Writing |
| GeoJournal | Teacher Resources |
| Student Resources | |

All digital resources and more information about them are available at **myNGconnect.com**. In addition, see the next page for specific instructions on how to use the **Interactive Map Tool**—a technology component that plays an integral part in the Teacher's Edition instruction.

## Interactive Map Tool

The **Interactive Map Tool** is an online mapmaker that allows students to draw and add labels and data layers to a map. For general use, follow the instructions below to navigate the map tool.

**1** Access the tool at **myNGconnect.com**.

**2** Select a region to explore. Click on the "Region" menu to select a continent and the "Country" menu to select a specific country, or simply click and drag the map to maneuver it to a specific location. You can also use the slider bar to zoom in and out.

**3** Choose the type of map you wish to view by clicking on the "Map Mode" menu. Options include terrain, topographic, satellite, street, National Geographic, and outline. The Outline mode allows you to click on a specific country and access a separate outline map of that country with features that you can turn on or off.

**4** Click on the THEMES tab to display categories of data layers that can be overlaid on the map. Availability of these data layers varies depending on the zoom level of the map. Each data layer also has a legend and a transparency control.

**5** Click on the DRAWING TOOLS tab to display a variety of tools that you can use to draw on the map. Most tools allow you to adjust the outline and fill colors, line width, and transparency. The tab can also be selected by clicking on the "Draw" icon.

**6** Click on the MARKERS tab to display a variety of markers that you can drag and drop on the map. You can set the markers at three different sizes. The MARKERS tab can also be selected by clicking on the "Markers" icon.

**7** To easily measure distances on the map, click on the "Measure" (ruler) icon. Click once on the map to start measuring, move the pointer to another spot, and click again to stop. The resulting line will display the distance in either kilometers or miles based on your selection from the dropdown menu.

# COOPERATIVE LEARNING

Cooperative learning strategies transform today's classroom diversity into a vital resource for promoting students' acquisition of both challenging academic content and language. These strategies promote active engagement and social motivation for all students.

| STRUCTURE & GRAPHIC | DESCRIPTION | BENEFITS & PURPOSES |
|---|---|---|
| **CORNERS**<br><br>A strongly agree<br>B disagree<br>C agree<br>D strongly disagree | • Corners of the classroom are designated for focused discussion of four aspects of a topic.<br>• Students individually think and write about the topic for a short time.<br>• Students group into the corner of their choice and discuss the topic.<br>• At least one student from each corner shares about the corner discussion. | • By "voting" with their feet, students literally take a position about a topic.<br>• Focused discussion develops deeper thought about a topic.<br>• Students experience many valid points of view about a topic. |
| **FISHBOWL** | • Part of the class sits in a close circle facing inward; the other part of the class sits in a larger circle around them.<br>• Students on the inside discuss a topic while those outside listen for new information and/or evaluate the discussion according to pre-established criteria.<br>• Groups reverse positions. | • Focused listening enhances knowledge acquisition and listening skills.<br>• Peer evaluation supports development of specific discussion skills.<br>• Identification of criteria for evaluation promotes self-monitoring. |
| **INSIDE-OUTSIDE CIRCLE** | • Students stand in concentric circles facing each other.<br>• Students in the outside circle ask questions; those inside answer.<br>• On a signal, students rotate to create new partnerships.<br>• On another signal, students trade inside/outside roles. | • Talking one-on-one with a variety of partners gives risk-free practice in speaking skills.<br>• Interactions can be structured to focus on specific speaking skills.<br>• Students practice both speaking and active listening. |
| **JIGSAW**<br><br>Expert Group 1   A's<br>Expert Group 2   B's<br>Expert Group 3   C's<br>Expert Group 4   D's | • Students are grouped evenly into "expert" groups.<br>• Expert groups study one topic or aspect of a topic in depth.<br>• Students regroup so that each new group has at least one member from each expert group.<br>• Experts report on their study. Other students learn from the experts. | • Becoming an expert provides in-depth understanding in one aspect of study.<br>• Learning from peers provides breadth of understanding of over-arching concepts. |

| STRUCTURE & GRAPHIC | DESCRIPTION | BENEFITS & PURPOSES |
|---|---|---|
| **NUMBERED HEADS** <br><br> Think Time <br> Talk Time <br> Share Time | • Students number off within each group. <br> • Teacher prompts or gives a directive. <br> • Students think individually about the topic. <br> • Groups discuss the topic so that any member of the group can report for the group. <br> • Teacher calls a number and the student with that number reports for the group. | • Group discussion of topics provides each student with language and concept understanding. <br> • Random recitation provides an opportunity for evaluation of both individual and group progress. |
| **ROUNDTABLE** | • Students sit around tables in groups of four. <br> • Teacher asks a question with many possible answers. <br> • Each student around the table answers the question a different way. | • Encouraging elaboration creates appreciation for diversity of opinion and thought. <br> • Eliciting multiple answers enhances language fluency. |
| **TEAM WORD WEBBING** | • Teams of students sit around a large piece of paper. Each team member has a different colored marker. <br> • Teacher assigns a topic for a Word Web. <br> • Each student adds to the part of the web nearest to him/her. <br> • On a signal, students rotate the paper and each student adds to the nearest part again. | • Individual input to a group product ensures participation by all students. <br> • Shifting point of view supports both broad and in-depth understanding of concepts. |
| **THINK, PAIR, SHARE** <br><br> Think <br> Pair <br> Share | • Students think about a topic suggested by the teacher. <br> • Pairs discuss the topic. <br> • Students individually share information with the class. | • The opportunity for self-talk during the individual think time allows the student to formulate thoughts before speaking. <br> • Discussion with a partner reduces performance anxiety and enhances understanding. |
| **THREE-STEP INTERVIEW** <br><br> GROUP | • Students form pairs. <br> • Student A interviews Student B about a topic. <br> • Partners reverse roles. <br> • Student A shares with the class information from Student B; then B shares information from Student A. | • Interviewing supports language acquisition by providing scripts for expression. <br> • Responding provides opportunities for structured self-expression. |

# TECHTREK

## myNGconnect.com

A musician and griot in Senegal

### Digital Library
**Unit 7 GeoVideo**
*Introduce Sub-Saharan Africa*

**Explorer Video Clip**
Dereck and Beverly Joubert, Conservationists
National Geographic Explorers-in-Residence

NATIONAL GEOGRAPHIC **PHOTO GALLERY**

Regional photos, including Kenya's
   savanna, Victoria Falls, Johannesburg,
   and the Great Rift Valley

**Music Clips**
Audio clips of music from the region

### Maps and Graphs
**Interactive Map Tool**

### Interactive Whiteboard GeoActivities
• Compare Precipitation Across Regions
• Locate a Wildlife Reserve
• Research Vanishing Cultures

### Connect to NG
Research links and current events in
   Sub-Saharan Africa

# NATIONAL GEOGRAPHIC
# ATLAS

Page numbers of maps match Student Edition.
For a full Atlas go to the Teacher's Reference Guide.

# World Physical

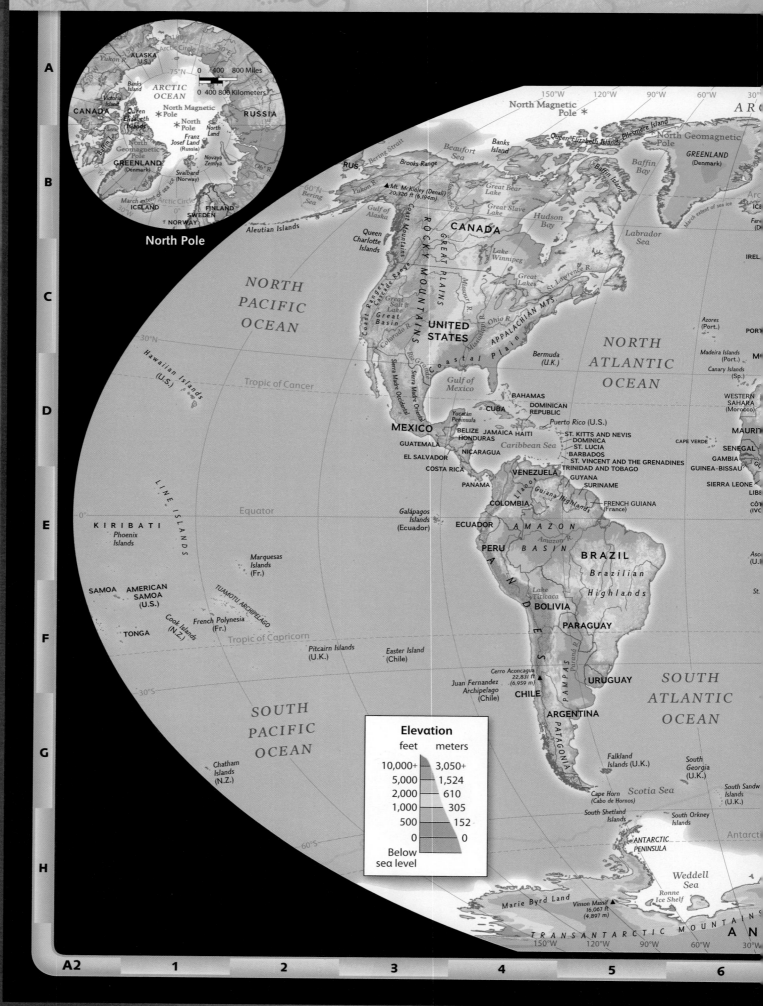

North Pole

ARCTIC OCEAN
North Magnetic Pole
North Pole
North Geomagnetic Pole
Franz Josef Land (Russia)
GREENLAND (Denmark)
CANADA
RUSSIA
ICELAND
NORWAY
SWEDEN
FINLAND
Yukon R.
ALASKA (U.S.)
Banks Island
Victoria Island
Queen Elizabeth Islands
Baffin Island
Novaya Zemlya
Ob' R.
Svalbard (Norway)
0 400 800 Miles
0 400 800 Kilometers
March extent of sea ice
Arctic Circle
75°N
60°N

NORTH PACIFIC OCEAN

SOUTH PACIFIC OCEAN

KIRIBATI
Phoenix Islands
LINE ISLANDS
SAMOA
AMERICAN SAMOA (U.S.)
TONGA
Cook Islands (N.Z.)
French Polynesia (Fr.)
TUAMOTU ARCHIPELAGO
Marquesas Islands (Fr.)
Pitcairn Islands (U.K.)
Easter Island (Chile)
Chatham Islands (N.Z.)
Hawaiian Islands (U.S.)

North Magnetic Pole
North Geomagnetic Pole
GREENLAND (Denmark)
Queen Elizabeth Islands
Ellesmere Island
Banks Island
Baffin Island
Baffin Bay
Labrador Sea
Beaufort Sea
Brooks Range
RUS.
Bering Strait
Bering Sea
Gulf of Alaska
Aleutian Islands
Mt. McKinley (Denali) 20,320 ft (6,194m)
Yukon R.
Coast Mountains
Great Bear Lake
Great Slave Lake
Hudson Bay
CANADA
Lake Winnipeg
ROCKY MOUNTAINS
GREAT PLAINS
Missouri R.
Great Lakes
St. Lawrence R.
APPALACHIAN MTS.
IRELAND
Queen Charlotte Islands
Cascade Range
Coast Ranges
UNITED STATES
Great Salt Lake
Great Basin
Colorado R.
Mississippi R.
Ohio R.
Coastal Plain
Sierra Nevada
Bermuda (U.K.)
Azores (Port.)
PORTUGAL
Madeira Islands (Port.)
Canary Islands (Sp.)
NORTH ATLANTIC OCEAN
WESTERN SAHARA (Morocco)
MAURITANIA
Gulf of Mexico
Sierra Madre Occidental
Sierra Madre Oriental
Yucatán Peninsula
MEXICO
Rio Grande
BAHAMAS
CUBA
DOMINICAN REPUBLIC
Puerto Rico (U.S.)
BELIZE
GUATEMALA
HONDURAS
JAMAICA HAITI
ST. KITTS AND NEVIS
DOMINICA
ST. LUCIA
BARBADOS
CAPE VERDE
SENEGAL
EL SALVADOR
NICARAGUA
Caribbean Sea
ST. VINCENT AND THE GRENADINES
TRINIDAD AND TOBAGO
GAMBIA
GUINEA-BISSAU
COSTA RICA
VENEZUELA
GUYANA
SURINAME
SIERRA LEONE
LIBERIA
PANAMA
Llanos
Guiana Highlands
FRENCH GUIANA (France)
COLOMBIA
CÔTE D'IVOIRE (IVORY COAST)
Galápagos Islands (Ecuador)
ECUADOR
AMAZON BASIN
Amazon R.
PERU
BRAZIL
Brazilian Highlands
Ascension (U.K.)
St. Helena
ANDES
Lake Titicaca
BOLIVIA
PARAGUAY
Cerro Aconcagua 22,831 ft (6,959 m)
Juan Fernandez Archipelago (Chile)
CHILE
PAMPAS
Paraná R.
URUGUAY
ARGENTINA
PATAGONIA
SOUTH ATLANTIC OCEAN
Falkland Islands (U.K.)
South Georgia (U.K.)
Cape Horn (Cabo de Hornos)
Scotia Sea
South Sandwich Islands (U.K.)
South Shetland Islands
South Orkney Islands
ANTARCTIC PENINSULA
Antarctic
Weddell Sea
Ronne Ice Shelf
Marie Byrd Land
Vinson Massif 16,067 ft (4,897 m)
TRANSANTARCTIC MOUNTAINS
ANTARCTICA

Tropic of Cancer
Equator
Tropic of Capricorn
150°W 120°W 90°W 60°W 30°W
30°N
0°
30°S
60°S

## Elevation

| feet | meters |
|---|---|
| 10,000+ | 3,050+ |
| 5,000 | 1,524 |
| 2,000 | 610 |
| 1,000 | 305 |
| 500 | 152 |
| 0 | 0 |
| Below sea level | |

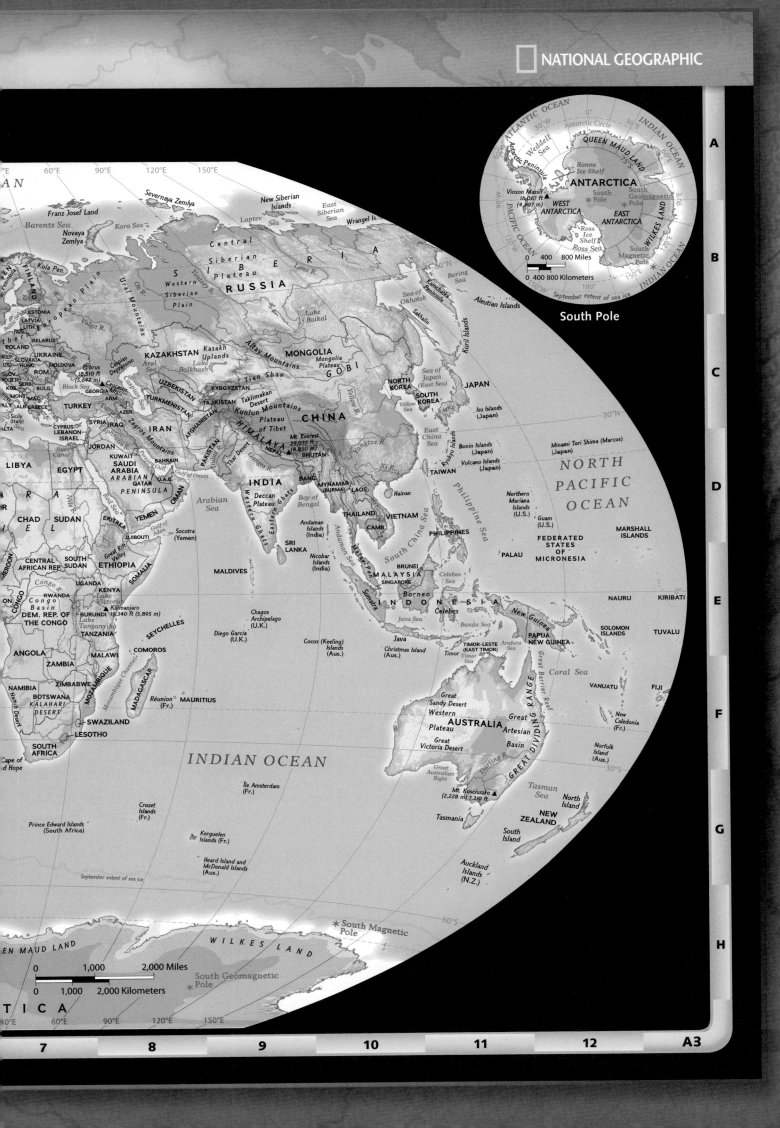

# World Political

Anchorage
ALASKA (U.S.)
Yukon R.
Arctic Circle
Yellowknife
CANADA
ARCTIC OCEAN
North Pole
Franz Josef Land (Russia)
RUSSIA
GREENLAND (Denmark)
Svalbard (Norway)
Nuuk (Godthåb)
Murmansk
Arkhangel'sk
ICELAND
Reykjavík
SWEDEN
FINLAND
NORWAY
Arctic Circle
0   400   800 Miles
0   400 800 Kilometers

**North Pole**

Bering Strait
RUS
ALASKA (U.S.)
Beaufort Sea
Banks Is.
Victoria Island
Baffin Island
Queen Elizabeth Islands
Ellesmere Island
ARC
GREENLAND (KALAALLIT NUNAAT) (Denmark)
Baffin Bay
Aleutian Islands
Bering Sea
Gulf of Alaska
Queen Charlotte Islands
CANADA
Hudson Bay
Labrador Sea
Nuuk (Godthåb)
Reykjavík
ICE
Faro
(D
Arc

NORTH PACIFIC OCEAN
Ottawa
St.-Pierre & Miquelon (France)
IREL
UNITED STATES
Washington, D.C.
NORTH ATLANTIC OCEAN
Azores (Port.)
POR
Li
30°N
Bermuda (U.K.)
Madeira Islands (Port.)
Tropic of Cancer
MEXICO
Gulf of Mexico
Canary Islands (Sp.)
Havana
Nassau
BAHAMAS
Laayoune
WESTERN SAHARA (Morocco)
Mexico City
CUBA
DOMINICAN REPUBLIC
Kingston
Port-au-Prince
Santo Domingo
PUERTO RICO (U.S.)
MAUR
Nouc
Belmopan
BELIZE
JAMAICA
HAITI
ST. KITTS AND NEVIS
DOMINICA
CAPE VERDE
Dakar
SENEGA
Guatemala City
HONDURAS
Praia
Banjul
GUATEMALA
Tegucigalpa
Caribbean Sea
ST. LUCIA
BARBADOS
GAMBIA
San Salvador
NICARAGUA
ST. VINCENT AND THE GRENADINES
GUINEA-BISSAU
Bissau
EL SALVADOR
Managua
TRINIDAD AND TOBAGO
Conakry
GUI
COSTA RICA
San José
Freetown
SIERRA LEONE
LIBERIA
VENEZUELA
Caracas
Georgetown
Panama City
PANAMA
Paramaribo
Yamou
Bogotá
GUYANA
Cayenne
CÔTE
COLOMBIA
FRENCH GUIANA (France)
(IVO
Galápagos Islands (Ecuador)
Quito
ECUADOR
SURINAME
Equator
0°
KIRIBATI
Phoenix Islands
LINE ISLANDS
PERU
BRAZIL
Asc (U.K
Marquesas Islands (Fr.)
Lima
SAMOA
AMERICAN SAMOA (U.S.)
Apia
TUAMOTU ARCHIPELAGO
Tahiti
French Polynesia (Fr.)
La Paz
Brasília
St.
BOLIVIA
Sucre
TONGA
Cook Islands (N.Z.)
PARAGUAY
Nuku'alofa
Tropic of Capricorn
Pitcairn Islands (U.K.)
Easter Island (Chile)
Asunción
São Paulo
Juan Fernandez Archipelago (Chile)
Santiago
URUGUAY
Montevideo
SOUTH ATLANTIC OCEAN
30°S
CHILE
Buenos Aires
ARGENTINA
SOUTH PACIFIC OCEAN
Chatham Islands (N.Z.)
Falkland Islands (U.K.)
South Georgia (U.K.)
South Sandw Islands (U.K.)
Scotia Sea
South Shetland Islands
South Orkney Islands
Antarct
60°S
Weddell Sea
AN

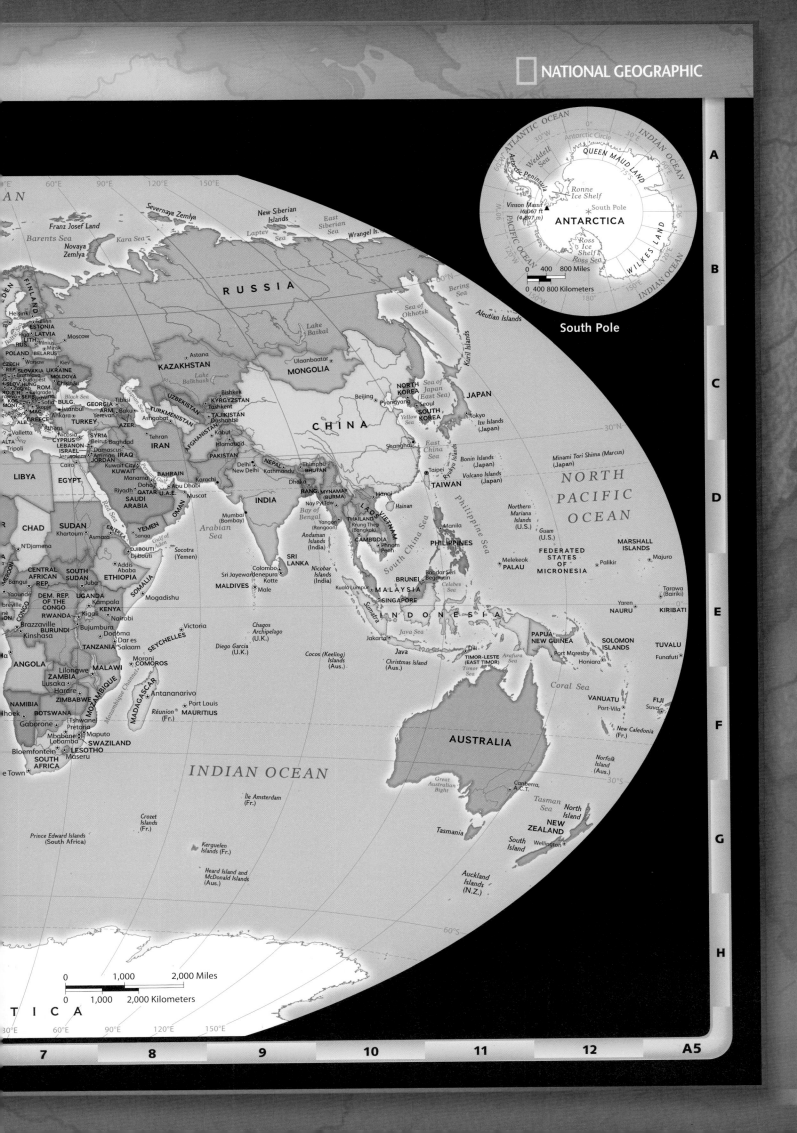

ATLANTIC OCEAN
Antarctic Circle
INDIAN OCEAN
Weddell Sea
QUEEN MAUD LAND
Antarctic Peninsula
Ronne Ice Shelf
South Pole
Vinson Massif 16,067 ft (4,897 m)
ANTARCTICA
WILKES LAND
PACIFIC OCEAN
Ross Ice Shelf
INDIAN OCEAN

0  400  800 Miles
0  400  800 Kilometers

South Pole

Franz Josef Land
Barents Sea
Novaya Zemlya
Kara Sea
Severnaya Zemlya
New Siberian Islands
East Siberian Sea
Laptev Sea
Wrangel Is.
Helsinki
FINLAND
ESTONIA
LATVIA
RUS.
LITH.
Minsk
Moscow
RUSSIA
Bering Sea
Aleutian Islands
Sea of Okhotsk
POLAND
BELARUS
Astana
Kiev
Warsaw
CZECH REP.
SLOVAKIA
UKRAINE
MOLDOVA
Bratislava
Budapest
HUNG.
ROM.
Chisinau
KAZAKHSTAN
Lake Balkhash
Ulaanbaatar
MONGOLIA
SERB.
Bucharest
Belgrade
BULG.
Black Sea
GEORGIA
Tbilisi
Bishkek
KYRGYZSTAN
Tashkent
Beijing
NORTH KOREA
Pyongyang
Sea of Japan (East Sea)
SOUTH KOREA
Seoul
JAPAN
MONT.
MAC.
Skopje
ALB.
GREECE
Athens
Istanbul
Ankara
TURKEY
ARM.
Yerevan
Baku
AZER.
Ashgabat
TURKMENISTAN
UZBEKISTAN
TAJIKISTAN
Dushanbe
CHINA
Yellow Sea
Tokyo
Izu Islands (Japan)
Valletta
MALTA
CYPRUS
Nicosia
SYRIA
Beirut
Damascus
LEBANON
ISRAEL
Baghdad
Tehran
Kabul
AFGHANISTAN
Islamabad
East China Sea
Shanghai
Bonin Islands (Japan)
Minami Tori Shima (Marcus) (Japan)
Tripoli
Jerusalem
Amman
JORDAN
IRAQ
KUWAIT
Kuwait City
IRAN
PAKISTAN
Delhi
New Delhi
NEPAL
Kathmandu
Thimphu
BHUTAN
Taipei
TAIWAN
Ryukyu Islands (Japan)
Volcano Islands (Japan)
LIBYA
EGYPT
Cairo
BAHRAIN
Manama
QATAR
Doha
Abu Dhabi
U.A.E.
Riyadh
Muscat
Dhaka
BANG.
MYANMAR (BURMA)
Hanoi
Hainan
NORTH PACIFIC OCEAN
SAUDI ARABIA
OMAN
INDIA
Mumbai (Bombay)
Bay of Bengal
Nay Pyi Taw
Krung Thep (Bangkok)
THAILAND
LAOS
VIETNAM
Northern Mariana Islands (U.S.)
CHAD
SUDAN
Khartoum
Asmara
ERITREA
YEMEN
Sanaa
Karachi
Arabian Sea
Andaman Islands (India)
CAMBODIA
Phnom Penh
Manila
Guam (U.S.)
FEDERATED STATES OF MICRONESIA
MARSHALL ISLANDS
N'Djamena
Djibouti
DJIBOUTI
Gulf of Aden
Socotra (Yemen)
Colombo
SRI LANKA
Nicobar Islands (India)
South China Sea
Philippine Sea
PHILIPPINES
Melekeok
PALAU
Palikir
CENTRAL AFRICAN REP.
SOUTH SUDAN
Juba
Addis Ababa
ETHIOPIA
SOMALIA
Sri Jayewardenepura Kotte
MALDIVES
Male
BRUNEI
Bandar Seri Begawan
Celebes Sea
Majuro
Bangui
DEM. REP. OF THE CONGO
UGANDA
Kampala
KENYA
Mogadishu
Kuala Lumpur
MALAYSIA
SINGAPORE
CAMEROON
Yaoundé
Libreville
GABON
CONGO
RWANDA
Kigali
BURUNDI
Bujumbura
Nairobi
Chagos Archipelago (U.K.)
INDONESIA
Yaren
NAURU
Tarawa (Bairiki)
KIRIBATI
Brazzaville
Kinshasa
TANZANIA
Dodoma
Dar es Salaam
Victoria
SEYCHELLES
Diego Garcia (U.K.)
Jakarta
Java Sea
PAPUA NEW GUINEA
Dili
SOLOMON ISLANDS
TUVALU
ANGOLA
Lilongwe
MALAWI
ZAMBIA
Lusaka
COMOROS
Moroni
MADAGASCAR
Antananarivo
Cocos (Keeling) Islands (Aus.)
Java
Christmas Island (Aus.)
TIMOR-LESTE (EAST TIMOR)
Timor Sea
Arafura Sea
Port Moresby
Honiara
Funafuti
Harare
ZIMBABWE
MOZAMBIQUE
Port Louis
MAURITIUS
Réunion (Fr.)
Coral Sea
VANUATU
Port-Vila
FIJI
Suva
NAMIBIA
Windhoek
BOTSWANA
Gaborone
Pretoria (Tshwane)
Mbabane
SWAZILAND
Maputo
AUSTRALIA
New Caledonia (Fr.)
Bloemfontein
LESOTHO
Maseru
SOUTH AFRICA
Cape Town
INDIAN OCEAN
Île Amsterdam (Fr.)
Great Australian Bight
Canberra, A.C.T.
Norfolk Island (Aus.)
Crozet Islands (Fr.)
Tasman Sea
North Island
Prince Edward Islands (South Africa)
Kerguelen Islands (Fr.)
Tasmania
NEW ZEALAND
South Island
Wellington
Heard Island and McDonald Islands (Aus.)
Auckland Islands (N.Z.)

0  1,000  2,000 Miles
0  1,000  2,000 Kilometers

ANTARCTICA

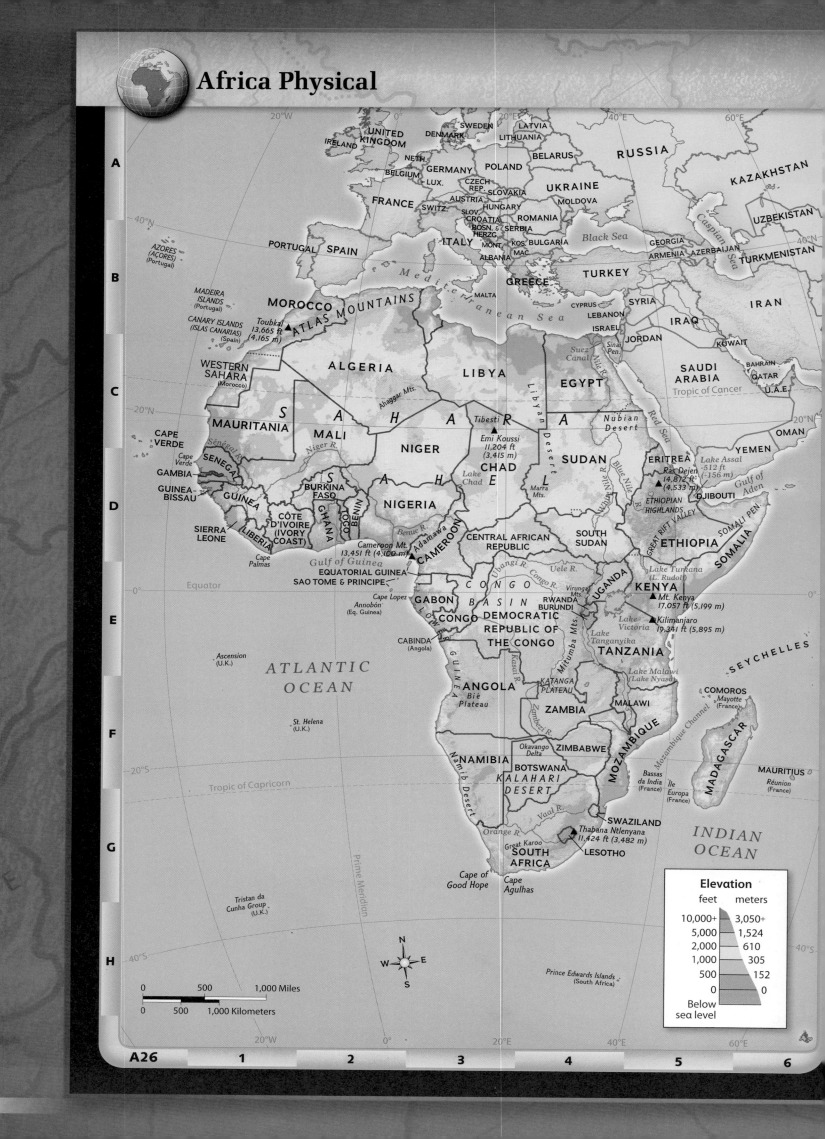

# Africa Physical

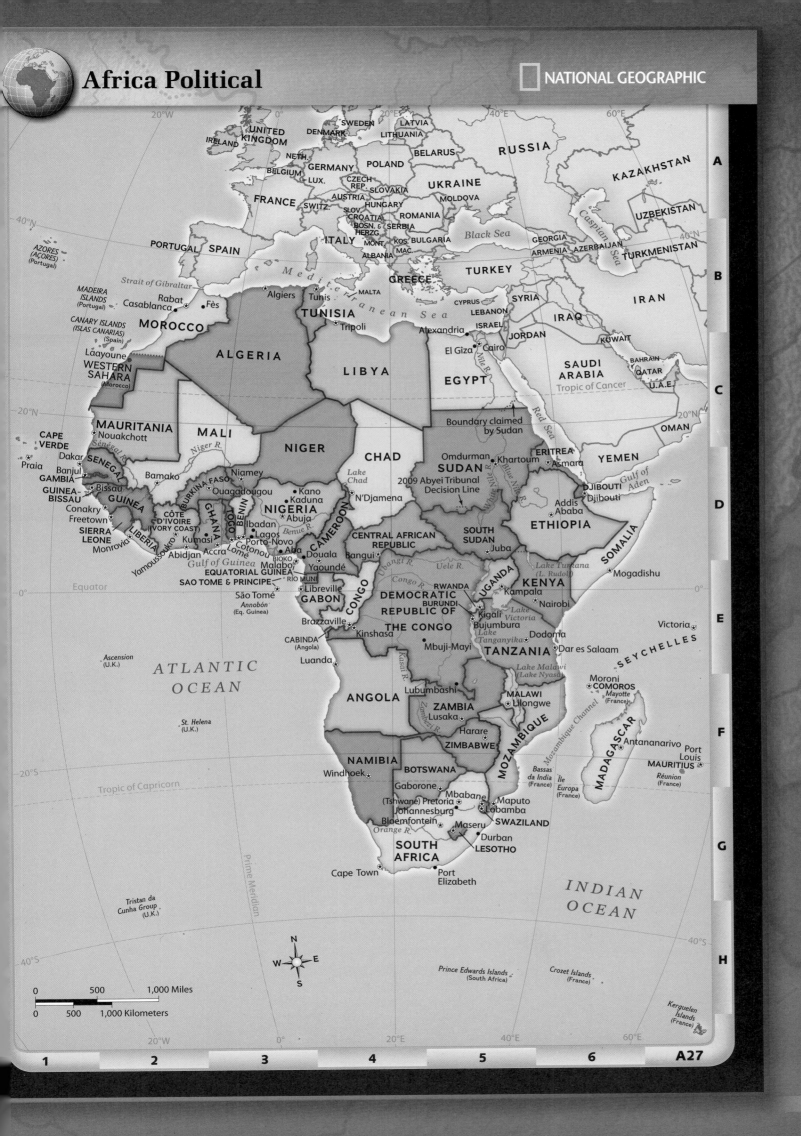

# Africa Political

AZORES (AÇORES) (Portugal)

MADEIRA ISLANDS (Portugal)

CANARY ISLANDS (ISLAS CANARIAS) (Spain)

UNITED KINGDOM
IRELAND
SWEDEN
DENMARK
LATVIA
LITHUANIA
NETH.
GERMANY
BELGIUM
LUX.
POLAND
BELARUS
RUSSIA
KAZAKHSTAN
FRANCE
SWITZ.
CZECH REP.
SLOVAKIA
AUSTRIA
HUNGARY
SLOV.
CROATIA
BOSN. & HERZG.
SERBIA
ROMANIA
MONT.
MAC.
ALBANIA
KOS.
BULGARIA
UKRAINE
MOLDOVA
Black Sea
GEORGIA
ARMENIA
AZERBAIJAN
Caspian Sea
TURKMENISTAN
UZBEKISTAN

PORTUGAL
SPAIN
ITALY
GREECE
MALTA
TURKEY
IRAN

Strait of Gibraltar
Mediterranean Sea

Algiers
Tunis
Rabat
Casablanca
Fès

MOROCCO
TUNISIA
Tripoli

CYPRUS
LEBANON
SYRIA
ISRAEL
Alexandria
El Gîza
Cairo
JORDAN
IRAQ
KUWAIT
SAUDI ARABIA
BAHRAIN
QATAR
U.A.E.

Lâayoune
WESTERN SAHARA (Morocco)

ALGERIA
LIBYA
EGYPT
Nile R.
Tropic of Cancer

OMAN

MAURITANIA
Nouakchott
MALI
NIGER
CHAD
Boundary claimed by Sudan
Red Sea

CAPE VERDE
Praia
Dakar
Senegal R.
SENEGAL
Bamako
Niger R.
Niamey
Lake Chad
N'Djamena
Omdurman
Khartoum
SUDAN
ERITREA
Asmara
YEMEN
Gulf of Aden
DJIBOUTI
Djibouti

GAMBIA
Banjul
GUINEA-BISSAU
Bissau
GUINEA
Conakry
Freetown
SIERRA LEONE
Monrovia
LIBERIA

BURKINA FASO
Ouagadougou
Kano
Kaduna
NIGERIA
Abuja
2009 Abyei Tribunal Decision Line
White Nile R.
Blue Nile R.
Addis Ababa
ETHIOPIA

CÔTE D'IVOIRE (IVORY COAST)
GHANA
TOGO
BENIN
Ibadan
Lagos
Porto-Novo
Cotonou
CAMEROON
CENTRAL AFRICAN REPUBLIC
SOUTH SUDAN
Juba
SOMALIA

Yamoussoukro
Kumasi
Abidjan
Accra
Lomé
Benue R.
Douala
Yaoundé
Bangui
Ubangi R.
Uele R.
UGANDA
Lake Turkana (L. Rudolf)

Gulf of Guinea
BIOKO
Malabo
EQUATORIAL GUINEA
RÍO MUNI
SAO TOME & PRINCIPE
São Tomé
Libreville
GABON
Congo R.
DEMOCRATIC REPUBLIC OF THE CONGO
RWANDA
Kigali
BURUNDI
Bujumbura
Lake Victoria
KENYA
Kampala
Nairobi
Mogadishu

Equator

CONGO
Brazzaville
Kinshasa
Mbuji-Mayi
Kasai R.
Dodoma
Lake Tanganyika
TANZANIA
Dar es Salaam
Victoria
SEYCHELLES

Annobón (Eq. Guinea)

CABINDA (Angola)
Luanda

ATLANTIC OCEAN

Ascension (U.K.)

St. Helena (U.K.)

ANGOLA
Lubumbashi
Zambezi R.
ZAMBIA
Lusaka
MALAWI
Lilongwe
Lake Malawi (Lake Nyasa)
Moroni
COMOROS
Mayotte (France)

Harare
ZIMBABWE
MOZAMBIQUE
Mozambique Channel
MADAGASCAR
Antananarivo
Port Louis
MAURITIUS
Réunion (France)

NAMIBIA
Windhoek
BOTSWANA
Gaborone
Bassas da India (France)
Île Europa (France)

Tropic of Capricorn

Prime Meridian

(Tshwane) Pretoria
Johannesburg
Bloemfontein
Mbabane
Lobamba
Maputo
SWAZILAND
Maseru
LESOTHO
Durban

Orange R.
SOUTH AFRICA
Cape Town
Port Elizabeth

INDIAN OCEAN

Tristan da Cunha Group (U.K.)

Prince Edwards Islands (South Africa)
Crozet Islands (France)

Kerguelen Islands (France)

N
W    E
S

0    500    1,000 Miles
0    500    1,000 Kilometers

20°W    0    20°E    40°E    60°E

40°N    20°N    Tropic of Cancer    0° Equator    20°S Tropic of Capricorn    40°S

A  B  C  D  E  F  G  H

1    2    3    4    5    6

# EXPLORE SUB-SAHARAN AFRICA

## WITH NATIONAL GEOGRAPHIC

### MEET THE EXPLORER

**NATIONAL GEOGRAPHIC**

Emerging Explorer Kakenya Ntaiya, educator and activist (shown at center), founded the first primary school for girls in her village. Her work provides African girls with an education and an opportunity to develop leadership skills.

### INVESTIGATE GEOGRAPHY

Giraffe mothers and their young run in Serengeti National Park, Tanzania. The Serengeti, connected to the Masai Mara National Park in neighboring Kenya, is the only place in Africa where large animal herds, including gnu, zebras, and gazelles, still make vast land migrations.

### STEP INTO HISTORY

This ancient Dogon village was built into the sandstone cliffs of Mali, West Africa. Today, most Dogon people are farmers, and practice the tradtional religion of their ancestors. Much of their social organization and cultural practices relates to this belief system.

Washington, D.C.

8,106 miles

Pretoria (Tshawne),
South Africa

Go to  myNGconnect.com  for maps of Sub-Saharan Africa.

## CONNECT WITH THE CULTURE

Musicians and griots—storytellers—
perform on the beach outside Dakar,
Senegal. The instrument is a kora. It has
21 strings and is similar to a lute.

355

# CHAPTER PLANNER

TE Resource Bank

myNGconnect.com

## SECTION 1 GEOGRAPHY

## 1.1 Physical Geography

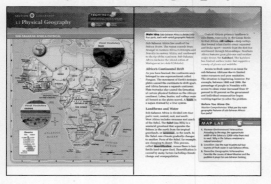

**OBJECTIVE** Locate and analyze the physical characteristics of the diverse areas of sub-Saharan Africa.

**Reading and Note-Taking**
Take Notes

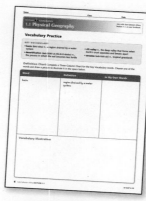

**Vocabulary Practice**
Definition Chart

Whiteboard Ready!

**GeoActivity**
Compare Precipitation Across Regions

## SECTION 1 GEOGRAPHY

## 1.2 East Africa and the Rift Valley

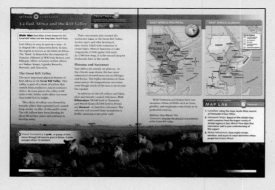

**OBJECTIVE** Identify and describe the physical features of East Africa and the Great Rift Valley.

**Reading and Note-Taking**
Describe Geographic Information

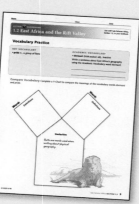

**Vocabulary Practice**
Comparison Chart

Whiteboard Ready!

**GeoActivity**
Relate Topography and Plate Tectonics

## SECTION 1 GEOGRAPHY

## 1.3 West Africa's Steppes

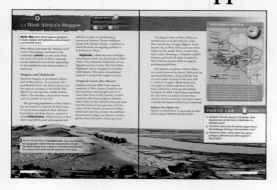

**OBJECTIVE** Analyze how West Africa's physical features, climate, precipitation, and access to coastal waters affect the population of the region.

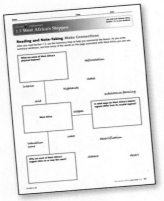

**Reading and Note-Taking**
Make Connections

**Vocabulary Practice**
Definition Chart

Whiteboard Ready!

**GeoActivity**
Graph Water Levels in Lake Chad

## ASSESSMENT

**Student Edition**

Ongoing Assessment: Map Lab

**Resource Bank and myNGconnect.com**

Review and Assessment, Sections 1.1–1.6

**ExamView®**
**Test Generator CD-ROM**

Section 1 Quiz in English and Spanish

---

**Student Edition**

Ongoing Assessment: Map Lab

**Resource Bank and myNGconnect.com**

Review and Assessment, Sections 1.1–1.6

**ExamView®**
**Test Generator CD-ROM**

Section 1 Quiz in English and Spanish

---

**Student Edition**

Ongoing Assessment: Photo Lab

**Resource Bank and myNGconnect.com**

Review and Assessment, Sections 1.1–1.6

**ExamView®**
**Test Generator CD-ROM**

Section 1 Quiz in English and Spanish

## TECHTREK  myNGconnect.com

 **» Fast Forward!**
**Core Content Presentations**
Teach *Physical Geography*

 **Connect to NG**
Research Links

 **Maps and Graphs**
Online World Atlas: Sub-Saharan
Africa Physical

**Interactive Whiteboard**
**GeoActivity** Compare
Precipitation Across Regions

**Also Check Out**
- NG Photo Gallery in **Digital Library**
- GeoJournal in **Student eEdition**

---

 **» Fast Forward!**
**Core Content Presentations**
Teach *East Africa and the Rift Valley*

 **Digital Library**
GeoVideo: *Introduce Sub-Saharan Africa*

 **Maps and Graphs**
- **Interactive Map Tool**
Connect Geography
and Imagery
- Online World Atlas: East Africa
Political; East Africa Climate

**Also Check Out**
- NG Photo Gallery in **Digital Library**
- GeoJournal in **Student eEdition**

---

 **» Fast Forward!**
**Core Content Presentations**
Teach *West Africa's Steppes*

 **Maps and Graphs**
Online World Atlas: West Africa
Political

 **Interactive Whiteboard**
**GeoActivity** Graph Water
Levels in Lake Chad

 **Connect to NG**
Research Links

**Also Check Out**
- NG Photo Gallery in **Digital Library**
- Graphic Organizers in **Teacher Resources**
- GeoJournal in **Student eEdition**

# CHAPTER PLANNER

TE Resource Bank

myNGconnect.com

## SECTION 1 GEOGRAPHY

### 1.4 Rain Forests and Resources

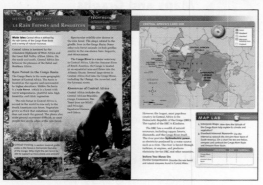

**OBJECTIVE** Describe the geography and resources of Central Africa and the rain forest.

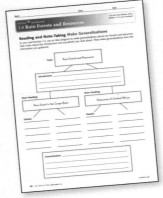

**Reading and Note-Taking**
Make Generalizations

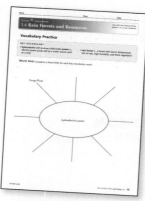

**Vocabulary Practice**
Word Web

**Whiteboard Ready!**

**GeoActivity**
Explore a Tropical Rain Forest

## SECTION 1 GEOGRAPHY

### 1.5 Southern Plateaus and Basins

**OBJECTIVE** Understand how Southern Africa's physical features and natural resources shape the land and its economic development.

**Reading and Note-Taking**
Describe Geographic Information

**Vocabulary Practice**
Vocabulary Pyramid

**Whiteboard Ready!**

**GeoActivity**
Research Copper Exports

## SECTION 1 GEOGRAPHY

### 1.6 Exploring Africa's Wildlife

**OBJECTIVE** Explain the importance of Africa's big cats and other wildlife, and describe efforts to protect the animals and their habitats.

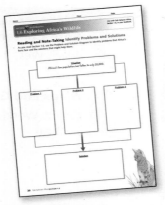

**Reading and Note-Taking**
Identify Problems and Solutions

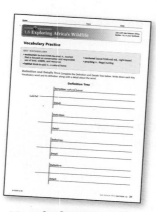

**Vocabulary Practice**
Definition and Details Tree

**Whiteboard Ready!**

**GeoActivity**
Locate a Wildlife Reserve

## ASSESSMENT

### TECHTREK  myNGconnect.com

**Student Edition**

Ongoing Assessment: Map Lab

**Resource Bank and myNGconnect.com**

Review and Assessment, Sections 1.1–1.6

 **ExamView®**
**Test Generator CD-ROM**
Section 1 Quiz in English and Spanish

 » **Fast Forward!**
**Core Content Presentations**
Teach *Rain Forests and Resources*

 **Digital Library**
• GeoVideo: *Introduce Sub-Saharan Africa*
• NG Photo Gallery, Section 1

 **Maps and Graphs**
• Interactive Map Tool
Analyze Patterns of Population
• Online World Atlas: Central Africa's Land Use

**Also Check Out**
GeoJournal in
**Student eEdition**

---

**Student Edition**

Ongoing Assessment: Map Lab

**Resource Bank and myNGconnect.com**

Review and Assessment, Sections 1.1–1.6

 **ExamView®**
**Test Generator CD-ROM**
Section 1 Quiz in English and Spanish

 » **Fast Forward!**
**Core Content Presentations**
Teach *Southern Plateaus and Basins*

 **Digital Library**
NG Photo Gallery, Section 1

 **Connect to NG**
Research Links

 **Maps and Graphs**
Interactive Map Tool
Analyze Climates in Southern Africa

**Also Check Out**
• Online World Atlas in
**Maps and Graphs**
• Graphic Organizers in
**Teacher Resources**
• GeoJournal in
**Student eEdition**

---

**Student Edition**

Ongoing Assessment: Reading Lab

**Teacher's Edition**

Performance Assessment: Create an Informational Brochure

**Resource Bank and myNGconnect.com**

Review and Assessment, Sections 1.1–1.6

 **ExamView®**
**Test Generator CD-ROM**
Section 1 Quiz in English and Spanish

 » **Fast Forward!**
**Core Content Presentations**
Teach *Exploring Africa's Wildlife*

  **Digital Library**
• Explorer Video Clip: *Dereck and Beverly Joubert*
• NG Photo Gallery, Section 1

 **Connect to NG**
Research Links

**Maps and Graphs**
Online World Atlas: African Wildlife Reserves

 **Interactive Whiteboard**
**GeoActivity** Locate a Wildlife Reserve

**Also Check Out**
GeoJournal in
**Student eEdition**

# CHAPTER PLANNER

## SECTION ② HISTORY

## 2.1 Bantu Migrations

**OBJECTIVE** Analyze the causes and effects of the Bantu migrations on Sub-Saharan Africa.

**Reading and Note-Taking**
Sentence Map

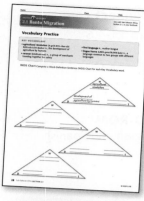

**Vocabulary Practice**
WDS Chart

**Whiteboard Ready!**

**GeoActivity**
Map the Swahili Language

## SECTION ② HISTORY

## 2.2 Early States and Trade

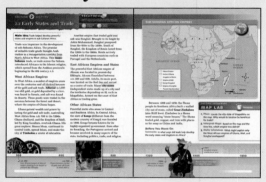

**OBJECTIVE** Examine the impact of trade on the development of states and empires in Africa.

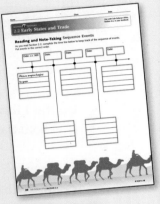

**Reading and Note-Taking**
Sequence Events

**Vocabulary Practice**
Descriptive Paragraph

**Whiteboard Ready!**

**GeoActivity**
Map Historic Trade Routes

## SECTION ② HISTORY

## 2.3 Impact of the Slave Trade

**OBJECTIVE** Understand the impact of the slave trade on sub-Saharan Africa's population.

**Reading and Note-Taking**
Find Main Idea and Details

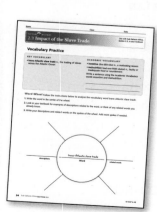

**Vocabulary Practice**
Word Wheel

**Whiteboard Ready!**

**GeoActivity**
Analyze Primary Sources: The Slave Trade

**Student Edition**
Ongoing Assessment: Map Lab

**Resource Bank and myNGconnect.com**
Review and Assessment, Sections 2.1–2.4

**ExamView®**
**Test Generator CD-ROM**
Section 2 Quiz in English and Spanish

**Fast Forward!**
**Core Content Presentations**
Teach *Bantu Migrations*

**Maps and Graphs**
Online World Atlas:
Bantu Migrations

**Interactive Whiteboard**
**GeoActivity** Map the
Swahili Language

**Also Check Out**
- NG Photo Gallery in **Digital Library**
- Graphic Organizers in **Teacher Resources**
- GeoJournal in **Student eEdition**

---

**Student Edition**
Ongoing Assessment: Map Lab

**Resource Bank and myNGconnect.com**
Review and Assessment, Sections 2.1–2.4

**ExamView®**
**Test Generator CD-ROM**
Section 2 Quiz in English and Spanish

**Fast Forward!**
**Core Content Presentations**
Teach *Early States and Trades*

**Digital Library**
- GeoVideo: *Introduce Sub-Saharan Africa*
- NG Photo Gallery, Section 2

**Connect to NG**
Research Links

**Maps and Graphs**
- **Interactive Map Tool** Analyze Movement
- Online World Atlas: Sub-Saharan African Empires

**Also Check Out**
- Graphic Organizers in **Teacher Resources**
- GeoJournal in **Student eEdition**

---

**Student Edition**
Ongoing Assessment: Data Lab

**Resource Bank and myNGconnect.com**
Review and Assessment, Sections 2.1–2.4

**ExamView®**
**Test Generator CD-ROM**
Section 2 Quiz in English and Spanish

**Fast Forward!**
**Core Content Presentations**
Teach *Impact of the Slave Trade*

**Connect to NG**
Research Links

**Interactive Whiteboard**
**GeoActivity** Analyze Primary
Sources: The Slave Trade

**Also Check Out**
- Charts & Infographics and Graphic Organizers in **Teacher Resources**
- GeoJournal in **Student eEdition**

## SECTION SUPPORT

TE Resource Bank

myNGconnect.com

## 2.4 Colonization to Independence

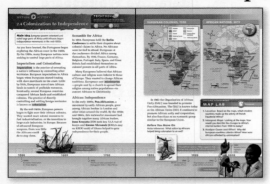

**OBJECTIVE** Describe the effects of European colonization in Africa and events that led to African independence.

### Reading and Note-Taking
Track Important Information

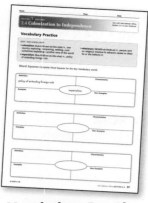

### Vocabulary Practice
Word Squares

**Whiteboard Ready!**

### GeoActivity
Build a Time Line of Ghana's Independence

## CHAPTER ASSESSMENT

### INFORMAL ASSESSMENT

TE Resource Bank

myNGconnect.com

### Review

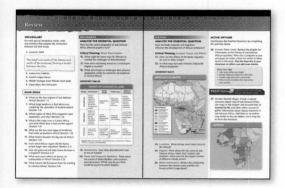

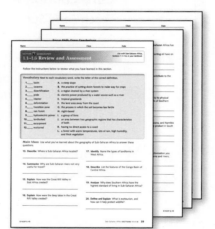

**Review and Assessment**

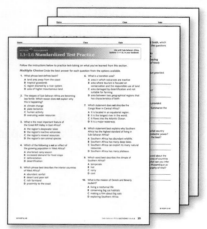

**Standardized Test Practice**

**Student Edition**
Ongoing Assessment: Map Lab

**Teacher's Edition**
Performance Assessment: Hold a Panel Discussion

**Resource Bank and myNGconnect.com**
Review and Assessment, Sections 2.1–2.4

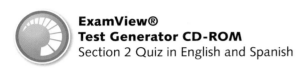

**ExamView®**
**Test Generator CD-ROM**
Section 2 Quiz in English and Spanish

**>> Fast Forward!**
**Core Content Presentations**
Teach *Colonization to Independence*

**Maps and Graphs**
Online World Atlas: European Colonies, 1938; African Nations, 2011

**Interactive Whiteboard**
**GeoActivity** Build a Time Line of Ghana's Independence

**Also Check Out**
- NG Photo Gallery in **Digital Library**
- GeoJournal in **Student eEdition**

## FORMAL ASSESSMENT

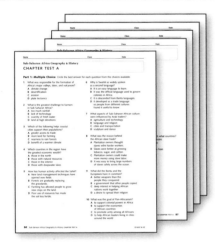

**Chapter Test A (on level)**

**Chapter Test B (modified)**

**ExamView®**
**Test Generator CD-ROM**
Chapter Tests

# STRATEGIES FOR DIFFERENTIATION

## STRIVING READERS  eEdition  Audiobook

### Strategy 1 • Play "ABC Brainstorm"

To elicit prior knowledge before reading, allow students to work in pairs to brainstorm words relating to Africa. Have them begin by making a chart that lists each letter of the alphabet and then trying to list at least one word starting with that letter next to the letter. You may ask students to keep their lists and add words to them as they progress through the lessons.

**Use with All Sections**

### Strategy 2 • Display a Graphic Summary

To give students a visual overview of the four areas of sub-Saharan Africa, display this graphic summary on the board and have students copy it in their notebooks.

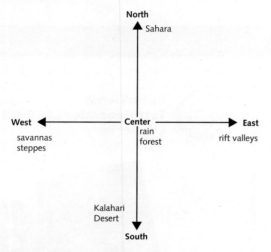

**Use with Section 1.1** *You may choose to have students revisit the graphic summary after reading Sections 1.2, 1.3, and 1.4 to add words about geographic features to each directional list.*

### Strategy 3 • Build a Cause-Effect Organizer

Before reading, display the following organizer and discuss what causes people to migrate. Ask students if they can volunteer a specific example of each of the kinds of causes listed. After reading, allow students to add examples under the word *Effects*. Students should add the examples from the reading—cultures blend, new languages develop, technology spreads, conflict occurs—as well as others they think of.

Causes ————————▶ Migration ————————▶ Effects
Economic
Political
Religious
Social
Environmental

**Use with Section 2.1**

### Strategy 4 • Create a 3-2-1 Summary

After they read a lesson, direct students to create a 3-2-1 summary by writing three important ideas under the number 3, two Key Vocabulary words and their definitions under the number 2, and one main idea question to ask another student. Students can share their summaries in pairs and answer each other's questions.

**Use with All Sections**

### Strategy 5 • Play the "I Am . . ." Game

To reinforce the meanings of key terms and names, assign every student one term or name that appears in the chapter and have them write a one-sentence clue beginning with "I am." Have students take turns reading clues and calling on students to guess answers.

**Use with All Sections**

## INCLUSION  eEdition  Audiobook

### Strategy 1 • Display Cardinal Points

Help students make and display a simple line drawing of a compass rose with the words *north, south, east,* and *west* written appropriately at the points. Allow students to keep the display on their desks as all areas of the region are discussed. Occasionally ask questions to verify that students can point to the direction appropriate to the area being discussed.

**Use with Sections 1.1–1.5**

### Strategy 2 • Prioritize Vocabulary Lists

Choose no more than two vocabulary words per lesson to focus on for mastery. Have students write the words on cards or in notebooks and draw a personal visual clue to the meaning. For visually impaired students, have them think of and record oral clues for their words.

**Use with All Sections**

# ENGLISH LANGUAGE LEARNERS

 **eEdition**    **Audiobook**    **Maps and Graphs**

## Strategy 1 • Display an "Out of Africa" Organizer

Use the following display to introduce key terms and features of sub-Saharan Africa before beginning to read:

**A**cross the continent
**F**our regions
**R**ain forests, rivers
**I**nterior countries
**C**ountries on coasts
**A**nimals

Use the map of the region at the beginning of the chapter or in the **Online World Atlas** to point out how sub-Saharan Africa stretches across the continent. Explain that students will learn about four different areas within sub-Saharan Africa, and explain that they will learn about rain forests and rivers as well. Use the map again to show that some of the countries are on the interior of the continent and some are along each coast. Finally, tell them that they can look forward to talking about the many kinds of animals that live in Africa.

**Use before Section 1.1** *You may also choose to revisit before and after Sections 1.1–1.6.*

## Strategy 2 • Preteach Key Terms

Because the terms *plateau* and *basin* are used frequently, introduce the following word sets before reading to make sure students have mental images for each concept.

**Plateau:** flat, high, tabletop
**Basin:** bottom of bowl, water drains, where rivers take water

**Use before Section 1.1**

## Strategy 3 • Teach Word Parts

Use examples from the Key Vocabulary lists to teach the following:

1. **Compound Words:** *highlands* (Section 1.3); *landlocked* (Section 1.5) Display the two words and explain that two words can be put together to make a new word. Ask students to circle the two words within each word. Ask for other examples of compound words.

2. **The Prefix** *Trans-: trans-Saharan* (Section 2.2); *trans-Atlantic* (Section 2.3) Explain that *trans-* is a word part added to the beginning of a word and that it means "across." Ask what the prefix *trans-* causes each of the two words to mean. Solicit one more example of a word beginning with the prefix *trans-*.

**Use with Sections 1.3, 1.5, 2.2, and 2.3**

# GIFTED & TALENTED

 **Connect to NG**

## Strategy 1 • Map the Congo River

Challenge students to work in pairs to create a large illustrated map of the Congo River. Students can use the **Research Links** to do research to show such details as countries and major cities and create symbols for a variety of important features of the area, such as rain forests and animals.

**Use with Section 1.4**

## Strategy 2 • Explain the Significance

Allow students to choose one term below to investigate and design a presentation that explains the significance of the term to the history of Africa.

Timbuktu
Kingdom of Mali
Mansa Musa

Great Zimbabwe
Kingdom of Aksum
Songhai Empire

**Use with Section 2.2**

# PRE-AP

 **Connect to NG**

## Strategy 1 • Defend a Position

Invite students to designate one of the four areas of sub-Saharan Africa (west, central, east, or south) as "Most Interesting to Visit" and write a position paper explaining the reasons for their choice. Direct them to the **Research Links** for information.

**Use with All Sections**

## Strategy 2 • Analyze Causes and Effects

Direct students to research the causes of European colonization in Africa and some effects of this colonization. They may want to focus on one or two European countries. Encourage them to show their work in the form of a graphic organizer.

**Use with Sections 2.3 and 2.4**

# Sub-Saharan Africa
## GEOGRAPHY & HISTORY

African elephants

## PREVIEW THE CHAPTER

**Essential Question** How has the varied geography of Sub-Saharan Africa affected people's lives?

**KEY VOCABULARY**

- basin
- savanna
- desertification
- rift valley
- pride
- interior
- deforestation
- transition zone
- highlands
- rain forest
- hydroelectric power
- landlocked
- escarpment
- habitat
- poaching
- nocturnal
- ecotourism

**ACADEMIC VOCABULARY**
dormant

**TERMS & NAMES**

- Sahel
- Kalahari
- Great Rift Valley
- Kilimanjaro
- Congo River
- Great Escarpment
- Zambezi River
- Okavango Delta

**Essential Question** How did trade networks and migration influence the development of African civilization?

**KEY VOCABULARY**

- agricultural revolution
- first language
- caravan
- lingua franca
- trans-Saharan
- alluvial
- city-state
- trans-Atlantic slave trade
- malnutrition
- imperialism
- colonialism
- missionary

**ACADEMIC VOCABULARY**
incentive

**TERMS & NAMES**

- Bantu
- Swahili
- Timbuktu
- Kongo
- Great Zimbabwe
- Middle Passage
- Berlin Conference
- Pan-Africanism
- Jomo Kenyatta
- Kwame Nkrumah

---

▶▶ **Fast Forward!**

**Core Content Presentations**
Introduce *Sub-Saharan Africa Geography & History*

**Digital Library**
GeoVideo: *Introduce Sub-Saharan Africa*

**Maps and Graphs**
- **Interactive Map Tool**
Explore Language Diversity
- **Online World Atlas**: Sub-Saharan Africa Political; North America Political

**Also Check Out**
Graphic Organizers in **Teacher Resources**

## INTRODUCE THE CHAPTER

### INTRODUCE THE MAP

Use the Sub-Saharan Africa Political map to familiarize students with the region. Remind students how to use the equator, the Tropic of Cancer, and the Tropic of Capricorn to identify a region's location and to predict the climate of the region. **ASK:** What does Congo's latitude suggest about its temperatures? (*Temperatures are probably high.*) Point out that of all continents, Africa has the greatest portion (four-fifths) of its area between the Tropics of Cancer and Capricorn.

### COMPARE ACROSS REGIONS

Show the North America Political map from the **Online World Atlas. ASK:** Which region is divided into the greater number of different countries, Sub-Saharan Africa or North America? (*Sub-Saharan Africa*) Point out that Africa has about the same number of countries as the United States has states. Have students discuss how life would be different if every state was a different country.

### AFRICAN COUNTRIES AND AMERICAN STATES

| AFRICAN COUNTRY | LAND AREA (SQ. MI.) | POPULATION (2010 EST.) |
|---|---|---|
| Democratic Republic of the Congo | 875,312 | 70,916,439 |
| Guinea-Bissau | 10,857 | 1,565,126 |
| Kenya | 219 746 | 40,046,566 |
| South Africa | 468,909 | 49,109,107 |

| AMERICAN STATE | LAND AREA (SQ. MI.) | POPULATION (2010 EST.) |
|---|---|---|
| California | 158,633 | 36,961,664 |
| Oregon | 97,047 | 3,825,657 |
| Rhode Island | 1,223 | 1,053,209 |
| Texas | 266,853 | 24,782,302 |

Source: CIA World Factbook and Britannica Online

# INTRODUCE THE ESSENTIAL QUESTIONS

## SECTION 1 • GEOGRAPHY
**How has the varied geography of Sub-Saharan Africa affected people's lives?**

**Jigsaw Activity: Geography of Africa**
Have students examine how living in different types of geographic areas affects people's lives. Assign students to expert groups, with each discussing one of the areas below. **ASK:** How would you expect the landforms, climate, elevation, and vegetation in this region to affect people's lives? Use the Jigsaw strategy to have experts share the predictions of their groups. See "Best Practices for Active Teaching" for a review of this strategy.

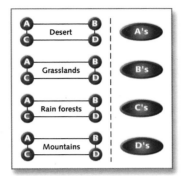

**A Desert** Lack or scarcity of water would significantly affect people's lives. Typically deserts are not heavily populated. Some deserts have oases where people can live. Irrigated desert areas, such as river valleys, can be excellent for farming. Animals can graze there after a rain. Some deserts have salt flats or mineral resources that boost local economies. Desert economies can benefit from selling to or trading with passing travelers.

**B Grasslands** With sufficient rainfall, grasslands are excellent for farming. Even dry grasslands are suitable for grazing, and if rivers or lakes can supply fresh water for irrigation, they make good cropland as well. Grasslands attract grazing wild animals, so hunters can find game. Tourists may be attracted by the animals.

**C Rain Forests** Rain forests are difficult to navigate, limiting transportation through them and isolating communities within them. Rain forests can be cleared, but their soil is not fertile and does not support crops for long. The forests contain many resources such as timber, medicinal plants, fruits, and nuts. Rich with plant and animal life, they provide game and attract tourists.

**D Mountains** Mountains may have fertile soil, but sloping, rocky land is difficult to farm. Mountains become barriers to transportation, sometimes isolating mountain communities. High-altitude regions are generally cooler than lowlands at comparable latitudes. At very high altitudes, people and animals must adapt in order to take in enough oxygen to work and function. **0:25** minutes

## SECTION 2 • HISTORY
**How did trade networks and migration influence the development of African civilization?**

**Think, Pair, Share Activity:** Have students use the Think, Pair, Share strategy to discuss the Essential Question. See "Best Practices for Active Teaching" for a review of this strategy. Allow students to look through this chapter, looking for clues in photos, maps, titles, and subheadings. Have them focus on each of the following aspects of the question:

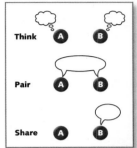

**A** How trade and migration might influence how and where civilizations grow

**B** How trade and migration can influence cultures

**C** How trade and colonialism can influence each other and civilizations in colonial territories **0:20** minutes

## ACTIVE OPTIONS

 **Interactive Map Tool**

**Explore Language Diversity**
**PURPOSE** Explore Sub-Saharan Africa's language regions
**SET-UP**
1. Open the **Interactive Map Tool,** set the "Map Mode" to National Geographic, and the "Region" to Africa.
2. Under "Human Systems—Populations & Cultures," turn on the Language Diversity layer. Set the transparency level to 40 percent.

**ACTIVITY**

Point out Sub-Saharan Africa's political borders and compare them with boundaries of the language diversity regions. Under "Country," select Nigeria, South Africa, and Somalia. Point out the language diversity in these countries. Then ask students why one language region might cross political borders. Tell them they will learn in this chapter about Africa's ethnic groups, how languages spread, and how Africa's political borders were drawn. **0:15** minutes

# INTRODUCE CHAPTER VOCABULARY  Teacher Resources

**Word Wheel** Download and distribute copies of the Word Wheel from the **Graphic Organizers.** Have students write a Key Vocabulary word in the center and write associated words on the spokes. Then have students write descriptive sentences about the word. Repeat with other Key Vocabulary words.

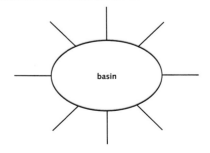

SECTION 1 GEOGRAPHY

## 1.1 Physical Geography

TECHTREK
myNGconnect.com For an online map
of Sub-Saharan Africa and Visual Vocabulary

Maps and Graphs    Digital Library

### SUB-SAHARAN AFRICA PHYSICAL

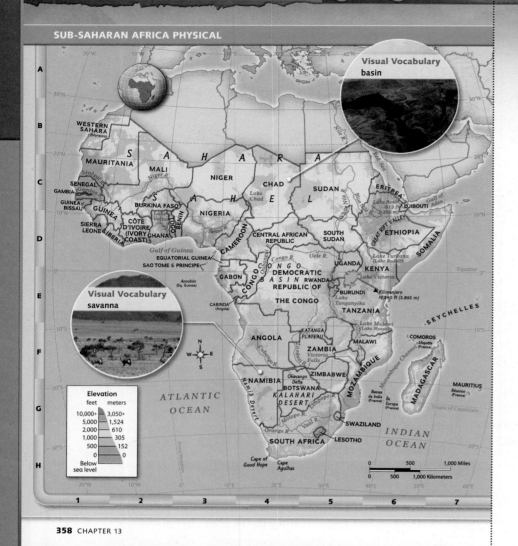

Visual Vocabulary
basin

Visual Vocabulary
savanna

**Elevation**

| feet | meters |
|------|--------|
| 10,000+ | 3,050+ |
| 5,000 | 1,524 |
| 2,000 | 610 |
| 1,000 | 305 |
| 500 | 152 |
| 0 | 0 |
| Below sea level | |

**Main Idea** Sub-Saharan Africa is divided into four parts, each with varied geographic features.

Sub-Saharan Africa lies south of the Sahara desert. The region extends from Senegal in western Africa to Ethiopia and Somalia in eastern Africa, and southward to the tip of the continent. Sub-Saharan Africa includes the island nation of Madagascar (ma duh GAS kahr).

#### Africa's Continental Drift

As you have learned, the continents once belonged to one supercontinent called Pangaea. The movement of Earth's tectonic plates caused the continents to drift apart, and Africa became a separate continent. Plate tectonics also caused the formation of certain physical features on the African continent. Lakes, basins, and valleys were all formed as the plates moved. A **basin** is a region drained by a river system.

#### Landforms and Water

Sub-Saharan Africa is divided into four parts: west, central, east, and south. West Africa includes savannas and much of the Sahel. The **Sahel** (saa HEL) is a semiarid grassland that separates the Sahara in the north from the tropical grasslands, or **savannas**, in the south. In the Sahel, one climate gradually changes to another. Parts of the Sahel, for example, are changing to desert. This process, called **desertification**, means there is less fertile land to grow food. Desertification is caused by many factors including climate change and overpopulation.

Central Africa's primary landform is rain forest, especially in the Congo Basin. In East Africa, **rift valleys**—deep valleys that formed when Earth's crust separated and broke apart—stretch from the Red Sea southward through Mozambique. Southern Africa features great plateaus and another major desert, the **Kalahari**. The Kalahari has limited surface water, but supports a variety of plants and wildlife.

Access to fresh water is an issue for sub-Saharan Africans due to limited water resources and poor sanitation. The situation is improving, however. For example, between 1990 and 2006, the percentage of people in Namibia with access to clean water increased from 57 percent to 93 percent as the government and individual communities began working together to solve the problem.

#### Before You Move On

**Monitor Comprehension** What are the main geographic features of sub-Saharan Africa's four parts?

**ONGOING ASSESSMENT**

## MAP LAB                    GeoJournal

1. **Human-Environment Interaction** According to the map, the approximate width of the Sahara is 3,000 miles from east to west. Why is the Sahara considered a natural boundary?

2. **Location** Use the map to point out two sources of fresh water in sub-Saharan Africa.

3. **Describe Geographic Information** Describe the causes of desertification and the problem it poses for sub-Saharan farming.

the steppes and Sahel of West Africa; the Rift Valley of East Africa; the rain forests of Central Africa; the plateaus and basins of Southern Africa

---

## PLAN

### OBJECTIVE
Locate and analyze the physical characteristics of the diverse areas of sub-Saharan Africa.

### CRITICAL THINKING SKILLS FOR SECTION 1.1

- Main Idea
- Monitor Comprehension
- Describe Geographic Information
- Summarize
- Analyze Cause and Effect
- Interpret Maps

### PRINT RESOURCES

*Teacher's Edition* Resource Bank

- Reading and Note-Taking: Take Notes
- Vocabulary Practice: Definition Chart
- **GeoActivity** Compare Precipitation Across Regions

TECHTREK  myNGconnect.com

**Fast Forward!**
**Core Content Presentations**
Teach *Physical Geography*

**Connect to NG**
Research Links

**Maps and Graphs**
Online World Atlas: Sub-Saharan Africa Physical

**Interactive Whiteboard**
**GeoActivity** Compare Precipitation Across Regions

**Also Check Out**
- NG Photo Gallery in **Digital Library**
- GeoJournal in **Student eEdition**

### BACKGROUND FOR THE TEACHER

Africa is mostly a huge plateau surrounded by narrow strips of lower coastal land. The equator runs almost midway between the northernmost and southernmost parts of Africa. Most of Africa's land mass is located north of the equator because of the bulge formed by western Africa. Most of the continent is located between the Tropic of Cancer and the Tropic of Capricorn. The prime meridian, or 0° longitude, runs from north to south through a portion of Africa.

### ESSENTIAL QUESTION

#### How has the varied geography of Sub-Saharan Africa affected people's lives?

Because of Africa's enormous size, much of the continent is distant from oceans and the moisture that oceans provide. Section 1.1 describes the physical features that can affect people's lives.

## INTRODUCE & ENGAGE  Maps and Graphs

**Turn and Talk** Project the Sub-Saharan Africa Physical map from the **Online World Atlas.** Have students share their prior knowledge of Africa with a classmate. Tell them to discuss books they have read, films they have seen, or information they have found on the Internet. Then have them describe to their partner the physical characteristics of the part of Africa featured in the book, film, or Internet source. Invite individual students to come forward, locate the featured countries or areas on the projected map, and describe their prior knowledge of that country or area. **0:15** minutes

## TEACH  Maps and Graphs

### Guided Discussion

1. **Summarize** What features of sub-Saharan Africa are caused by plate tectonics? *(lakes, basins, and valleys)*

2. **Analyze Cause and Effect** Which features of sub-Saharan Africa's climate and geography might cause challenges for its people? *(Possible response: large dry regions, limited supply of and access to fresh water, distance between interior and coast, rivers that do not connect coast with interior, rivers hard to travel)*

**Interpret Maps** Help students interpret the Sub-Saharan Africa Physical map. Explain how to use the legend to determine elevation. Call on volunteers to identify countries with some of the highest and lowest elevations. **ASK:** Which country has both very high and very low elevations? *(Kenya)* **0:15** minutes

## DIFFERENTIATE  Connect to NG

**Striving Readers   Summarize** Use Strategy 2 from Strategies for Differentiation. Have students refer to the graphic summary in their notebooks, work in pairs, and add words from the lesson that describe the four areas of sub-Saharan Africa.

**Pre-AP Compare Across Regions** Have students use the **Research Links** to conduct Internet research and create a chart that compares rivers and lakes in a sub-Saharan country with rivers and lakes in their own region. Have them consider the following:

- Do people depend on the river or lake for fresh water?
- How is the river or lake important economically?
- Is the river or lake useful as transportation?
- Does the river or lake provide a boundary between countries, states, or cities?

**ASK:** What generalization can you make about similarities between the two regions? What might be some reasons for the differences between the two regions?

Examples:

Generalization 1: We do not depend on the river for fresh water because we have plenty of rainfall and other water sources in our community. That is not true of Sudan.

Generalization 2: Rivers and lakes are very important sources of water for my community. This is also true for Tanzania.

 **Interactive Whiteboard**
## GeoActivity

**Compare Precipitation Across Regions** Have students examine the precipitation map in groups of four. Tell each group to assign each member a different continent. Have each group member use a Venn diagram to record regional comparisons. Then have group members ask a question comparing precipitation in Africa as a whole with precipitation on the assigned continent. Other group members should use the map to answer the question. Then group members should ask questions comparing precipitation in one smaller area of Africa, such as the Sahel, with that in a smaller area on another continent. Monitor groups as they ask and answer questions. As a class, discuss some of the questions and answers that were shared in the groups. **0:20** minutes

## On Your Feet

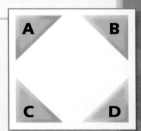

**Four Corners** Have students meet in corners to discuss the different areas of sub-Saharan Africa. Post signs in four corners of the classroom, each labeled with one of these areas: West Africa, Central Africa, East Africa, Southern Africa. Ask students to discuss what they know of their chosen area from the text, the map, or prior knowledge. Then have one member from each group report to the class. Students might record the information about each area in a single table such as the one shown below, which can then be shared as part of the final report. **0:25** minutes

| Area of Africa | What We Know |
|---|---|
| West Africa | |
| Central Africa | |
| East Africa | |
| South Africa | |

## ONGOING ASSESSMENT
## MAP LAB  GeoJournal

### ANSWERS

1. The desert is a natural feature that limits human movement and settlement.
2. lakes and rivers
3. Desertification is the process by which semiarid grasslands are becoming less fertile due to climate change and human activities. With the loss in fertility, it becomes more difficult to farm.

# 1.2 East Africa and the Rift Valley

**TECHTREK**
myNGconnect.com For online maps of
East Africa and photos of the Great Rift Valley

Maps and Graphs    Digital Library

**Main Idea** East Africa is best known for the Great Rift Valley and the deep lakes found there.

East Africa is easy to spot on a map—it is shaped like a rhinoceros horn. In fact, the region is known as the Horn of Africa. The "horn" is formed by the countries of Somalia, Djibouti (ji BOO tee), Eritrea, and Ethiopia. Other countries in East Africa are Sudan, Kenya, Uganda, Rwanda, Burundi, and Tanzania.

## The Great Rift Valley

The most important physical feature of East Africa is the **Great Rift Valley**. This valley is part of a chain of valleys that stretch from southwest Asia to southern Africa. In some places the valley is 60 miles wide. Valley walls often rise more than 6,000 feet in height.

This chain of valleys was formed by tectonic plates that separated and created deep cracks, or rifts, in the earth's crust. The rift valleys have been forming for about 20 million years and continue to develop today.

Plate movements also created the freshwater lakes in the Great Rift Valley. As low spots and rifts developed, they slowly filled with rainwater to create lakes. West of Tanzania is Lake Tanganyika (TANG guhn YEE kuh). At 4,700 feet deep, it is the second deepest freshwater lake in the world.

## Plateaus and Savannas

East Africa sits mostly on plateaus. As the climate map shows, the two most substantial elevated areas are in Ethiopia and Kenya. The higher elevations of these areas means the temperatures are cooler, even though much of the area is on or near the equator.

In addition to the rift valleys and lakes, plate movements created volcanoes. Both **Kilimanjaro** (19,340 feet) in Tanzania and Mount Kenya (17,058 feet) in Kenya are **dormant**, or inactive, volcanoes. The volcanic soil around these mountains is fertile, meaning crops grow well.

### EAST AFRICA POLITICAL

### EAST AFRICA CLIMATE

Both Tanzania and Kenya have vast savannas where wildlife such as lions, giraffes, and elephants roam freely or in protected reserves.

**Before You Move On**
Summarize  Describe the physical characteristics of the Great Rift Valley. *chain of valleys with very high walls and deep freshwater lakes; limited rainfall*

> **Visual Vocabulary** A pride, or group, of lions moves through tall savanna grass in Kenya. A pride averages about 15 members.

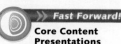

**ONGOING ASSESSMENT**
## MAP LAB

GeoJournal

1. **Location**  Using the maps, locate three sources of freshwater in East Africa.
2. **Interpret Maps**  Based on the climate map, which countries have the largest variety of climate regions in East Africa? How does that information add to your understanding of this region?
3. **Make Inferences**  How might climate, elevation, and access to water determine where people live in East Africa?

# PLAN

## OBJECTIVE Identify and describe the physical features of East Africa and the Great Rift Valley.

### CRITICAL THINKING SKILLS FOR SECTION 1.2

- Main Idea
- Summarize
- Interpret Maps
- Make Inferences
- Interpret Models
- Categorize
- Identify

## PRINT RESOURCES

*Teacher's Edition* Resource Bank

- Reading and Note-Taking: Describe Geographic Information
- Vocabulary Practice: Comparison Chart
- **GeoActivity**  Relate Topography and Plate Tectonics

**TECHTREK** myNGconnect.com

**Fast Forward!**
**Core Content Presentations**
Teach *East Africa and the Rift Valley*

**Digital Library**
GeoVideo: *Introduce Sub-Saharan Africa*

**Maps and Graphs**
- **Interactive Map Tool** Connect Geography and Imagery
- Online World Atlas: East Africa Political; East Africa Climate

**Also Check Out**
- NG Photo Gallery in **Digital Library**
- GeoJournal in **Student eEdition**

## BACKGROUND FOR THE TEACHER

The Great Rift Valley extends 3,000 miles. It runs south through Syria and Lebanon, and on through the Jordan Valley, the Dead Sea, the Gulf of Aqaba, and the Red Sea. The main branch in Africa continues southwest from the Red Sea across Ethiopia. It then runs south across Kenya, Tanzania, and Malawi to the Zambezi River Valley in Mozambique. The lowest part of the Great Rift Valley is the Dead Sea, 1,300 feet below sea level. The highest is in southern Kenya.

## ESSENTIAL QUESTION

### How has the varied geography of Sub-Saharan Africa affected people's lives?

The nature and quality of people's lives in East Africa depend on their access to water, coasts, and natural resources. Section 1.2 describes the location and characteristics of these features.

## INTRODUCE & ENGAGE  Digital Library

**GeoVideo:** *Introduce Sub-Saharan Africa* Show the section comparing the different areas of Africa to acquaint students with the dramatic physical features of the region. **ASK:** What image from the video do you most remember? *(Students' responses will vary.)*

**Interpret Models** East Africa is home to the Great Rift Valley, which includes some very deep lakes. To show students how the valley was formed, have pairs of students place two paperback books of equal thickness lengthwise between them, then pull the books until they are about a half inch away from each other. Explain that the books represent plates of land that pull apart, leaving deep valleys between them. Explain that the Great Rift Valley formed this way. `0:15` minutes

## TEACH  Maps and Graphs

### Guided Discussion

1. **Categorize** Which features of East Africa are caused by plate tectonics? *(Great Rift Valley, deep lakes, and volcanoes)*

2. **Identify** What are the characteristics of East Africa's plateaus and savannas? *(cooler temperatures on the plateaus; savannas are home to wildlife such as lions, giraffes, and elephants)* Remind students that the savannas are an important habitat, a home to particular species, some of which are endangered.

3. **Make Inferences** Which features of East Africa might be most likely to draw tourists? *(Responses will vary. Best responses: high mountains and savannas full of wildlife)*

**Interpret Maps** Project the East Africa Climate map from the **Online World Atlas.** Explain how to use the legend to determine climate in the various areas. Have students point to the driest and most humid areas. **ASK:** In which countries are the most humid areas located? *(Ethiopia, Sudan, Kenya, Uganda, and Tanzania)* `0:20` minutes

## DIFFERENTIATE

**Inclusion Display Cardinal Points** Use Inclusion Strategy 1 from Strategies for Differentiation. As students read and discuss the text encourage them to refer to the drawing of the compass rose and point to the direction being referenced. Ask occasional questions such as "Which country is south of Kenya? Which country is east of Kenya?"

**English Language Learners Teach Compound Words** Remind students that sometimes two words can be put together to make a new word. Write these words and have students copy them.

- rainwater
- freshwater
- wildlife

**Example:**

Ask students to circle the two words within each word. Then help them define each of the two smaller words and the resulting compound word.

## ACTIVE OPTIONS

 **Interactive Map Tool**

**Connect Geography and Imagery**

**PURPOSE** Visualize earthquake activity in East Africa

**SET-UP**

1. Open the **Interactive Map Tool,** set the "Map Mode" to Satellite, set the "Region" to Africa, and zoom in to East Africa.

2. Under "Physical Systems—Land," turn on the Earthquakes layer.

**ACTIVITY**

1. Point out the crescent-shaped lakes in East Africa. Explain that these are clear visual indicators of where valleys are located. Explain that the lakes were created as a result of tectonic activity in the area.

2. Turn the Earthquakes layer off and on to illustrate that earthquakes in the area occur along the valleys.

3. Ask students to explain this relationship. *(The valleys were created by tectonic forces, so it should be no surprise that earthquakes occur along the valleys.)* `0:25` minutes

### On Your Feet

**Numbered Heads** Have students get into groups of four and number off within each group. Assign Map Lab Question 3. Have students discuss their answers as a group. Students should write down the facts from the text and their prior knowledge that form the basis of their inferences. Then call a number and the student from each group with that number reports for the group. `0:20` minutes

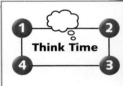 Think Time

 Talk Time

 Share 2's Time

## ONGOING ASSESSMENT

### MAP LAB  GeoJournal

**ANSWERS**

1. Students may identify any of the lakes or rivers shown.

2. Kenya and Ethiopia each have four climate regions. This information is helpful to know because it can provide an understanding of why people live where they do and how different countries can face similar issues due to their shared climate.

3. People tend to live close to freshwater sources or in areas with temperate climates and elevations favorable to farming.

**TECHTREK**
myNGconnect.com For an online
map and photos of desertification
Maps and Graphs | Digital Library

**Main Idea** West Africa's physical geography includes steppes and highlands as well as tropical coast and dry desert.

West Africa runs from the Atlantic coast south of the Sahara, eastward to the continent's **interior**, or area away from the coast. This part of Africa supports several different ways of life, depending on the landforms and climates found in each area.

### Steppes and Highlands

Semiarid steppes, or grasslands, define part of West Africa. As you know, the grassland between the Sahara desert and the tropical savannas is the Sahel. The Sahel runs through the middle of West Africa. The area has a short rainy season and, as a result, is very dry.

The growing population in West Africa has increased the demand for food crops. To create more cropland, West Africans have had to cut down forests, a practice called **deforestation**. Deforestation in West Africa has left the arid soil unprotected.

Soil has eroded, or washed away, because of overuse. These conditions, along with climate change, contribute to desertification, an ongoing problem in sub-Saharan Africa.

**Highlands**, which are areas of higher mountainous land, are also found in West Africa. The Adamawa Highlands are on Nigeria's eastern border. The Futa Jallon Highlands rise in Senegal on its border with Guinea. This series of sandstone plateaus is marked by rugged canyons.

### Tropical Coast, Dry Desert

Coastal countries differ from interior countries in West Africa. Countries on the coast have more people and more cities than those in the interior. Coastal countries often have tropical climates. Some cities on the Gulf of Guinea get more than 80 inches of rain per year, and the coast of Côte d'Ivoire can get more than 10 feet per year. In contrast, the northern desert areas of Niger, an interior country, get less than 10 inches of rain per year.

The largest cities in West Africa are located near or on the Atlantic coast. The coastal city of Lagos, Nigeria, is the largest city in West Africa and one of the largest in the world. Such coastal cities have many advantages. Adequate rainfall, fishing, and trade all make it easier for West African coastal cities to support growing populations.

The interior countries of West Africa are mostly covered by desert. Deforestation and desertification, along with the lack of water, make farming in the poor soil a constant struggle. About 80 percent of people in Chad make their living from subsistence farming and raising livestock. In 2003, Chad began exporting oil. This new economic resource may improve Chad's economy and make money available for improved farming technology.

**Before You Move On**
**Monitor Comprehension** In what ways are West Africa's steppes different from the coasts?
*The steppes have less rainfall than the coasts and the steppes are not as densely populated.*

### WEST AFRICA POLITICAL

**CITIES AND WATER** Nearly all of the West African capitals are either near the coast or near a river. Water is essential for cities to grow. Areas with good access to water have better farming, more industry, and the ability to support larger populations. Large cities around the world tend to build up around good sources of water.

**ONGOING ASSESSMENT**

## PHOTO LAB
GeoJournal

1. **Analyze Visuals** Based on the photo, what characteristics of the Sahel in Mali make it a transition zone?

2. **Location** What does the photo suggest about the challenges of living in this transition zone?

3. **Interpret Maps** What makes the capital of Nigeria different from other capitals in West Africa?

> **Visual Vocabulary** A **transition zone** is an area between two geographic regions that has characteristics of both. The Sahel (shown here in Mali) is a transition zone between the Sahara in the north and the savannas in the south.

## PLAN

### OBJECTIVE Analyze how West Africa's physical features, climate, precipitation, and access to coastal waters affect the population of the region.

### CRITICAL THINKING SKILLS FOR SECTION 1.3

- Main Idea
- Monitor Comprehension
- Analyze Visuals
- Interpret Maps
- Analyze Cause and Effect
- Contrast

### PRINT RESOURCES

*Teacher's Edition* Resource Bank

- Reading and Note-Taking: Make Connections
- Vocabulary Practice: Definition Chart
- **GeoActivity** Graph Water Levels in Lake Chad

**TECHTREK** myNGconnect.com

**Fast Forward!**
**Core Content Presentations**
Teach *West Africa's Steppes*

**Maps and Graphs**
Online World Atlas: West Africa Political

**Interactive Whiteboard GeoActivity** Graph Water Levels in Lake Chad

**Connect to NG**
Research Links

**Also Check Out**
- NG Photo Gallery in **Digital Library**
- Graphic Organizers in **Teacher Resources**
- GeoJournal in **Student eEdition**

### BACKGROUND FOR THE TEACHER

Water levels in Lake Chad have been receding for thousands of years. Lake Chad is a transnational wetland. Chad, Nigeria, Niger, and Cameroon each have some of its wetlands within their borders. During the 2000s, each of these countries declared Lake Chad a wetland of international importance and agreed to take steps toward its protection.

### ESSENTIAL QUESTION

### How has the varied geography of Sub-Saharan Africa affected people's lives?

Section 1.3 describes various geographic processes, such as desertification and deforestation, and their impact on settlement patterns and economies.

## INTRODUCE & ENGAGE

**Team Up** Have students work in pairs to discuss the main economic activities in their community. Assign them to brainstorm any ways that these activities might depend on local geographic features, such as fertile soil, rainfall, or mineral resources. If your community is near an ocean, lake, or river, have students focus on the role it plays in such economic factors as transportation, sources of fresh water, or fishing. Provide each pair with a T-Chart like the one shown at right and have them list geographic features and the importance of each feature. Tell students that they will learn about the resources of West Africa and they can add information on Africa to the T-Chart. `0:20` minutes

| Geographic Feature | Why Important |
|---|---|
| | |

## TEACH  Maps and Graphs

### Guided Discussion

1. **Analyze Cause and Effect** Why did West Africa's largest cities arise near or on the coast? *(The coast has more rainfall and fresh water. It is better for farming, so the region can feed its people. Being on the coast allows for better transportation and trade.)*

2. **Contrast** How are coastal regions in West Africa different from interior regions? *(Coastal areas have tropical climates with plenty of rain. Interior areas are dry.)*

**Interpret Maps** Project the West Africa Political map from the **Online World Atlas.** Have students point to cities that are located on or near rivers. Then have them point to the cities that are on the coast at the mouth of a river. **ASK:** What is the advantage to being both on a river and on the coast? *(Such a location offers easy transportation from port to port, across the ocean, and to the interior. The river may also be a source of fresh water, unlike the ocean.)* `0:15` minutes

## DIFFERENTIATE  Connect to NG

**English Language Learners Study Word Parts** Explain that *semi-* is a prefix, or word part added to the beginning of a word. It means "half or partly." Ask students to define the word *arid,* and then the word *semiarid.* Ask for one more example of a word beginning with the prefix *semi-.* Then tell students that the prefix *de-* means "make opposite or remove." Ask students what it would mean to deforest an area of land. Then explain that the suffix *-ation* means "act, process, or result of." Have students use these word parts to define *deforestation.* Ask for one more example of a word beginning with the prefix *de-.*

**Gifted & Talented Write Feature Articles** Assign students the role of journalists reporting on deforestation in two parts of Sub-Saharan Africa. At least one part should be in West Africa. Show examples of feature articles from a major newspaper. Have students use the **Research Links** to learn more about deforestation in two parts of Africa. Tell students to compare the causes, extent, and effects of deforestation in the two parts. Ask them to focus in particular on the type of economic activity that has led to deforestation.

### Interactive Whiteboard
## GeoActivity

**Graph Water Levels in Lake Chad** Have students work in groups of four to answer the questions as presented in the activity. Have each group then take a turn creating the graph on the whiteboard. When students have finished, have them discuss as a class the effects that climate change and human activity can have on the environment of this region. `0:20` minutes

**EXTENSION** For more practice in plotting information on a graph, have groups of students research to find data on the levels of other lakes in different parts of Africa. For example, they might consider Lake Victoria or Lake Tanganyika. Students should determine how to set up the graph on their own. When they are finished, have them compare the effects of climate change and human activity across the two parts of Africa. `0:25` minutes

### On Your Feet

**Demonstrate Deforestation and Erosion** Take students outside or prepare some buckets for use indoors to simulate conditions. Use a hose or large container of water to run water over a patch of ground that is grassy or covered with other vegetation. Point out that the water does not move soil or pick it up. Then find or create a patch of bare soil or sand. Run water over the bare patch and have students compare the results with what happened when water ran over the planted area. Remind students that erosion becomes worse after deforestation. `0:30` minutes

### ONGOING ASSESSMENT
## PHOTO LAB  GeoJournal

#### ANSWERS
1. The Sahel is a transition zone between the Sahara in the north and the savannas in the south. As a transition zone, it has characteristics of both the desert (sand) and the savanna (grasses).
2. The photo shows that the physical features of this transition zone would make it hard to establish agriculture. Living in a transition zone could mean dealing with an unpredictable climate.
3. Abuja, Nigeria's capital, is not located on a coast or a river.

# 1.4 Rain Forests and Resources

TECHTREK
myNGconnect.com For a land use map and photos of wildlife

Maps and Graphs  Digital Library

**Main Idea** Central Africa is defined by the rain forests of the Congo River Basin and a variety of natural resources.

Central Africa is bordered by the Adamawa Highlands of West Africa and the Great Rift Valley of East Africa. On the north and south, Central Africa lies between the plateaus of the Sahel and Southern Africa.

## Rain Forest in the Congo Basin

The Congo Basin is the main geographic feature of Central Africa. The basin is located on the equator and surrounded by higher elevations. Within the basin is a **rain forest**, which is a forest with warm temperatures, plentiful rain, high humidity, and thick vegetation.

The rain forest in Central Africa is second in the world in size only to the South American rain forest. Vegetation grows so thick that sometimes sunlight does not reach the ground. The plants also make ground movement difficult, so most people live on the edges of the rain forest.

> **Critical Viewing** A western lowland gorilla walks in the forest in Democratic Republic of the Congo. Why might the rain forest be able to support so many plants and animals?
>
> because it has warm temperatures, gets a great deal of rainfall, and has thick vegetation that offers protection to animals

Spectacular wildlife also thrives in the rain forest. The okapi, related to the giraffe, lives in the Congo Basin. Some other rain forest animals include gorillas similar to the one shown here, leopards, and rhinoceroses.

The **Congo River** is a major waterway in Central Africa. Like the Amazon River of South America, the Congo is located in an equatorial area and flows into the Atlantic Ocean. Several large rivers in Central Africa feed into the Congo River, including the Ubangi, the Aruwimi, and the Lomami rivers.

## Resources of Central Africa

Central Africa includes the Central African Republic, Congo, Cameroon, São Tomé (sow too MAY) and Príncipe, Equatorial Guinea, and Gabon.

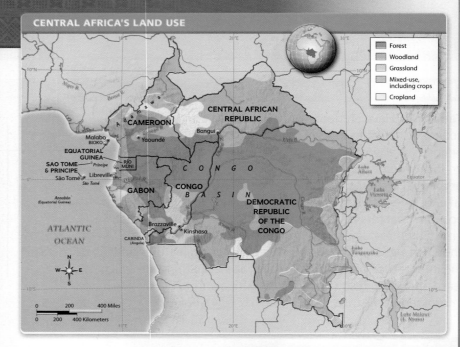

CENTRAL AFRICA'S LAND USE

Forest
Woodland
Grassland
Mixed-use, including crops
Cropland

However, the largest, most populous country in Central Africa is the Democratic Republic of the Congo (DRC). The capital of the DRC is Kinshasa.

The DRC has a wealth of natural resources, including copper, forests, diamonds, and the Congo River itself. The river provides **hydroelectric power**, or electricity produced by a water source such as a river. The river is forced through turbines, or engines, and produces electricity for the DRC and other countries.

### Before You Move On

**Monitor Comprehension** Describe the rain forest and natural resources found in Central Africa.
The rain forest is an area of heavy rainfall, warm temperatures, and dense vegetation. The resources are copper, timber, diamonds, and hydroelectric power.

ONGOING ASSESSMENT

## MAP LAB

GeoJournal

1. **Interpret Maps** How does the latitude of the Congo Basin help explain its climate and vegetation?

2. **Conduct Internet Research** Use the Internet to research the Amazon River Basin of South America. On a chart like the one below, compare and contrast the Congo River Basin and Amazon River Basin.

| | LOCATION | SIZE | RAINFALL |
|---|---|---|---|
| Congo River Basin | | | |
| Amazon River Basin | | | |

SECTION 1.4 **365**

---

## PLAN

### OBJECTIVE Describe the geography and resources of Central Africa and the rain forest.

### CRITICAL THINKING SKILLS FOR SECTION 1.4

- Main Idea
- Monitor Comprehension
- Interpret Maps
- Conduct Internet Research
- Analyze Cause and Effect
- Explain

### PRINT RESOURCES

*Teacher's Edition* Resource Bank

- Reading and Note-Taking: Make Generalizations
- Vocabulary Practice: Word Web
- **GeoActivity** Explore a Tropical Rain Forest

TECHTREK myNGconnect.com

 Fast Forward!
**Core Content Presentations**
Teach *Rain Forests and Resources*

 **Digital Library**
- GeoVideo: *Introduce Sub-Saharan Africa*
- NG Photo Gallery, Section 1

 **Maps and Graphs**
- **Interactive Map Tool** Analyze Patterns of Population
- Online World Atlas: Central Africa's Land Use

**Also Check Out**
GeoJournal in **Student eEdition**

### BACKGROUND FOR THE TEACHER

Including all the area drained by the Congo River and its tributaries, the Congo Basin is the world's second largest river basin. Rain falls most of the year, totaling, on average, between five and eight feet of rain yearly. During parts of the year, the river floods a floodplain and spills into the rain forest. The runoff contains nutrients from the forest and helps feed the fish.

### ESSENTIAL QUESTION

#### How has the varied geography of Sub-Saharan Africa affected people's lives?

The rain forest of Central Africa offers timber and other resources, but it is thick and difficult to navigate. This can make transportation, communication, and national unity difficult. Section 1.4 describes the resources and navigation difficulties of the rain forest.

## INTRODUCE & ENGAGE  Digital Library

**GeoVideo:** *Introduce Sub-Saharan Africa* Show the portion of the video that shows the rain forest so that students understand how this area differs from other parts of Africa. Discuss as a class what the differences are.

**Express Ideas Through Speech** Have students work in groups of four. Based on prior knowledge, have students brainstorm and list animals and plants they associate with the rain forest. Then have students view the diagram of the rain forest from the **GeoActivity.** Preview the activity with the class, and tell them to keep the activity in mind as they read this lesson. `0:15` minutes

## TEACH  Maps and Graphs

### Guided Discussion

1. **Analyze Cause and Effect** Remind students that in Section 1.1 they learned that the Congo River is hard to navigate because of rapids and waterfalls. **ASK:** Based on this and information from this lesson, why might it be hard to unify the large Democratic Republic of the Congo? *(The rain forest is thick and difficult to navigate. Where the Congo River is also hard to navigate, it is hard to travel from one part of the country to another.)*

2. **Explain** Where would you expect the primary economic activities of Central Africa to be located? Explain. *(Responses will vary: On the edge of the rain forest, because people live there; where the copper and diamonds are located, because they would need to be mined and processed; and on the coast where shipping and trade are most possible)*

**Interpret Maps** Project the Central Africa's Land Use map from the **Online World Atlas.** Point out that much of the mixed-use land and cropland in the Democratic Republic of the Congo lies along its eastern border. Ask students how its location might account for its use as cropland. *(It is next to lakes or rivers. The lakes and rivers might provide water and transportation for crops.)* `0:20` minutes

## DIFFERENTIATE  Digital Library

**Inclusion Analyze Visuals** Provide questions to help students describe the photograph of the gorilla and surrounding rain forest: What is the animal in the picture? What is surrounding the animal? What characteristics of the rain forest might help protect the animal?

**Pre-AP Create Multimedia Presentations** Have students extend their knowledge about the rain forest, its layers, its wildlife, and the fierce competition for nutrients. Ask them to create a multimedia presentation that describes and illustrates the organization and life in a rain forest. Tell them to include information about where several types of plants or animals get their nutrients and describe adaptations to conditions in the rain forest such as darkness in the understory or lack of soil in the canopy. Students can include digital photos, original artwork, video, and/or text to explain what is happening and why. Suggest that they may want to start with photos from the **NG Photo Gallery.**

## ACTIVE OPTIONS

###  Interactive Map Tool

#### Analyze Patterns of Population

PURPOSE Understand patterns of population density in Central Africa

##### SET-UP

1. Open the **Interactive Map Tool,** set the "Map Mode" to Satellite, and show Central Africa.

2. Under "Human Systems—Populations & Culture," turn on the Population Density layer. Move the transparency slider back and forth to alternately show and hide the population density.

##### ACTIVITY

1. Point out areas on the Central Africa's Land Use map that are very green and show how those areas become light under the population density layer.

2. Ask students to explain this relationship. *(The dark green areas on the satellite image show heavy vegetation, and the light areas on the Population Density layer show low population density. Thus, fewer people live in the dense vegetation.)* `0:15` minutes

### On Your Feet

**Display Card Responses** Have half of the class write ten True-False questions based on the lesson. Have the other half create individual answer cards, writing "True" on one side and "False" on the other side of each card. Students from the first group take turns asking their questions. Students from the second group hold up their cards, showing either "True" or "False." Have students keep track of their correct answers. `0:20` minutes

### ONGOING ASSESSMENT

## MAP LAB  GeoJournal

#### ANSWERS

1. The Congo Basin sits on the equator and receives direct sunlight all year. This—along with other factors such as elevation and wind patterns—explains its climate and vegetation.

2. Possible responses below:

| | LOCATION | SIZE | RAINFALL |
|---|---|---|---|
| Congo River Basin | Central Africa | 1.3 million square miles | between 80 and 120 inches annually |
| Amazon River Basin | Central South America | 2.3 million square miles | between 60 and 120 inches annually |

# 1.5 Southern Plateaus and Basins

**Main Idea** Southern Africa's physical geography offers opportunities for economic development.

Southern Africa has fertile farmland, valuable natural resources, and abundant wildlife. The income from exporting natural resources gives Southern Africa the highest standard of living in sub-Saharan Africa.

## Basins and Plateaus

The Congo Basin extends into the Southern African countries of Angola and Zambia. From there, the land rises to a large plateau that spans most of Southern Africa. Six of the area's countries are **landlocked**, or have no direct access to a coast. Another major African basin, the Kalahari in Southern Africa, includes the Kalahari Desert. However, the basin also has areas rich with wildlife.

The plateau of Southern Africa is defined by the **Great Escarpment**. An **escarpment** is a steep slope. The Great Escarpment is the steep slope from the plateau down to the coastal plains of Southern Africa. The Great Escarpment is most dramatic in the countries of South Africa and Lesotho. It also extends northeast into Zimbabwe and northwest into Namibia and Angola.

The **Zambezi River** in Southern Africa collects water from the entire south-central part of Africa. The Zambezi flows through Angola, Zambia, along Zimbabwe's border, and through Mozambique (mo zam BEEK) to the Indian Ocean. The Kariba Dam on the Zambezi provides hydroelectric power. In fact, the countries of Zambia and Zimbabwe get most of their electricity from the dam.

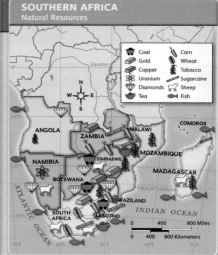

SOUTHERN AFRICA
Gross Domestic Product Per Capita, 2009

More than $4,000
$1,000–$4,000
Less than $1,000

SOUTHERN AFRICA
Natural Resources

Coal    Corn
Gold    Wheat
Copper    Tobacco
Uranium    Sugarcane
Diamonds    Sheep
Tea    Fish

## Mining and Farming

A zone of mineral deposits winds through Zambia, Zimbabwe, and South Africa. Copper, gold, and diamonds are mined in this zone, and destined for jewelry and industrial uses. In fact, South Africa is one of the world's largest gold producers. Many people migrate there to work in the mines even though the work can be dangerous.

Southern Africa's temperate climate supports a variety of crops. For example, South Africa has many vineyards that thrive on its plateau, and Zimbabwe has tea plantations on its eastern escarpment. Angola produced nearly 20 percent of the world's coffee until 1975 when a civil war began. When the war ended in 2002, coffee production started again. Fruits, such as bananas, pineapples, and apples, are grown throughout Southern Africa. Corn, wheat, and other grains can also be found across the area.

South Africa, Botswana, and Namibia have the highest Gross Domestic Product in Southern Africa. Other countries are working to overcome factors that have weakened their economies, such as civil war and disease. For them, economic success is a goal for the future.

### Before You Move On
Monitor Comprehension In what ways do the area's resources and crops support its economy?
by providing valuable commodities for export

### ONGOING ASSESSMENT
## MAP LAB    GeoJournal

1. **Compare and Contrast** According to the Gross Domestic Product map, which countries have the highest GDP? The lowest GDP?

2. **Interpret Maps** In what ways might South Africa's natural resources contribute to differences on the GDP map?

3. **Movement** What circumstances have led many workers to migrate to Southern Africa?

**Critical Viewing** Miners near Johannesburg, South Africa, work deep underground to extract resources. Based on the photo, what are some of the dangers that miners might face?
mine collapse, pollution that might damage lungs, poisonous gases

---

# PLAN

## OBJECTIVE Understand how Southern Africa's physical features and natural resources shape the land and its economic development.

## CRITICAL THINKING SKILLS FOR SECTION 1.5

- Main Idea
- Monitor Comprehension
- Compare and Contrast
- Interpret Maps
- Make Predictions
- Describe Geographic Information
- Analyze Cause and Effect

## PRINT RESOURCES

*Teacher's Edition* Resource Bank

- Reading and Note-Taking: Describe Geographic Information
- Vocabulary Practice: Vocabulary Pyramid
- **GeoActivity** Research Copper Exports

## TECHTREK    myNGconnect.com

**Fast Forward!**
**Core Content Presentations**
Teach *Southern Plateaus and Basins*

**Digital Library**
NG Photo Gallery, Section 1

**Connect to NG**
Research Links

**Maps and Graphs**
**Interactive Map Tool**
Analyze Climates in Southern Africa

**Also Check Out**
- Online World Atlas in **Maps and Graphs**
- Graphic Organizers in **Teacher Resources**
- GeoJournal in **Student eEdition**

## BACKGROUND FOR THE TEACHER

In the dry Kalahari, seasonal streams empty into depressions known as pans. There the water from the streams dries up. As it evaporates, the water leaves its salt and some minerals behind. The Kalahari was not always as dry as it is now. Streams and large rivers once emptied into a huge lake. Makgadikgadi (mah KAH dee KAH dee) pans are the footprints of the ancient lake.

## ESSENTIAL QUESTION

### How has the varied geography of Sub-Saharan Africa affected people's lives?

Southern Africa has widely varying climates, elevations, physical features, and natural resources, creating a wide diversity of economic activities. Section 1.5 describes this varied topography and natural resources.

## INTRODUCE & ENGAGE  Digital Library

**Make Predictions** As a class, discuss the gems and precious metals found in Southern Africa. Display or show some photos of gems from the **NG Photo Gallery.** Encourage students to discuss items of jewelry they have seen. Then have them discuss the likely economic effects of mineral resources such as diamonds or gold. Have them predict effects on the national economy, the owners of the mines, and the workers who work in the mines, and list their predictions on a graphic organizer similar to the one at right. Suggest that they save the graphic organizers so they can revisit them at the end of the unit. **0:15** minutes

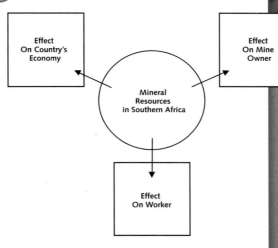

## TEACH

### Guided Discussion

1. **Describe Geographic Information** Remind students that geographic features are not necessarily confined to one area. **ASK:** Which two basins are found in Southern Africa? *(parts of the Congo Basin and the Kalahari Basin)*

2. **Analyze Cause and Effect** Remind students that geography is not just the study of physical features, but also the study of how people interact with the environment and each other. **ASK:** Other than physical features and natural resources, what factors have affected the economies of Southern African countries? *(civil war and disease)*

### MORE INFORMATION

**Waterholes** The National Geographic film, *ROAR: Lions of the Kalahari,* was filmed at a waterhole in the Nxai Pan, a small pan near the larger Makgadikgadi pans. The waterhole is surrounded by dry grass plains with a few bushes and scattered trees. The only water for miles, this waterhole was a magnet for prey animals during the dry season and therefore an excellent hunting ground for the lion pride that lived there.

## DIFFERENTIATE  Digital Library  Connect to NG

**Inclusion Build Models** After showing the photo of the Great Escarpment from the **NG Photo Gallery** and reviewing what a plateau is, have students use modeling clay to demonstrate their understanding. Tell them to form a plateau in clay and create escarpments on its borders. Help them label the plateau and escarpments.

**Pre-AP Hold Panel Discussions** Have students use the **Research Links** to conduct research about mining in South Africa. Different students should research effects on the economy, the mine owners and operators, and the mine workers. Tell them to assume the roles of experts and hold a panel discussion in front of the class. Students can download digital photos to support their discussion. Suggest that they may want to start with photos from the **NG Photo Gallery.**

---

## ACTIVE OPTIONS

### Interactive Map Tool

#### Analyze Climates in Southern Africa

**PURPOSE** Understand climate variation in Southern Africa

**SET-UP**

1. Open the **Interactive Map Tool,** set the "Map Mode" to Satellite, and zoom in on Southern Africa.

2. Under "Physical Systems—Climate," turn on the Climate Zones layer.

**ACTIVITY**

Have students compare the climate regions with the locations of crops in Southern Africa. Ask how the climate map might explain why the various crops are grown where they are and why sheep graze where they do. Help them relate the growth of sugarcane to humid areas, and the growth of other crops to areas that are dry in only one season. Remind them that sheep can be grazed in drier areas. **0:20** minutes

**EXTENSION** Have students compare the climate zone map on the **Interactive Map Tool** to the physical map in Section 1.1. Help them locate physical features on the satellite images. Ask how those physical features might play a role in the climate zones shown on the **Interactive Map Tool.** **0:15** minutes

### On Your Feet

**Create a Map** Have students get into groups of four to complete a sketch map of Southern Africa's resources. One group member should sketch the outline of Southern Africa, another should draw the country borders, and the other two divide up the resources and place them on the map. If time permits, have a member from each group visit another group to share and discuss the map. **0:20** minutes

---

## ONGOING ASSESSMENT

# MAP LAB  GeoJournal

### ANSWERS

1. highest: Botswana, Lesotho, Namibia, South Africa, Swaziland; lowest: Madagascar, Malawi, Mozambique, Zambia, Zimbabwe

2. Southern Africa has a wide variety of natural resources, but countries with diamonds—such as South Africa—seem to have higher GDPs.

3. the availability of mining jobs with good pay

# Exploring
# Africa's Wildlife
### with Dereck and Beverly Joubert

**Main Idea** Humans are working to protect endangered African big cats and their homes.

## Big Cats in Africa

Big cats, such as lions, cheetahs and leopards, are a vital part of African wildlife. Since the 1940s, the number of lions in Africa has been reduced from about 450,000 to 20,000—and humans caused most of this reduction. Hunting, movement into big cat **habitats** (natural homes), and **poaching** (illegal hunting) all contribute to fewer big cats in the wild.

## Working to Protect Habitats

"It seems like we were explorers from birth, wandering the wild Earth with a passion," said Dereck Joubert. The Jouberts, who are National Geographic Explorers-in-Residence, learned about wildlife on game reserves in Southern Africa. Today, they live in Botswana. "On our first trip to Botswana and the **Okavango** (oh kuh VAANG oh) **Delta**, in 1981, we felt we had come home," the Jouberts noted.

That same year, the Jouberts joined the Chobe Lion Research Institute in Botswana. They began an intensive study of lions,

**myNGconnect.com**
For more on Dereck and Beverly Joubert in the field today

which included adopting a **nocturnal**, or night-based, lifestyle. They worked during the night in the African wilderness for months at a time. Since leaving the Chobe Institute, the Jouberts have worked on their own in many different filmmaking, photography, and conservation projects.

The Jouberts have a mission: conserving big cat habitats. Protecting habitats also protects the biodiversity, or variety of life, in the habitat. The Jouberts' projects draw attention to the plight of big cats in Africa. Their knowledge of how big cats live helps other conservationists to develop habitat protection programs.

The Jouberts also support **ecotourism**, which is tourism that is focused on wildlife protection and responsible use of land and resources. Ecotourism teaches visitors about conservation issues. For the Jouberts, teaching is an essential part of their work. Ultimately, they believe that "We are part of a global community of lions and leopards, buffalo, dung beetles, snakes, trees, and ice caps, not somehow apart from it all."

**Before You Move On**
Summarize What are some ways of protecting African big cats? protecting habitats, educating people about the importance of the big cats, setting up reserves, targeting poachers

**AFRICAN WILDLIFE RESERVES**
National Park, Wildlife Reserve
Chobe Lion Research Institute

**BIG CATS BY THE NUMBERS**

**5**
Distance in miles from which a lion's roar can be heard

**12**
Average life span of a male lion in the wild

**23**
Distance in feet a cheetah can cover in one stride

**70**
A cheetah's top speed in miles per hour

**550**
Weight in pounds of a fully grown male lion

**Source:** Smithsonian National Zoo, National Geographic Society

**ONGOING ASSESSMENT**
## READING LAB  GeoJournal

1. **Make Inferences** Using what you know about sub-Saharan geography, what might explain the lack of wildlife reserves in the north?
2. **Interpret Data** What do the cheetah's speed and stride distance imply about its ability as a hunter?

SECTION 1.6 **369**

---

## PLAN

**OBJECTIVE** Explain the importance of Africa's big cats and other wildlife, and describe efforts to protect the animals and their habitats.

### CRITICAL THINKING SKILLS FOR SECTION 1.6

- Main Idea
- Summarize
- Make Inferences
- Interpret Data
- Identify Problems and Solutions
- Find Main Idea and Details
- Interpret Maps

### PRINT RESOURCES

*Teacher's Edition* Resource Bank

- Reading and Note-Taking: Identify Problems and Solutions
- Vocabulary Practice: Definition and Details Tree
- **GeoActivity** Locate a Wildlife Reserve

 myNGconnect.com

**Fast Forward!**
**Core Content Presentations**
Teach *Exploring Africa's Wildlife*

**Digital Library**
- Explorer Video Clip: Dereck and Beverly Joubert
- NG Photo Gallery, Section 1

**Connect to NG**
Research Links

**Maps and Graphs**
Online World Atlas: African Wildlife Reserves

**Interactive Whiteboard**
**GeoActivity** Locate a Wildlife Reserve

**Also Check Out**
GeoJournal in **Student eEdition**

### BACKGROUND FOR THE TEACHER

Researchers have agreed that conflict between lions and livestock owners is a major cause of lion endangerment. In Kenya, the Predator Compensation Fund of the Maasailand Preservation Trust compensates local Maasai herders for livestock kills by lions in and around Kenya's Amboseli National Park. Reports indicate that lion deaths have dropped since the project began.

### ESSENTIAL QUESTION

#### How has the varied geography of Sub-Saharan Africa affected people's lives?

As the economic and political geography of Africa have changed, the habitats of big cats have been disappearing. Section 1.6 describes some of these economic changes, their effects, and the contributions of two individuals to the survival of big cats.

## INTRODUCE & ENGAGE  Digital Library

**Explorer Video Clip:** *Dereck and Beverly Joubert* Show the **Explorer Video Clip** to provide background information on the Jouberts and their work in Africa. As a class, discuss what it would be like to devote your life to a particular cause, as the Jouberts have done. **ASK:** What kind of personal traits do you think such a person might have? *(curiosity, determination, courage, perseverance)*

**Identify Problems and Solutions** After students view the video, have them work in pairs and take notes using a T-Chart. One student completes the Problems column and the other completes the Proposed Solutions column. Replay the video and have them switch columns and take additional notes. Discuss the problems and solutions as a class.
`0:20` minutes

| Problems | Proposed Solutions |
|---|---|
| | |

## TEACH  Maps and Graphs

### Guided Discussion

**1. Find Main Idea and Details** How are the Jouberts contributing to the environment and economy of Botswana? *(They are conserving species and promoting ecotourism, which helps build the local and national economies.)*

**2. Make Inferences** How can promoting ecotourism help save endangered cats? *(Botswana's people are more likely to protect the cats if they can see their economic value.)*

**Interpret Maps** Look at the African Wildlife Reserves map in the **Online World Atlas.** How do wildlife reserves help protect big cat populations? *(People cannot build or farm in these areas, so cats do not lose their habitats or prey. These areas are patrolled to discourage illegal hunters.)* `0:15` minutes

## DIFFERENTIATE  Connect to NG

**Striving Readers Build a Cause-Effect Chart** Before reading, display this chart and have students copy it. With the class, discuss what sometimes causes species to decline or go extinct. Have students use the chart to take notes as they read. After reading, discuss the causes and allow students to add examples to their charts.

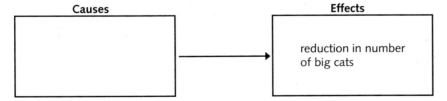

Causes → Effects: reduction in number of big cats

**Gifted & Talented Make Recommendations** Have students select an endangered or vulnerable African species and conduct research about the causes of its endangerment, starting with the **Research Links**. Tell them to research solutions that have been proposed and tried, and any available results of implemented solutions. Then have them write a list of recommendations to propose to the government of an African country where the species is endangered.

## ACTIVE OPTIONS

### Interactive Whiteboard
### GeoActivity

**Locate a Wildlife Reserve** Project the map and the set of criteria. Have students work in groups of four and discuss the criteria. Students select the location and write the reasons for their choice. Allow time for students to compare their chosen locations and explain their reasons.
`0:20` minutes

### On Your Feet

**Think, Pair, Share** Have students use the Think, Pair, Share strategy to discuss the Before You Move On question. See "Best Practices for Active Teaching" for a review of this cooperative learning strategy.
`0:20` minutes

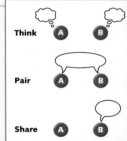

### Performance Assessment

**Create an Informational Brochure** Encourage students to use knowledge from the lessons to create a colorful informational brochure about the physical geography and natural wonders of Africa. They should focus on what landforms, climate, plant life, and animal life travelers to Africa can expect to see in each part. Brochures should include information about seasonal changes as well. Suggest that students include information about ongoing changes from human activity, such as deforestation, desertification, or endangerment of species. Students may use the **NG Photo Gallery** for photos to include in the brochures. Go to **myNGconnect.com** for the Performance Assessment rubric.

## ONGOING ASSESSMENT
## READING LAB  GeoJournal

### ANSWERS

1. Possible response: Large areas of desert in the north would help explain the lack of reserves.
2. The cheetah's speed and stride distance imply that it is a very effective hunter.

## 2.1 Bantu Migrations

TECHTREK
myNGconnect.com For a map of the
Bantu migrations and photos of Bantu culture

Maps and
Graphs

Digital
Library

**Main Idea** Bantu-speaking people migrated from West Africa and influenced the language and culture of the African continent.

As you have read, sub-Saharan Africa's varied physical features support a variety of crops today. About 10,000 years ago an agricultural revolution began in Central Africa. During the **agricultural revolution**, humans began to grow crops instead of gathering plants. Sometime after the agricultural revolution, around 2000 B.C., one of the greatest migrations in human history began—the **Bantu** migration. By A.D. 1000, Bantu peoples had spread from their Central African homeland south and east across sub-Saharan Africa.

### The Bantu People

People migrate for economic, political, religious, social, and environmental reasons. When groups of people move, cultures blend, new languages form, technology spreads—and sometimes conflict occurs.

> **Critical Viewing** Bantu descendants pick tea in South Africa. One possible reason for the Bantu migration was to find better farmland. What does this photo suggest about farming methods in South Africa today?
> The photo suggests that farming has not changed much and still relies on traditional methods like hand-picking.

**370** CHAPTER 13

Historians and anthropologists are not certain why the Bantu chose to migrate when and where they did. Whatever the reason, the Bantu people began to move and carried their cultural traits and skills along with them.

The Bantu had knowledge of iron working, and their use of iron weapons gave them an advantage over other tribal groups. As the Bantu people moved, they forced other groups to move or become absorbed into Bantu culture.

The many different groups that became part of Bantu culture kept much of their own culture as well. As a result, the nearly 85 million people who trace their history to the Bantu migrations share a very diverse culture today.

### Bantu Languages

Today, people whose ancestors were Bantu exist in more than 400 ethnic groups, including the Zulu, the Swahili, and the Kikuyu. Original Bantu languages have evolved into more than 450 languages.

**Swahili** (also known as Kiswahwali) is one of the best-known of the surviving Bantu languages. For more than 5 million people, Swahili is the language they learn as children, or their **first language**. For 30 million other people, Swahili is their second language. Swahili is spoken mainly in East Africa and can be heard in several different forms, or dialects.

Swahili is heavily influenced by the Arabic language. Arab traders from northern Africa and Bantu-speaking people of eastern Africa met and exchanged goods over many centuries. Over time, Swahili became the language used to conduct trade.

Beginning in the early 19th century, Arab trade **caravans**—groups of merchants traveling together for safety—traveled farther into the interior of Africa, spreading Swahili to more people. Eventually, Swahili would be used by some Europeans who colonized parts of Africa where the language was spoken.

Today, many areas in Africa have two groups of people with different first languages. In these areas, Swahili is frequently spoken by both groups as a way to communicate. As a result, Swahili is the **lingua franca** (LEEN gwa FRAWN kah), or common language between multiple groups of people.

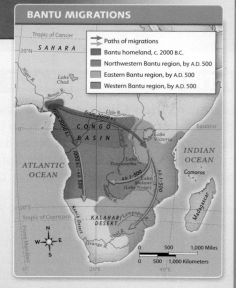

**BANTU MIGRATIONS**

Paths of migrations
Bantu homeland, c. 2000 B.C.
Northwestern Bantu region, by A.D. 500
Eastern Bantu region, by A.D. 500
Western Bantu region, by A.D. 500

**Before You Move On**
**Summarize** How did the Bantu influence the culture and language of the African continent?

**ONGOING ASSESSMENT**
### MAP LAB    GeoJournal

1. **Interpret Maps** What landform in Africa might have influenced the Bantu people to migrate south instead of north?

2. **Movement** Based on the map, over what period of time did the Bantu migration take place?

3. **Draw Conclusions** How was the migration of the Bantu people supported by their use of metal-working technology?

4. **Make Inferences** Why might it be important for an area to have a *lingua franca*, or common language?

The Bantu brought their own knowledge and skills, such as iron-working, everywhere they migrated. Their languages still survive today.

SECTION 2.1 **371**

---

## PLAN

### OBJECTIVE Analyze the causes and effects of the Bantu migrations on Sub-Saharan Africa.

### CRITICAL THINKING SKILLS FOR SECTION 2.1

- Main Idea
- Summarize
- Interpret Maps
- Draw Conclusions
- Make Inferences
- Analyze Cause and Effect

### PRINT RESOURCES

*Teacher's Edition* Resource Bank

- Reading and Note-Taking: Create a Sentence Map
- Vocabulary Practice: WDS Chart
- **GeoActivity** Map the Swahili Language

TECHTREK    myNGconnect.com

**Fast Forward!**
**Core Content Presentations**
Teach *Bantu Migrations*

**Maps and Graphs**
Online World Atlas: Bantu Migrations

**Interactive Whiteboard**
**GeoActivity** Map the Swahili Language

**Also Check Out**
- NG Photo Gallery in **Digital Library**
- Graphic Organizers in **Teacher Resources**
- GeoJournal in **Student eEdition**

### BACKGROUND FOR THE TEACHER

Arab ivory and slave caravans were instrumental in spreading the use of Swahili and making it a dominant language. A number of Arabic words have been incorporated into Swahili. The word *Swahili* itself is from Arabic and means "of the coast." Originally, Bantu languages had no written form. Swahili was first written using Arabic script. Today, the language is written using the Roman alphabet.

### ESSENTIAL QUESTION

### How did trade networks and migration influence the development of African civilization?

The Bantu migrations enriched the culture of Africa, spreading the Bantu language as well as agriculture and technologies. Section 2.1 describes the Bantu migrations as well as the technologies and languages they spread.

# INTRODUCE & ENGAGE

**Activate Prior Knowledge** Have students discuss migrations to your community and region, as well as other migrations they have studied. Then have students work in pairs, using a graphic organizer like the one at the right to list effects of migrations they have observed or studied.

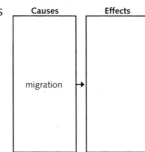

Causes      Effects

migration →

If students need prompting, ask about languages spoken in the community; restaurants and stores that offer food or goods from other countries; and customs such as festivals that have been established. When students have finished, have them share their organizers with the class. Explain that they will study Bantu migrations in Africa and their effect. `0:20` **minutes**

# TEACH  Maps and Graphs

## Guided Discussion

1. **Analyze Cause and Effect** Besides spreading their language, how might the Bantu have influenced or contributed to the cultures whose territory they entered? *(They probably introduced iron-working.)*

2. **Make Inferences** Why might governments need a *lingua franca* in a multi-cultural country? What is the lingua franca in the United States? *(They need a language in which to conduct business and issue government literature. Leaders need a language in which to address all the people of the country; English.)*

**Interpret Maps** Project the Bantu Migrations map from the **Online World Atlas.** Explain how to use the legend to locate the original homelands of the Bantu and the pattern of their migrations over the years. As students refer to the map on the chapter introduction in their textbooks, call on a volunteer to point out the approximate location of modern-day Nigeria on the projected map. **ASK:** Which modern countries have part of their territories located in the original Bantu homelands? *(Nigeria and Cameroon)* `0:15` **minutes**

# DIFFERENTIATE

**Striving Readers Use Visuals to Support the Main Idea** Help students break down the Main Idea statement using the map and the map legend. Have students trace the path of the arrows to see where the Bantu migrated from and where they migrated to. As they trace the path of each arrow, have them name each Bantu region that the arrow leads to. **ASK:** Based on the map, why do you think the Bantu people influenced language in Africa? *(Possible response: The Bantu people migrated to many different regions and spread the Bantu language to different parts of Africa.)*

**English Language Learners Identify Spanish Cognates** Explain that just as Swahili has many Arabic words, English has many words that are taken from other languages. As a result, it has many cognates, or words that share a common origin and meaning with words in other languages. These words have similar spellings and pronunciations. In Section 2.1, point out words with Spanish cognates, such as *migration, economic, political, religious, anthropologists, technology.* Invite Spanish-dominant students to pronounce the Spanish cognates for other students. Encourage students to identify other cognates as they read.

# ACTIVE OPTIONS

 **Interactive Whiteboard**
## GeoActivity

**Map the Swahili Language** Use this activity to help students understand the importance of a common language for government, culture, and trade. Have students work in groups to create their own maps of the Swahili language. Tell them to create a legend that distinguishes between countries where Swahili is spoken as a primary language and countries where Swahili is spoken as a secondary language. Then have them discuss the influence and cultural contributions of the Bantu migrations on contemporary societies. `0:20` **minutes**

**EXTENSION** Suggest that interested students do more reading about Swahili and its widespread use in Africa. Pairs of students can focus on one of the following topics:

- differences among three main forms of the language: Kiunguja, Kimvita, or Kiamu
- similarities between the Swahili and Arabic languages
- the ways that Swahili spread

Students should go back to their Swahili maps and add or correct any information as needed. `0:25` **minutes**

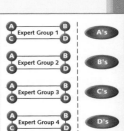

## On Your Feet

**Jigsaw** Identify four significant migrations of human populations. Use the Jigsaw strategy to have students compare and contrast the Bantu migration with migrations in Europe or North America, such as the Great Atlantic migration. Each group member is to become an expert on a different migration. Have experts report their findings to different groups. See "Best Practices for Active Teaching" for a review of this cooperative learning strategy. `0:30` **minutes**

## ONGOING ASSESSMENT
# MAP LAB  GeoJournal

### ANSWERS
1. the Sahara
2. The Bantu migration started about 3000 B.C. By A.D. 1000, the Bantu had spread to Southern Africa. The migration took place over thousands of years.
3. Access to iron-working supported the Bantu migration by giving them superior weapons and tools.
4. A common language facilitates unity socially, culturally, and economically.

## 2.2 Early States and Trade

**Main Idea** Trade helped develop powerful states and empires in sub-Saharan Africa.

Trade was important in the development of sub-Saharan Africa. The promise of valuable trade goods brought Arab traders to a transportation corridor from North Africa to West Africa. This **trans-Saharan** trade, or trade across the Sahara, introduced Africans to the Islamic religion, which spread from the Arabian peninsula beginning in the 8th century A.D.

### West African Empires

In West Africa, a number of empires arose over the centuries and all thrived because of the gold and salt trade. **Alluvial** (a LOO vee ahl) gold, or gold deposited by a river, was found in forests, and salt was found in deserts. These goods were traded in the savanna between the forest and desert, where the empire of Ghana began.

Ghana gained wealth and power by taxing the gold and salt trade, controlling West Africa from A.D. 700 to the 1200s. Ghana declined, and the kingdom of Mali, led by King Sundiata, overtook Ghana. His great-nephew, Mansa Musa, continued to control trade, spread Islam, and make the city of **Timbuktu** a center of education.

Another empire that traded gold and salt was Songhai. Brought to its height by Askia Muhammad, Songhai prospered from the 900s to the 1400s. South of Songhai, the kingdom of Benin lasted from the 1200s to the 1800s. Benin actively traded with European countries such as Portugal and the Netherlands.

### East African Empires and States

The powerful East African empire of Aksum was located in present-day Ethiopia. Aksum flourished between A.D. 300 and 600. Adulis, its main port, was located on the Red Sea and served as a center of trade. Many **city-states** (independent states made up of a city and the territories depending on it), such as Mogadishu, formed on the coast of East Africa as trading grew.

### Other African States

Powerful states also arose in Central and Southern Africa. In Central Africa, the state of **Kongo** (different from the modern country of Congo) was founded in 1390. Kongo became known for its highly-organized government. Soon after its founding, the Portuguese arrived and became involved in many aspects of the state, including politics, trade, and religion.

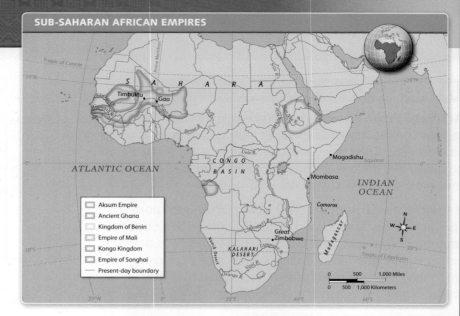

### SUB-SAHARAN AFRICAN EMPIRES

- Aksum Empire
- Ancient Ghana
- Kingdom of Benin
- Empire of Mali
- Kongo Kingdom
- Empire of Songhai
- Present-day boundary

Between 1200 and 1450, the Shona people in Southern Africa built a walled city out of stone, called **Great Zimbabwe** (zim BAH bwe). *Zimbabwe* is a Shona word meaning "stone houses." The Shona traded gold, copper, and iron with places as far away as China and India.

#### Before You Move On

**Summarize** In what ways did trade help develop the early states and kingdoms in Africa? Each rose to power because of trade of products such as gold and salt.

### ONGOING ASSESSMENT
## MAP LAB    GeoJournal

1. **Place** Locate the city-state of Mogadishu on the map. Why would its location be beneficial for trade?
2. **Interpret Maps** Based on the map and the time line, which empire was oldest?
3. **Make Inferences** What might explain why the West African empires of Ghana, Mali, and Songhai overlapped?

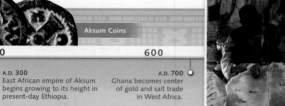

**Aksum Coins**

**300**

**600**

**900**

**1200**

**1500**

**1800**

A.D. 300
East African empire of Aksum begins growing to its height in present-day Ethiopia.

A.D. 700
Ghana becomes center of gold and salt trade in West Africa.

Modern vendor cuts a slab of salt to sell in a Mali market.

1300s
Mali empire in West Africa at its height

Mansa Musa ruled Mali for about 25 years.

○ 1591
Songhai empire comes to an end.

---

## PLAN

### OBJECTIVE Examine the impact of trade on the development of states and empires in Africa.

### CRITICAL THINKING SKILLS FOR SECTION 2.2

- Main Idea
- Summarize
- Interpret Maps
- Make Inferences
- Analyze Cause and Effect
- Draw Conclusions

### PRINT RESOURCES

*Teacher's Edition* Resource Bank

- Reading and Note-Taking: Sequence Events
- Vocabulary Practice: Descriptive Paragraph
- **GeoActivity** Map Historic Trade Routes

**TECHTREK**    myNGconnect.com

>> **Fast Forward!**
**Core Content Presentations**
Teach *Early States and Trade*

**Digital Library**
- GeoVideo: *Introduce Sub-Saharan Africa*
- NG Photo Gallery, Section 2

**Connect to NG**
Research Links

**Maps and Graphs**
- **Interactive Map Tool** Analyze Movement
- Online World Atlas: Sub-Saharan African Empires

**Also Check Out**
- NG Photo Gallery in **Digital Library**
- Graphic Organizers in **Teacher Resources**
- GeoJournal in **Student eEdition**

### BACKGROUND FOR THE TEACHER

Locations of ancient rain forest gold mines were secret. Gold and salt were bartered without face-to-face meetings between traders. Traders piled salt along a stream or river. Drumbeats announced the beginning of trading, and the traders left. The gold traders came, placed bags of gold dust next to each pile of salt, and left. The salt traders returned. If they were satisfied with the amount of gold offered, they took it and left. If not, the process continued until both sides were satisfied.

### ESSENTIAL QUESTION

### How did trade networks and migration influence the development of African civilization?

States and empires were built on local natural resources. Section 2.2 describes ancient sub-Saharan African resources, kingdoms, and trading.

# INTRODUCE & ENGAGE  Digital Library

**GeoVideo:** *Introduce Sub-Saharan Africa* Show the video and emphasize for students the importance of trade to the development of sub-Saharan Africa. Tell students that remnants of the gold and salt trade still exist today and that camel caravans have not disappeared as a means of transporting goods. **ASK:** What challenges to trade might still exist today? *(Students' responses will vary.)*

**Create Web Diagrams** Tell students that in this lesson they will read about several early kingdoms in sub-Saharan Africa. Suggest that they create a web diagram similar to the one shown here and that they use it to track dates and other details about each empire. Remind the class that they can add to this diagram at any time and use it to review information at the end of the unit. **0:10** minutes

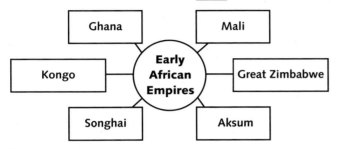

# TEACH  Maps and Graphs

## Guided Discussion

1. **Analyze Cause and Effect** What was one effect of Ghana taxing the gold and salt trade? *(Ghana became wealthy from taxing trade within its borders.)*

2. **Draw Conclusions** How did the gold and salt trade lead to the development of the city-state of Aksum in sub-Saharan Africa? *(Aksum became a center of the gold and salt trade because it had a major port on the Red Sea.)*

**Interpret Maps** Project the Sub-Saharan African Empires map from the **Online World Atlas.** Explain how to use the legend to locate the ancient kingdoms. Have students turn to the political map in the chapter introduction in their textbooks. As students refer to their map, call on a volunteer to point out the approximate location of modern day Ghana on the projected map. **ASK:** How did ancient Ghana's location help it benefit from the salt trade? *(It was just south of the Sahara and north of the rain forests, so trade took place on its borders or as traders passed through.)* **0:15** minutes

# DIFFERENTIATE

**Inclusion Interpret Maps** Point to the different colors in the legend that represent the different kingdoms. Model using color to locate the first empire, Axum, and run your finger around it. Then have students work in pairs and provide these steps and questions to interpret the map:

1. One partner uses the color on the legend to locate a kingdom or empire and traces his or her finger around it.

2. The first asks the other partner, "When did this kingdom exist?" The responding partner uses the legend to find the dates.

---

# ACTIVE OPTIONS

##  Interactive Map Tool

### Analyze Movement

**PURPOSE** Analyze the relationship between geography and movement in West Africa

**SET-UP**

1. Open the **Interactive Map Tool,** set the "Map Mode" to Topographic, and show West Africa. Point out Mauritania's southern border with Mali—an area where Ghana, Mali, and Songhai overlapped.

2. Under "Environment and Society," turn on the Land Cover layer and go through the legend.

3. Under "Physical Systems—Land," turn on the Surface Elevation layer.

**ACTIVITY**

1. Point out Mauritania's southern border with Mali. Alternate between showing the Land Cover and Surface Elevation layers while students take note of the information shown.

2. Ask students to use these two pieces of data to draw conclusions about their possible impact on ancient trade in the area. *(The closed and open scrubland shown on the Land Cover layer along with the generally uniform elevations might mean that the area could be easily traveled.)* **0:20** minutes

##  On Your Feet

**Living Time Line** Ask for volunteers to create a living time line. Assign each volunteer a kingdom from the time line in the textbook. Ask students to collect facts about the assigned empire from the textbook or the **Research Links.** Then students should make large cards with the name and dates of their kingdoms and line up chronologically. Students with kingdoms that coexisted during the same period should stand side-by-side. In order, they should inform the class about the assigned empire. **0:25** minutes

**ONGOING ASSESSMENT**

# MAP LAB  GeoJournal

## ANSWERS

1. It is located on the coast near the horn of Africa, making coastal trade as well as trade with India and Asia possible.
2. Aksum
3. West African control of the gold and salt trade was located in the same area, and as a result, different groups sought to control the same area.

## 2.3 Impact of the Slave Trade

TECHTREK
myNGconnect.com For research
links on the slave trade and Guided Writing

Connect to NG    Student Resources

**Main Idea** The European slave trade involved millions of people and had lasting effects on Africa and the Americas.

Slavery existed in Africa for many years before European contact. For example, African tribal groups turned male war captives into slaves. Women and children were often incorporated into families, and the children of some slaves could be born free. When Islam came to Africa beginning in the A.D. 700s, some Muslims began to capture and sell Africans to North Africa and Southwest Asia.

### European Slave Trade Begins

The Portuguese were the first Europeans to explore the African coast in the 1400s. The **trans-Atlantic slave trade**, or trading of slaves across the Atlantic Ocean, started around 1500. Enslaved people were brought to African coastal cities and held captive until sold. The Portuguese, Spanish, Dutch, French, and English all purchased slaves at African coastal ports.

After purchase, enslaved Africans were crowded onto large ships headed for European colonies in the Americas. This trip across the Atlantic Ocean, known as the **Middle Passage**, could take several months. About 2 million people died in the Middle Passage, many due to **malnutrition** (inadequate food or nourishment) or disease.

Once slaves arrived in the Americas, they were sold at auction, often to go to work on large farms called plantations. Sugar, tobacco, and cotton were some of the major plantation crops. European demand for these crops increased and the plantations got bigger. As the plantations grew, so did the demand for slave labor.

The **incentive**, or motivating reason, for slavery was profit. Europeans bought enslaved people in order to have a cheap and captive labor source. The plantation owners made more money because they did not have to pay the slaves.

### Consequences of the Slave Trade

The trans-Atlantic slave trade lasted from the 1500s to the mid-1800s. Historians estimate that more than 12 million Africans were enslaved and shipped to the Western Hemisphere. The majority of slaves were sent to Brazil and the Caribbean.

People forced into slavery were generally young because they had a better chance of surviving the Middle Passage. Also, when they arrived at their destination, it was expected that young people would be able to work longer and harder in the fields.

### THE MIDDLE PASSAGE

| | LEFT FROM AFRICA | ARRIVED IN THE AMERICAS |
|---|---|---|
| **1500–1600** | 277,506 | 199,285 |
| **1601–1700** | 1,875,631 | 1,522,677 |
| **1701–1800** | 6,494,619 | 5,609,869 |
| **1801–1867** | 3,873,580 | 3,370,825 |
| **TOTAL** | 12,521,336 | 10,702,656 |

**Source:** http://slavevoyages.org/tast/assessment/estimates.faces

Many Africans taken were male, and many were potential leaders in their community. Families were often torn apart. These losses weakened many African communities and completely destroyed others.

Millions of people in North America, the Caribbean, and South America are descendents of enslaved Africans. These people have shaped cultures in those regions by sharing their languages, customs, and traditions. The impact of the slave trade has lasted for centuries.

**Before You Move On**
**Summarize** How did the European slave trade develop and how did it change cultures?

3.25 feet

The journey across the Atlantic could take up to 90 days depending on the weather. Enslaved Africans were packed onto ships and chained below deck. They were only taken above deck for brief periods. Unable to stand up or move, many Africans died where they sat.

### ONGOING ASSESSMENT
## DATA LAB
GeoJournal

1. **Interpret Charts** Based on the chart, how many people died during the Middle Passage?
2. **Analyze Data** During which time period did the greatest number of enslaved Africans die?
3. **Movement** How did the forced movement of Africans affect communities around the world?
4. **Write Reports** Research one of the following topics and then write a short report on how each affected sub-Saharan Africa: sugar plantations, the triangular trade, or slave ports. Go to **Student Resources** for Guided Writing support.

**Critical Viewing** This is a European ship used to transport enslaved Africans. What does this illustration suggest about conditions on the ships for enslaved Africans?
It suggests that conditions were terrible, with extremely cramped space and no fresh air.

The European slave trade developed because workers were needed on plantations in the Americas. The slave trade devastated African cultures and brought African cultural influences to the Americas.

SECTION 2.3 **375**

---

## PLAN

### OBJECTIVE Understand the impact of the slave trade on sub-Saharan Africa's population.

### CRITICAL THINKING SKILLS FOR SECTION 2.3

- Main Idea
- Summarize
- Interpret Charts
- Analyze Data
- Compare and Contrast
- Analyze Cause and Effect

### PRINT RESOURCES

*Teacher's Edition* Resource Bank

- Reading and Note-Taking: Find Main Idea and Details
- Vocabulary Practice: Word Wheel
- **GeoActivity** Analyze Primary Sources: The Slave Trade

**Fast Forward!**
**Core Content Presentations**
Teach *Impact of the Slave Trade*

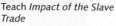

**Interactive Whiteboard**
**GeoActivity** Analyze Primary Sources: The Slave Trade

**Connect to NG**
Research Links

**Also Check Out**
- Charts & Infographics and Graphic Organizers in **Teacher Resources**
- GeoJournal in **Student eEdition**

### BACKGROUND FOR THE TEACHER

Long before people were sent as slaves to the Americas, the trans-Saharan slave trade had supplied enslaved Africans as laborers in the Mediterranean. These Africans worked alongside slaves from Russia and the Balkans. The number of enslaved Africans jumped astronomically after plantation owners in the Americas began to use slaves.

### ESSENTIAL QUESTION

### How did trade networks and migration influence the development of African civilization?

Europeans established the slave trade by trading for slaves with African merchants and rulers. Section 2.3 describes the history, causes, and effects of the slave trade in Africa.

## INTRODUCE & ENGAGE

**K-W-L Chart** Provide each student with a K-W-L chart like the one below. Have students brainstorm what they know about slavery and the African slave trade. Then ask them to write questions that they would like to have answered as they study the lesson. Allow time at the end of the lesson for students to fill in what they have learned. `0:15` minutes

| WHAT DO I KNOW? | WHAT DO I WANT TO KNOW? | WHAT DID I LEARN? |
|-----------------|--------------------------|--------------------|
|  |  |  |
|  |  |  |

## TEACH

### Guided Discussion

1. **Compare and Contrast** How was slavery in Africa different before the arrival of the Europeans? *(At first slaves were captured in war rather than bought and sold. Then Arab traders began capturing and selling Africans but not in as great numbers as the Europeans.)*

2. **Analyze Cause and Effect** Why did the slave trade increase after the arrival of the Europeans? *(Demand for plantation crops was high, and Europeans wanted cheap, captive labor to work on plantations.)*

### MORE INFORMATION

**Back to Africa: Liberia** Some African slaves migrated back to Africa. As its name suggests, Liberia, Africa's oldest republic, was settled by a group of freed American slaves in 1820. A group of abolitionists, the American Colonization Society, resettled more than 10,000 freed slaves in Liberia. In 1847, the independent country modeled its constitution on that of the United States.

Liberian flag

## DIFFERENTIATE  Connect to NG

**Striving Readers Analyze Cause and Effect** Provide students with a chart like the one at right to help them organize the main ideas from the lesson. Have students work in pairs. One student completes the left column and a partner completes the right column. Students then discuss the benefits of slave-trading to the traders and owners and the effects on the slaves and their communities.

| Reasons for Slavery | Effects of Slavery |
|---------------------|--------------------|
|  |  |

**Gifted & Talented Compare Across Regions** Have students use the **Research Links** to conduct research about what happened to enslaved Africans when they arrived at their destinations. Suggest, for example, that one group of students research slavery in Central America and the Caribbean, and another research slavery in the southern United States. Groups should look for statistics on the numbers of slaves in each of those regions and the conditions under which they lived and worked. Have each group share their findings with the class as a whole.

---

## ACTIVE OPTIONS

### Interactive Whiteboard
### GeoActivity

**Analyze Primary Sources: The Slave Trade** To help students understand that people may see an event in different ways depending on their point of view and vested interests, project and supply students with the two accounts. One is told by a slave and one by an English slave ship captain. Have students read the two accounts and answer critical-thinking questions. `0:15` minutes

**EXTENSION** Provide students with two more primary sources about the slave trade. Ask students to compose their own critical-thinking questions about the passages. Ask for volunteers to share their questions and then answer them as a class. `0:20` minutes

### On Your Feet

**Walk the Triangle** Have students research the different parts of the triangular trade, and then label points in the classroom to represent each destination: Great Britain, the Americas, and Africa. After research is complete, have students who researched the middle passage stand on that portion of the triangular route, the ones who researched sugar plantations stand at the Americas point, and the ones who researched slave ports stand at Africa. At each of these points, call on volunteers to report briefly on their research. Then all students walk the triangle and return to their seats. `0:30` minutes

### ONGOING ASSESSMENT
### DATA LAB  GeoJournal

#### ANSWERS

1. 12,521,336 were put on ships in Africa; 10,702,656 survived the journey. 1,818,680 died during the Middle Passage.

2. between 1701 and 1800—884,750 people died; 1500–1600: 78,221; 1601–1700: 352,954; 1801–1867: 502,755

3. African villages and communities were devastated by the loss of young people, especially young men. Village leadership was disrupted. Many parts of Africa were weakened by the slave trade. Cultures in the Americas were shaped by the enslaved Africans and continue to be shaped by their descendents.

4. Students' reports should show evidence of research, observe the rules of grammar and punctuation, and present reasonable findings.

## 2.4 Colonization to Independence

**Main Idea** European powers colonized and ruled large parts of Africa until Africans began independence movements in the mid-1900s.

As you have learned, the Portuguese began exploring the African coast in the 1400s. By the 1500s, many European nations were seeking to control large parts of Africa.

### Imperialism and Colonialism

**Imperialism** is the practice of extending a nation's influence by controlling other territories. European imperialism in Africa began when Europeans started trading with slave merchants on the coast. Little by little, Europeans moved into African lands in search of profitable resources. Eventually, several European countries conquered African lands and established colonies. The practice of directly controlling and settling foreign territories is known as **colonialism**.

By the mid-1800s, European powers began to fight over their African colonies. They wanted more natural resources to fuel industrialization, or the transition to large-scale industries, in Europe. Because of advanced European weapons, there was little the Africans could do to stop them.

### Scramble for Africa

In 1884, Europeans held the **Berlin Conference** to settle their disputes about colonial claims in Africa. No Africans were invited to attend. Europeans at the conference divided Africa among themselves. By 1910, France, Germany, Belgium, Portugal, Italy, Spain, and Great Britain had established themselves as colonial powers in all parts of Africa.

Many Europeans believed that African culture and religion were inferior to those of Europe. They wanted to change African traditions. Europeans sent **missionaries** —people sent by a church to spread their religion among native populations—to convert Africans to Christianity.

### African Independence

In the early 1900s, **Pan-Africanism**, a movement to unify African people, grew among African leaders in London and other cities around the world. By the 1950s and 1960s, this nationalist movement had brought together many African leaders. **Jomo Kenyatta** (JOH moh ken YAA taa) of Kenya and **Kwame Nkrumah** (KWAA may en KROO mah) of Ghana helped to gain independence for their people.

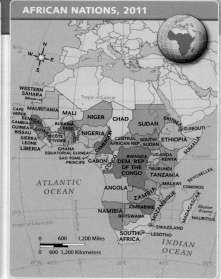

**EUROPEAN COLONIES, 1938**

Belgian
British
French
British & French
Italian
Portuguese
Spanish
Independent countries
— 1938 boundaries

**AFRICAN NATIONS, 2011**

In 1963 the Organization of African Unity (OAU) was founded to promote Pan-Africanism. The OAU is known today as the African Union (AU). It continues to promote African unity and cooperation, but also functions as an economic group similar to the European Union.

**Before You Move On**
Make Inferences What action by Africans helped bring colonialism to an end? African leaders started a Pan-Africanism movement to help unify the people.

**ONGOING ASSESSMENT**
## MAP LAB   GeoJournal

1. **Location** Based on the maps, which modern countries made up the colony of French Equatorial Africa?

2. **Interpret Maps** Looking at the maps, how would you describe the changes to Africa's internal borders from 1938 to today?

3. **Analyze Cause and Effect** Why did European countries colonize Africa? How were Africans affected by colonization?

A caravel ship used in trade voyages

This political cartoon (1892) suggests that Europe now controls the African continent.

Jomo Kenyatta

1500 — 1600 — 1700 — 1800 — 1900 — 2000

○ 1500s
European imperialism in Africa begins.

○ 1642
The Dutch take possession of Portuguese forts in West Africa.

○ 1884
Berlin Conference divides Africa.

○ 1963
Organization of African Unity (OAU) is founded.

○ 2002
African Union replaces OAU.

**376** CHAPTER 13

---

## PLAN

### OBJECTIVE Describe the effects of European colonization in Africa and events that led to African independence.

### CRITICAL THINKING SKILLS FOR SECTION 2.4

• Main Idea
• Make Inferences
• Interpret Maps
• Analyze Cause and Effect
• Make Generalizations

### PRINT RESOURCES

*Teacher's Edition* Resource Bank

• Reading and Note-Taking: Track Important Information
• Vocabulary Practice: Word Squares
• **GeoActivity** Build a Time Line of Ghana's Independence

**TECHTREK** myNGconnect.com

**Fast Forward!**
**Core Content Presentations**
Teach *Colonization to Independence*

**Maps and Graphs**
Online World Atlas: European Colonies, 1938; African Nations, 2011

**Interactive Whiteboard**
**GeoActivity** Build a Time Line of Ghana's Independence

**Also Check Out**
• NG Photo Gallery in **Digital Library**
• GeoJournal in **Student eEdition**

### BACKGROUND FOR THE TEACHER

The Berlin Conference was held at a time when 80 percent of Africa remained under local control. Only the coastal areas had been colonized by European countries. At the Berlin Conference, colonial powers wrestled for control over the interior of the continent. Europeans imposed their map of Africa over cultures and regions, ignoring long established cultural and linguistic boundaries.

### ESSENTIAL QUESTION

### How did trade networks and migration influence the development of African civilization?

European countries divided up Africa so that Britain, France, Germany, the Netherlands, Belgium, Italy, and other countries controlled different parts of the continent. Section 2.4 describes the beginning of colonialism and the lasting effects of colonization in sub-Saharan Africa.

# INTRODUCE & ENGAGE

**Activate Prior Knowledge** Explain that in this section, students will learn about European colonial rule in Africa. For hundreds of years, European powers claimed parts of Africa as colonies. By the late 1800s most parts of Africa were ruled as colonies.

Have students draw on their knowledge of colonialism in the Americas and the founding of the United States to discuss these questions:

- What is colonialism? *(the practice of directly controlling and settling foreign territories)*
- Why did countries want colonies? *(for new markets and control of profitable natural resources; in the United States, for freedom of religion; in Africa, to spread Christianity)*
- What geographic factors made Africa a desirable continent to colonize? *(abundant natural resources)*

Discuss again after completing the reading to assure accuracy of responses.
`0:15` minutes

# TEACH  Maps and Graphs

## Guided Discussion

1. **Make Inferences** What can you infer about European attitudes from the fact that no African leaders were invited to attend the Berlin Conference? *(Europeans considered Africans to be inferior and without rights to a say in their future. Europeans assumed that Africa was theirs to divide.)*

2. **Make Generalizations** How did Europeans want to change the people of Africa? *(They wanted them to adopt Christianity and other European values.)*

**Interpret Maps** Project the European Colonies map and the African Nations map from the **Online World Atlas.** Explain how to use the legend to locate the European colonies and spheres of influence. Have students locate Nigeria on both maps. Ask students to compare and contrast the two maps. **ASK:** How did some borders change after African colonies became independent? *(Some African colonies were further divided, becoming more than one country.)* `0:15` minutes

# DIFFERENTIATE

**English Language Learners Study Word Parts** Explain that -*ism* is a suffix, or word part added to the end of another word. It means "action, process, practice, or state." Ask students to define the word *colonial* and then the word *colonialism*. Repeat with the word *imperialism*. Ask for one more example of a word ending with the suffix -*ism*. Then tell students that the prefix *pan-* means "all." Ask students what the word *Pan-American* would mean. Have students explain how the prefix *pan-* and the suffix -*ism* contribute to the meaning of the word *Pan-Africanism*.

**Inclusion Complete Time Lines** Have students complete the **GeoActivity.** As students work on the time line for the activity, provide them with either the date or the event for each entry on the time line. Have pairs use the information provided to complete the time line by filling in the missing dates and events. Pair visually impaired students with partners who can read the dates or events aloud to them.

# ACTIVE OPTIONS

 **Interactive Whiteboard**
## GeoActivity

**Build a Time Line of Ghana's Independence** Have students build a time line of the events before and after Ghana's independence. Project the information and have students identify significant events that should be part of the time line. Have students work in groups to complete the time line. They can use a Round Table strategy in which each group member adds an event to the time line until it is complete. `0:25` minutes

## On Your Feet

**Numbered Heads** Have students get into groups of four and number off within each group. Assign the Before You Move On question. Have students discuss their answers as a group. Students should write down the facts from the text and their prior knowledge that form the basis of their inferences. Then call a number and the student from each group with that number reports for the group. `0:20` minutes

## Performance Assessment

**Hold a Panel Discussion** Have students work in groups of five to conduct a panel discussion. One group member is the moderator, posing the question, "How did trade networks and migration influence the development of African civilization?" Other group members will report on the influence of one of the following: Bantu migrations, early states and trade, the slave trade, and how colonialism grew out of slavery and trade. Go to **myNGconnect.com** for the rubric.

## ONGOING ASSESSMENT
# MAP LAB  GeoJournal

### ANSWERS

1. Chad, Central African Republic, Cameroon, Gabon, and Congo
2. Responses will vary, but students may recognize that many of the borders remained the same between 1938 and 2011.
3. The slave trade brought a European presence and encouraged economic interactions and settlement by Europeans. This led to the colonizing of Africa. Africa lost millions of people to the slave trade, and African communities were weakened.

# Photo Gallery • Nigerian Salt Ponds

For more photos from the National Geographic Photo Gallery, go to the **Digital Library** at myNGconnect.com.

Mountain gorilla, Africa

Nigerian camel caravan

South African women

**Critical Viewing** These circular ponds contain a mixture of water and salty earth. The mud is moved to evaporation areas where salt is left behind. The color of the salt depends on where the mud came from.

Students in Botswana

African lions

Victoria Falls, Zimbabwe

Zulu village, South Africa

## VOCABULARY

For each pair of vocabulary words, write one sentence that explains the connection between the two words.

1. savanna; Sahel

> *The Sahel runs south of the Sahara and north of the savannas, forming a border between the two.*

2. ecotourism; habitats
3. Swahili; *lingua franca*
4. Middle Passage; trans-Atlantic slave trade
5. imperialism; Pan-Africanism

### MAIN IDEAS

6. What are the four regions of sub-Saharan Africa? (Section 1.1)
7. Which large landform in East Africa was created by the separation of tectonic plates? (Section 1.2)
8. Which region of West Africa supports more population, and why? (Section 1.3)
9. What is the major river in Central Africa, and what effect does it have on the region? (Section 1.4)
10. What are the two main types of landforms that make up Southern Africa? (Section 1.5)
11. What factors threaten the big cats of Africa? (Section 1.6)
12. From what African region did the Bantu people begin their migration? (Section 2.1)
13. How did gold and salt help Ghana develop as a kingdom? (Section 2.2)
14. What were some effects of slavery on communities in Africa? (Section 2.3)
15. What reasons did Europeans have for wanting to colonize Africa? (Section 2.4)

## GEOGRAPHY

### ANALYZE THE ESSENTIAL QUESTION

How has the varied geography of sub-Saharan Africa affected people's lives?

**Critical Thinking: Draw Conclusions**

16. What might be some ways for Africans to combat the challenges of desertification?
17. How does not having access to a coastal port impact a country?
18. What advantages or challenges does physical geography create for economic development in Central Africa?

### INTERPRET TABLES

#### IMPACT OF CHANGES IN LAND

| Change | Environment | Human Health | Safety Issues | Politics & Economics |
|---|---|---|---|---|
| Desertification | Loss of habitat; decline in variety of plant and animal life; increased soil erosion | Malnutrition, hunger | Wars over arable land and limited water resources | Poverty; decreased political and economic influence; population movement |
| Deforestation | Decline in variety of plant and animal life; loss of habitat; reduced resources | Loss of potential new medical products | Increased landslides and flooding | Loss of forest products; loss of indigenous communities; loss of tourism opportunities |
| Soil Erosion | Loss of soil and habitat; loss of farmland | Loss of food and water; hunger, malnutrition | Risk of flooding and landslides | Loss of property; reduced farm development |

Source: http://www.eoearth.org/article/Global_Environment_Outlook_(GEO-4):_Chapter_3#Introduction

19. **Summarize** How does desertification lead to loss of habitat?
20. **Form and Support Opinions** Think about the causes of desertification, deforestation, and soil erosion. Which one do you think would be easiest to solve? Explain.

## HISTORY

### ANALYZE THE ESSENTIAL QUESTION

How did trade networks and migration influence the development of African civilization?

**Critical Thinking: Analyze Cause and Effect**

21. How can the effects of the Bantu migration be seen in Africa today?
22. In what ways did trade networks help build African kingdoms?

### INTERPRET MAPS

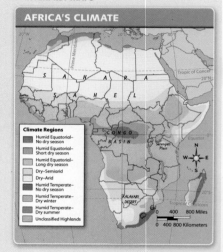

AFRICA'S CLIMATE

**Climate Regions**
- Humid Equatorial—No dry season
- Humid Equatorial—Short dry season
- Humid Equatorial—Long dry season
- Dry—Semiarid
- Dry—Arid
- Humid Temperate—No dry season
- Humid Temperate—Dry winter
- Humid Temperate—Dry summer
- Unclassified Highlands

23. **Location** What climate zone covers most of the Sahara?
24. **Region** Think about the four areas of sub-Saharan Africa: West, East, Central, and Southern. What area has the largest number of different climate zones?
25. **Make Inferences** What is the relationship between the climate zones and the rain forests of the Congo Basin?

## ACTIVE OPTIONS

**Synthesize** the Essential Questions by completing the activities below.

26. **Create Time Lines** Review this chapter for information on the history of sub-Saharan African countries. Then use a computer or pen and paper to create a time line similar to those found in this book. **Post the time line in your classroom so others can add more entries.**

> **Time Line Tips**
> - Take notes before you begin.
> - Include important dates for a time line.
> - Include important rulers and events.
> - Find at least one photo that represents your country.

**TECHTREK** myNGconnect.com For research links on Sub-Saharan Africa

27. **Create Sketch Maps** Create a natural resources sketch map of sub-Saharan Africa. Use maps in this chapter and research links at **Connect to NG** and other online sources to gather information about natural resources in sub-Saharan Africa. Add them to an outline map similar to the one below. Use a map key to show the resources.

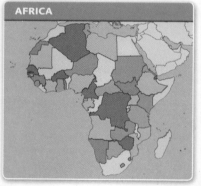

AFRICA

---

# CHAPTER Review

## VOCABULARY ANSWERS

1. > *The Sahel runs south of the Sahara and north of the savannas, forming a border between the two.*

2. The Jouberts promote ecotourism as a way of protecting habitats.
3. More than 30 million people in Africa use Swahili as a *lingua franca*, a language common to two groups with different languages.
4. The Middle Passage was a particularly brutal part of the trans-Atlantic slave trade.
5. Pan-Africanism was the response of African countries to decades of European imperialism.

## MAIN IDEAS ANSWERS

6. West Africa, East Africa, Central Africa, Southern Africa
7. Movement between plates formed the Great Rift Valley of East Africa.
8. The coastal countries of West Africa are more populous because of their access to fresh water and a climate that is good for agriculture.
9. The Congo River. It provides a means of local travel, and dams on the river produce hydroelectric power for the area.
10. basins and plateaus
11. loss of habitat, hunting, and poaching
12. Central Africa
13. Ghana developed as a kingdom by controlling and taxing the gold and salt trade.
14. weakened or destroyed communities, torn apart families, loss of potential leaders
15. access to natural resources

# GEOGRAPHY

## ANALYZE THE ESSENTIAL QUESTION ANSWERS

16. Possible response: build fences that stabilize the sands and allow crops to grow

17. It inhibits trade and makes communication and transportation difficult, which can stall progress.

18. One advantage of physical geography in Central Africa is the Congo River: damming the river has provided electricity for the area. One challenge is the dense forest, which hinders the movement of economic goods in the area.

## INTERPRET TABLES

19. Desertification is the process by which soil becomes less fertile, usually permanently. Less fertile soils tend not to support vegetation. Lack of vegetation leads to soil erosion and loss of habitat.

20. Responses will vary, but students should use specific examples from sub-Saharan Africa to support their opinions.

## ACTIVE OPTIONS

### CREATE TIME LINES

26. Students' time lines should
    • include appropriate dates;
    • cover important rulers and events;
    • include at least one photo.

### CREATE SKETCH MAPS

27. Students' maps should
    • show location of natural resources in sub-Saharan Africa;
    • indicate the names of the natural resources;
    • use colors appropriately;
    • include a key or legend.

# HISTORY

## ANALYZE THE ESSENTIAL QUESTION ANSWERS

21. Many people trace their ancestry to Bantu groups and some Bantu languages, such as Swahili, serve as a *lingua franca* between groups who speak different languages.

22. Trade networks established an exchange of desired goods and African kingdoms were built, in part, by controlling and taxing this exchange.

## INTERPRET MAPS

23. Dry–Arid

24. Southern Africa, which includes the island of Madagascar, has six climate zones. In fact, Madagascar itself has five climate zones.

25. The climate zones of the Congo Basin rain forests have no long or short dry periods.

Possible resources and locations:

• Coal—in southern Africa, Democratic Republic of the Congo, and Nigeria

• Oil reserves—West African coastal basin: mainly in Nigeria and also in Cameroon, Gabon, and Republic of Congo; Angola

• Uranium—Southern Africa is said to be one of the world's seven major uranium provinces. Other countries with significant uranium deposits are Niger, Gabon, Democratic Republic of the Congo, and Namibia.

• Iron ore—The most significant iron reserves are to be found in western and southern Africa. The most significant deposits are in Liberia, Guinea, Nigeria, Mauritania, Gabon. In southern Africa most iron ore reserves lie in South Africa itself. There are also substantial reserves in Zimbabwe.

• Copper—Most of Africa's copper is contained in the Central African Copperbelt, stretching across Zambia and into the Democratic Republic of the Congo.

• Aluminum ore—Africa has about one-fourth of the world's reserves of bauxite, the chief aluminum ore. Virtually all of this occurs in a major belt stretching some 1,200 miles from Guinea to Togo. The largest reserves are in Guinea.

• Gold—The greatest concentrations are in South Africa, where reserves of gold probably constitute about half of the world total. Gold is also found in Zimbabwe, in the Democratic Republic of the Congo, and in Ghana. There are numerous alluvial sources of gold in Burundi, Côte d'Ivoire, and Gabon.

• Diamonds—The principal known reserves of diamonds in their primary form are in the South African Vaal belt. Elsewhere in Africa, primary deposits are found in Tanzania, Botswana, and Lesotho. Industrial diamonds are found in the Democratic Republic of the Congo, which contains the majority of Africa's reserves, Central African Republic, and Angola. In West Africa, diamonds are found in Sierra Leone, Guinea, Côte d'Ivoire, Liberia, and Ghana.

# CHAPTER PLANNER

## SECTION 1 CULTURE

## 1.1 Africa's Borders and Cultures

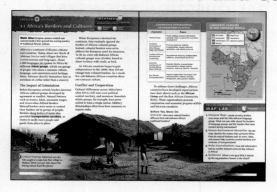

**OBJECTIVE** Understand the legacy of colonialism and the steps that Africa is taking to form stable countries.

## SECTION 1 CULTURE

## 1.2 African Music Goes Global

**OBJECTIVE** Examine the role of music in Africa's cultures and its influence around the world.

## SECTION 1 CULTURE

## 1.3 Kenya Modernizes

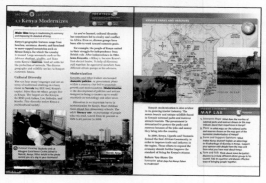

**OBJECTIVE** Analyze the challenges Kenya has faced and the progress it has made.

---

# SECTION SUPPORT

TE Resource Bank

myNGconnect.com

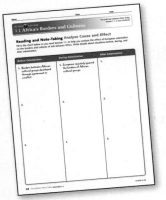

**Reading and Note-Taking**

Analyze Cause and Effect

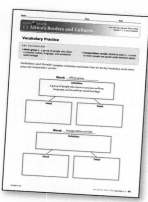

**Vocabulary Practice**

Definition and Details

**Whiteboard Ready!**

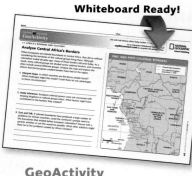

**GeoActivity**

Analyze Central Africa's Borders

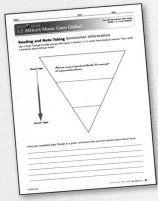

**Reading and Note-Taking**

Summarize Information

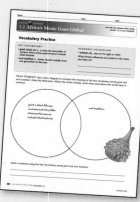

**Vocabulary Practice**

Venn Diagram

**Whiteboard Ready!**

**GeoActivity**

Solve a Puzzle About African Music

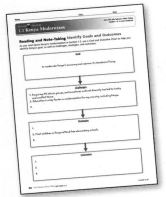

**Reading and Note-Taking**

Identify Goals and Outcomes

**Vocabulary Practice**

Definition Clues

**Whiteboard Ready!**

**GeoActivity**

Graph Kenya's Economic Indicators

## ASSESSMENT

**Student Edition**

Ongoing Assessment: Map Lab

**Resource Bank and myNGconnect.com**

Review and Assessment, Sections 1.1–1.4

 **ExamView®**
**Test Generator CD-ROM**
Section 1 Quiz in English and Spanish

**Student Edition**

Ongoing Assessment: Photo Lab

**Resource Bank and myNGconnect.com**

Review and Assessment, Sections 1.1–1.4

 **ExamView®**
**Test Generator CD-ROM**
Section 1 Quiz in English and Spanish

**Student Edition**

Ongoing Assessment: Map Lab

**Resource Bank and myNGconnect.com**

Review and Assessment, Sections 1.1–1.4

 **ExamView®**
**Test Generator CD-ROM**
Section 1 Quiz in English and Spanish

## TECHTREK  myNGconnect.com

 >> **Fast Forward!**
**Core Content Presentations**
Teach *Africa's Borders and Cultures*

 **Digital Library**
NG Photo Gallery, Section 1

 **Connect to NG**
Research Links

**Interactive Whiteboard**
**GeoActivity** Analyze Central Africa's Borders

**Also Check Out**
• Charts & Infographics in **Teacher Resources**
• Online World Atlas in **Maps and Graphs**
• GeoJournal in **Student eEdition**

 >> **Fast Forward!**
**Core Content Presentations**
Teach *African Music Goes Global*

**Digital Library**
• Music Clip, Section 1
• NG Photo Gallery, Section 1

 **Magazine Maker**

 **Connect to NG**
Research Links

**Interactive Whiteboard**
**GeoActivity** Solve a Puzzle About African Music

**Also Check Out**
GeoJournal in **Student eEdition**

 >> **Fast Forward!**
**Core Content Presentations**
Teach *Kenya Modernizes*

 **Digital Library**
NG Photo Gallery, Section 1

 **Connect to NG**
Research Links

 **Maps and Graphs**
**Interactive Map Tool**
Analyze Patterns of Population

**Also Check Out**
• Online World Atlas in **Maps and Graphs**
• Graphic Organizers in **Teacher Resources**
• GeoJournal in **Student eEdition**

# CHAPTER PLANNER

## SECTION SUPPORT

### SECTION 1 CULTURE

## 1.4 Exploring Traditional Cultures

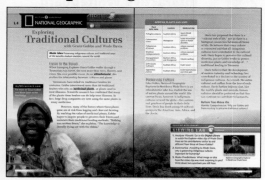

**OBJECTIVE** Understand the scientific value of traditional healing methods and the need to preserve traditional cultures.

**Reading and Note-Taking**

Make Generalizations

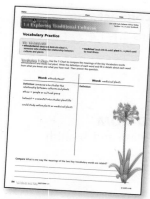

**Vocabulary Practice**

Vocabulary T-Chart

**Whiteboard Ready!**

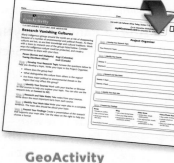

**GeoActivity**

Research Vanishing Cultures

### SECTION 2 GOVERNMENT & ECONOMICS

## 2.1 Prized Mineral Resources

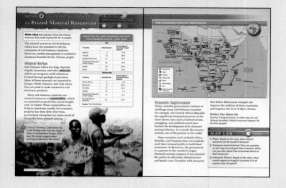

**OBJECTIVE** Learn about the mineral resources of Sub-Saharan Africa, their economic potential, and the challenges in extracting them.

**Reading and Note-Taking**

Outline and Take Notes

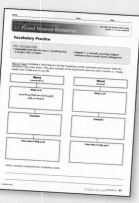

**Vocabulary Practice**

Word Map

**Whiteboard Ready!**

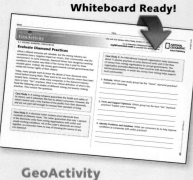

**GeoActivity**

Evaluate Diamond Practices

### SECTION 2 GOVERNMENT & ECONOMICS

## 2.2 Nigeria and Oil

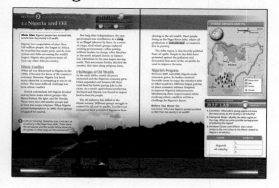

**OBJECTIVE** Understand the challenges in unifying Nigeria and in harnessing its oil wealth to modernize its economy.

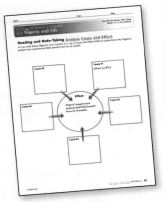

**Reading and Note-Taking**

Analyze Cause and Effect

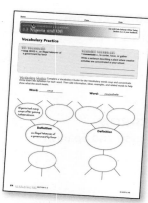

**Vocabulary Practice**

Vocabulary Cluster

**Whiteboard Ready!**

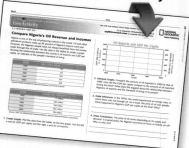

**GeoActivity**

Compare Nigeria's Oil Revenue and Incomes

**Student Edition**
Ongoing Assessment: Viewing Lab

**Teacher's Edition**
Performance Assessment: Create a Visual Aid

**Resource Bank and myNGconnect.com**
Review and Assessment, Sections 1.1–1.4

**ExamView®**
**Test Generator CD-ROM**
Section 1 Quiz in English and Spanish

>> **Fast Forward!**
**Core Content Presentations**
Teach *Exploring Traditional Cultures*

**Digital Library**
Explorer Video Clips: Grace Gobbo and Wade Davis

**Connect to NG**
Research Links

**Maps and Graphs**
**Interactive Map Tool**
Analyze Land Use

**Also Check Out**
- Charts & Infographics in **Teacher Resources**
- NG Photo Gallery in **Digital Library**
- GeoJournal in **Student eEdition**

---

**Student Edition**
Ongoing Assessment: Map Lab

**Resource Bank and myNGconnect.com**
Review and Assessment, Sections 2.1–2.6

**ExamView®**
**Test Generator CD-ROM**
Section 2 Quiz in English and Spanish

>> **Fast Forward!**
**Core Content Presentations**
Teach *Prized Mineral Resources*

**Teacher Resources**
Chart: Selected Oil and Diamond Exports

**Connect to NG**
Research Links

**Maps and Graphs**
- **Interactive Map Tool** Analyze the Human Footprint in Sub-Saharan Africa
- Online World Atlas: Sub-Saharan Africa's Resources

**Also Check Out**
- NG Photo Gallery in **Digital Library**
- GeoJournal in **Student eEdition**

---

**Student Edition**
Ongoing Assessment: Map Lab

**Resource Bank and myNGconnect.com**
Review and Assessment, Sections 2.1–2.6

**ExamView®**
**Test Generator CD-ROM**
Section 2 Quiz in English and Spanish

>> **Fast Forward!**
**Core Content Presentations**
Teach *Nigeria and Oil*

**Digital Library**
NG Photo Gallery, Section 2

**Connect to NG**
Research Links

**Maps and Graphs**
- **Interactive Map Tool** Population and Oil
- Online World Atlas: Ethnic Groups and Oil

**Also Check Out**
GeoJournal in **Student eEdition**

# SECTION SUPPORT

SECTION **2** GOVERNMENT & ECONOMICS

## 2.3 Agriculture and Food Supply

**OBJECTIVE** Identify and describe the challenges of improving agriculture and increasing food output for Africa's growing population.

### Reading and Note-Taking
Find Main Idea and Details

### Vocabulary Practice
Descriptive Paragraph

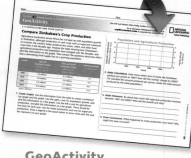

Whiteboard Ready!

### GeoActivity
Compare Zimbabwe's Crop Production

---

SECTION **2** GLOBAL ISSUES

## 2.4 Improving Public Health

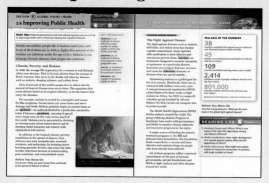

**OBJECTIVE** Examine the steps Africa is taking to fight disease and improve public health.

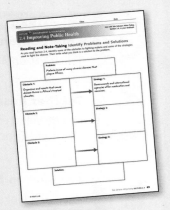

### Reading and Note-Taking
Identify Problems and Solutions

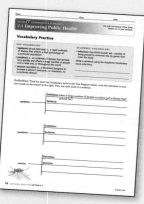

### Vocabulary Practice
Definition Tree

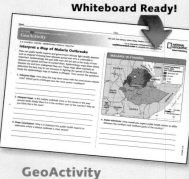

Whiteboard Ready!

### GeoActivity
Interpret a Map of Malaria Outbreaks

---

SECTION **2** GOVERNMENT & ECONOMICS

## 2.5 Sudan and Somalia

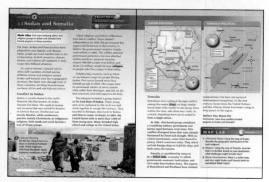

**OBJECTIVE** Compare and contrast the problems in Sudan and Somalia.

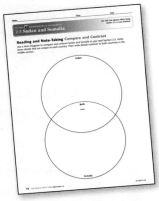

### Reading and Note-Taking
Compare and Contrast

### Vocabulary Practice
Four-Column Chart

Whiteboard Ready!

### GeoActivity
Build a Time Line of Events

**Student Edition**

Ongoing Assessment: Writing Lab

**Resource Bank and myNGconnect.com**

Review and Assessment, Sections 2.1–2.6

**ExamView®**
**Test Generator CD-ROM**
Section 2 Quiz in English and Spanish

 **» Fast Forward!**
**Core Content Presentations**
Teach *Agriculture and Food Supply*

 **Maps and Graphs**
*Interactive Map Tool*
Analyze Agriculture and Land

**Digital Library**
• GeoVideo: *Introduce Sub-Saharan Africa*
• NG Photo Gallery, Section 2

**Also Check Out**
• Graphic Organizers in **Teacher Resources**
• GeoJournal in **Student eEdition**

---

**Student Edition**

Ongoing Assessment: Reading Lab

**Resource Bank and myNGconnect.com**

Review and Assessment, Sections 2.1–2.6

**ExamView®**
**Test Generator CD-ROM**
Section 2 Quiz in English and Spanish

 **» Fast Forward!**
**Core Content Presentations**
Teach *Improving Public Health*

 **Interactive Whiteboard**
**GeoActivity** Interpret a Map of Malaria Outbreaks

 **Connect to NG**
Research Links

**Also Check Out**
• NG Photo Gallery in **Digital Library**
• Charts & Infographics in **Teacher Resources**
• GeoJournal in **Student eEdition**

---

**Student Edition**

Ongoing Assessment: Map Lab

**Resource Bank and myNGconnect.com**

Review and Assessment, Sections 2.1–2.6

**ExamView®**
**Test Generator CD-ROM**
Section 2 Quiz in English and Spanish

 **» Fast Forward!**
**Core Content Presentations**
Teach *Sudan and Somalia*

 **Maps and Graphs**
• **Interactive Map Tool**
Analyze Borders and Language Diversity
• Online World Atlas: Sudan Political; Somalia Political

**Also Check Out**
• NG Photo Gallery in **Digital Library**
• GeoJournal in **Student eEdition**

SECTION **2** GOVERNMENT & ECONOMICS

## 2.6 Ending Apartheid

**OBJECTIVE** Explain how apartheid came to an end and how democratic government was founded in South Africa.

## SECTION SUPPORT

**Whiteboard Ready!**

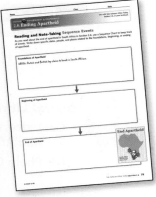

**Reading and Note-Taking**
Sequence Events

**Vocabulary Practice**
Definition Chart

**GeoActivity**
Analyze Primary Sources: Apartheid and Segregation

## CHAPTER ASSESSMENT

### Review

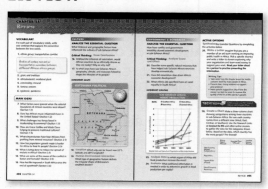

## INFORMAL ASSESSMENT

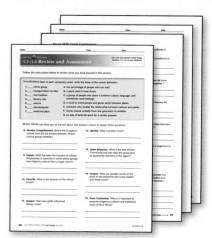

**Review and Assessment**

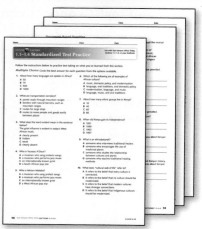

**Standardized Test Practice**

### Student Edition
Ongoing Assessment: Reading Lab

### Teacher's Edition
Performance Assessment: Create a Group Presentation

### Resource Bank and myNGconnect.com
Review and Assessment, Sections 2.1–2.6

**ExamView®**
**Test Generator CD-ROM**
Section 2 Quiz in English and Spanish

**Fast Forward!**
### Core Content Presentations
Teach *Ending Apartheid*

### Digital Library
NG Photo Gallery, Section 2

### Connect to NG
Research Links

### Interactive Whiteboard
**GeoActivity** Analyze Primary Sources: Apartheid and Segregation

### Also Check Out
• Graphic Organizers in **Teacher Resources**
• GeoJournal in **Student eEdition**

## FORMAL ASSESSMENT

**Chapter Test A (on level)**

**Chapter Test B (modified)**

**ExamView®**
**Test Generator CD-ROM**
Chapter Tests

# STRATEGIES FOR DIFFERENTIATION

## STRIVING READERS  eEdition  Audiobook

### Strategy 1 • Use Sentence Starters

Provide these sentence starters for students to complete after reading. You can also have students use the sentences as a preview to set a purpose for reading.

**1.1** Africa is a continent of diverse cultures and countries because _____.

**1.2** Griots are important in West African cultures because _____.

**1.3** Some of the challenges of modernization in Kenya include _____.

**1.4** Many indigenous African cultures understand the value of plants for _____.

**Use with Sections 1.1–1.4**

### Strategy 2 • Build Word Maps

Display the Word Map and have students fill in the information for the Key Vocabulary words listed below. Work together as a class for words that may be challenging.

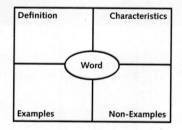

**1.4** medicinal plant   **2.3** famine
**2.1** mineral   **2.4** pandemic

**Use with Sections 1.4, 2.1, 2.3, and 2.4**

### Strategy 3 • Set a Purpose for Reading

Direct students to read and find at least six causes of famine in Africa. After reading, have students record the causes in a list. Allow partners to compare lists and then list the effects of famine.

**Use with Section 2.3**

### Strategy 4 • Use a Venn Diagram Summary

Display the completed Venn diagram below for students to use as they read.

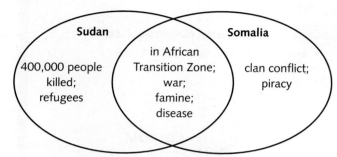

**Use with Section 2.5** *Make sure students are able to explain what each entry means.*

### Strategy 5 • Create a Time Line

Display the following events and direct students to arrange them in order on a time line:

ANC protests apartheid          Union of South Africa formed
Mandela elected president     All South Africans given the vote
Boers form republics               de Klerk begins change
Biko arrested and killed          Apartheid laws created

**Use with Section 2.6** *Suggest that students start by finding the part of the lesson that mentions each listed event and then identifying the date associated with each. You might assign each event and date to a student and have them line up according to chronology. Then students can transfer the dates and events to a poster board time line or a time line on the interactive whiteboard.*

## INCLUSION  eEdition  Audiobook

### Strategy 1 • Preview Lessons

Give students copies of these summaries before beginning the lessons.

1. Malaria is a chronic disease carried by mosquitoes. Sleeping under nets and draining water where mosquitoes breed can prevent it. Government agencies are working to prevent its spread.

2. In the past, laws in South Africa separated races, and only white South Africans could vote. Black South Africans protested, and the laws were changed to allow them to vote. Work is still going on to promote racial equality.

After students have read the section, put them in groups and ask them to add details to the summaries.

**Use with Sections 2.4 and 2.6**

### Strategy 2 • Mark Up Maps

Provide a printout of a map of the continent of Africa for students to keep on their desks. Have students outline in color the borders of the country as it is discussed and then circle the country's name.

**Use with Sections 1.3, 1.4, 2.1, 2.2, and 2.5** *As an alternative, give students a copy of a blank outline map of Africa. Have them add country labels and any other relevant labels as they study sub-Saharan Africa.*

## ENGLISH LANGUAGE LEARNERS  eEdition  Audiobook

### Strategy 1 • Review Key Concepts

Because the concept of colonialism is important to understanding the main ideas in this chapter, review the meaning for students. Display the following words:

| | |
|---|---|
| colony | colonialism |
| colonial | colonization |

Remind students that in the past, many European countries sent explorers and armies to other countries to claim land and set up colonies, places for people to live that were under the rule of the exploring country. Explain that this practice of setting up and ruling colonies in other lands is called *colonialism.* Ask them if they remember which countries set up colonies in Africa. Tell them they will read to find out some results of colonialism in the countries of Africa. Have them look for sentences in which each word is used, read them orally, and write a similar one.

**Use with Section 1.1**

### Strategy 2 • Pair Partners for Dictation

After reading a lesson, direct each student to write one sentence about a main idea from the reading. Pair students and let them take turns dictating their sentences to each other. Then allow them to work together to check spelling and accuracy of sentences.

**Use with All Sections**

### Strategy 3 • Use Photos to Predict Content

Direct students to look at each photo in the lesson and write one sentence predicting what the caption will be about. After reading, you may wish to have students verify their predictions and reword any sentences if necessary.

**Use with Sections 2.1–2.3** *Ask for volunteers to hold one-minute discussions of each photo in the lesson. They should explain what they had predicted about the photo and what the photo actually depicts. Point out that the photos shown in these lessons show work being done by traditional methods.*

## GIFTED & TALENTED  Connect to NG

### Strategy 1 • Explore Ethnic Cultures

Allow students to choose one of the ethnic groups below (or another of their choosing). Have them use the **Research Links** to research and report about the group's culture and cultural contributions.

| | |
|---|---|
| Kikuyu | Swazi |
| Mandinka | Zulu |

**Use with Section 1.1**

### Strategy 2 • Retell Traditional Tales

Tell students to find and read a traditional African tale and prepare an oral retelling for the class. Ask them to give details about where the story comes from before they begin their retellings.

**Use with Section 1.2** *Encourage students to find illustrations that could accompany their oral retelling of the tales.*

## PRE-AP  Connect to NG  Teacher Resources

### Strategy 1 • Evaluate Solutions

Have students make a Pros and Cons chart for possible solutions in the fight against malaria. Then direct them to use their charts to write a letter to a fictional aid agency about which solution they believe holds the most promise for eliminating malaria.

**Use with Section 2.4** *There is a wealth of information online about the fight against malaria. Have students use the* **Research Links** *to check out non-governmental organizations (NGOs) around the world that are working—with some success—to help control the disease. Students can also use a* **Writing Template** *to help them construct their letter.*

### Strategy 2 • Synthesize Information

Suggest that students first review what they learned in all lessons in Section 2 and use that information to decide and explain what they believe are the three greatest challenges facing countries in sub-Saharan Africa today. Remind them to give reasons for their decisions. Students can use the chart below to record their ideas.

| COUNTRY | CHALLENGE | REASON |
|---|---|---|
| | | |
| | | |

**Use with Sections 2.1–2.6**

# CHAPTER 14

# Sub-Saharan Africa
## TODAY

## PREVIEW THE CHAPTER

**Essential Question** What historical and geographic factors have influenced the cultures of sub-Saharan Africa?

**KEY VOCABULARY**
- ethnic group
- transportation corridor
- griot
- oral tradition
- reserve
- domestic policy
- modernization
- literacy rate
- ethnobotanist
- medicinal plant

**ACADEMIC VOCABULARY**
evident

**TERMS & NAMES**
- African Union
- Youssou N'Dour
- Nairobi
- Jomo Kenyatta

**Essential Question** How have conflict and government instability slowed economic development in sub-Saharan Africa?

**KEY VOCABULARY**
- mineral
- commodity
- coup
- famine
- erosion
- legume
- microcredit
- epidemic
- pandemic
- vaccine
- infectious
- refugee
- clan
- failed state
- segregation
- apartheid
- homeland

**ACADEMIC VOCABULARY**
concentrated

**TERMS & NAMES**
- Lost Boys of Sudan
- African National Congress
- Nelson Mandela
- Steve Biko

Traditional Masai in Tanzania herd a flock of goats into a pen.

---

 **Fast Forward!**
**Core Content Presentations**
Introduce *Sub-Saharan Africa Today*

 **Digital Library**
- GeoVideo: *Introduce Sub-Saharan Africa*
- NG Photo Gallery

 **Maps and Graphs**
**Interactive Map Tool**
Examine Land Cover

**Also Check Out**
Research Links in
**Connect to NG**

## INTRODUCE THE CHAPTER

### INTRODUCE THE PHOTOGRAPH

Use the photo as a springboard for discussion about traditional sub-Saharan African culture. Call on volunteers to point out elements of traditional Masai culture that are evident in the photo. Discuss with students what the photo suggests about the economy of Masai societies and the age at which children begin to participate. **ASK:** How might the Masai culture come into conflict with groups that have different economic activities and lifestyles? *(The needs of nomadic herders might conflict with the needs of settled farmers, developers of land, parks that set aside land for wildlife protection, or people who want to protect populations of predators such as lions.)*

### COMPARE ACROSS REGIONS

The Masai are nomadic people living mostly in Kenya and northern Tanzania. As cattle and goat herders, they base their economy almost completely on livestock, consuming mostly meat and milk. They build their huts from dried cattle dung. The Masai probably migrated from Ethiopia and Sudan. Masai warriors were once feared by other tribes, but they lost power during the late 1800s.

### CONNECT

Traditionally, Masai groups have defined their wealth by the size of their livestock herds, and they have resisted a money-based economy. Today, many Masai are participating in money-based economies. Some have settled on farms. Others have moved to cities for jobs.

# INTRODUCE THE ESSENTIAL QUESTIONS

## SECTION 1 • CULTURE
**What historical and geographic factors have influenced the cultures of sub-Saharan Africa?**

**Fishbowl Activity: Cultures of Sub-Saharan Africa** Use a Fishbowl strategy to examine how geographic and historical factors shape cultures in general and sub-Saharan African cultures in particular. Encourage students to use prior knowledge of factors that have shaped previously studied regions. Suggest that they also draw on what they learned about sub-Saharan Africa from the previous chapter. **ASK:** How would you expect the landforms, climate, elevation, vegetation, and historical factors to shape cultures? Use the notes below to prompt students while they share their knowledge and exchange ideas. See "Best Practices for Active Teaching" for a review of this cooperative learning strategy. `0:20` minutes

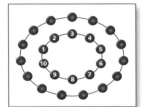

**1 Geographic Factors** Scarcity of water would affect cultures by expanding or limiting their options for obtaining or producing food. Temperatures and elevations also affect what can be grown or raised. For example, areas with game and wild plants would permit a hunter-gatherer lifestyle. Fertile land and available water encourage growing crops and settled communities. Dry areas with sparse vegetation might make nomadic herding the only option. Areas rich in mineral resources might encourage cultures based on mining and metal working crafts. Groups near bodies of water might be fishing cultures.

**2 Historical Factors** Migrations might affect cultural development. Migrants may displace, merge cultures with, impose their cultures on, or be absorbed by resident cultures. Immigrant groups might need to change lifestyles based on the geography of the new home. Wars and conquests might displace or destroy some cultures. The development of states with codes of law and enforcement might force changes in cultures that expand by conquest or gain livestock by raiding other groups. When people trade and interact, they may largely replace their own languages with a *lingua franca*.

Colonists might draw borders that split up cultural groups or kingdoms. They may outlaw certain cultural practices. They usually bring elements of their own culture that are forced upon or adopted by indigenous people.

## SECTION 2 • HISTORY
**How have conflict and government instability slowed economic development in sub-Saharan Africa?**

**Three Corner Activity: Economic Development** Adapt the Four-Corner strategy to a Three-Corner strategy to show how historical and geographic factors have affected economic development in the region. Tell students to pick the factor they think has the most influence on the region's economic development and explain why. See "Best Practices for Active Teaching" for a review of this strategy. `0:20` minutes

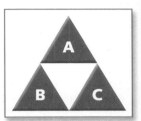

**A Physical Geography** How geographic factors might influence the type of economies that can develop and how events such as earthquakes, volcanic eruptions, drought, or flood can impact established economies

**B Historical Events** How historical events such as conquest, war, or increasing or decreasing demand for materials and products can affect economies

**C Colonialism** How colonialism can influence local economies

## ACTIVE OPTIONS

 **Interactive Map Tool**

**Examine Land Cover**

PURPOSE Make inferences about parts of Tanzania where the introductory photo could have been taken

**SET-UP**

1. Open the **Interactive Map Tool**, set the "Map Mode" to National Geographic, and set the "Region" to Africa. Zoom in on Tanzania.

2. Under "Environment and Society," turn on the Land Cover layer. Set the transparency level to 40 percent.

**ACTIVITY**

Point out Tanzania's political borders and compare them with boundaries of the land cover regions. Have students make inferences about parts of Tanzania where the photo could have been taken. *(in regions with shrubland or grassland)* Then have them point out areas where it was not taken. *(regions marked as woodland or cropland)* `0:10` minutes

# INTRODUCE CHAPTER VOCABULARY

**Around the World** Display the list of Key Vocabulary words for the chapter. Select a student "traveler," who moves and stands by a student in the next seat. The student in the seat becomes the challenger. Present a definition of one of the words. Whoever says the matching word first becomes the new traveler and stands by the student in the next seat. A traveler who keeps responding first and returns to his or her seat or finishes the list of vocabulary words has gone "around the world."

# 1.1 Africa's Borders and Cultures

TECHTREK
myNGconnect.com For a language map and photos of African culture

Maps and Graphs  Digital Library

**Main Idea** European powers created new colonial borders that ignored the existing borders of traditional African cultures.

Africa is a continent of diverse cultures and countries. Today, about two thirds of Africans live in rural villages that have varied customs and languages. About 1,000 languages are spoken in Africa by different **ethnic groups**, which are groups of people who share a common culture, language, and sometimes racial heritage. Many Africans identify themselves first as members of a tribe rather than a country.

## The Impact of Colonialism

Before Europeans arrived, borders between African cultural groups developed by agreement or conflict. Natural features such as oceans, lakes, mountain ranges, and rivers often defined borders. Natural borders were easier to control than borders set by groups of people. Borders along bodies of water also provided **transportation corridors**, or routes to easily move people and goods from place to place.

When Europeans colonized the continent, they routinely ignored the borders of African cultural groups. Instead, colonial borders were set to address the European need for resources. To do so, some sub-Saharan African cultural groups were divided, forced to share territory with rivals, or both.

As African countries began to gain independence in the 1900s, they did not change their colonial borders. As a result, few sub-Saharan African countries share one common culture.

## Conflict and Cooperation

Cultural differences across Africa have often led to civil wars over political control, territory, and resources. Somalia's ethnic groups, for example, have never united to form a single nation. Military dictatorships often have been necessary to impose order.

To address these challenges, African countries have developed organizations (see chart above) such as the **African Union** and the East African Community (EAC). These organizations promote cooperation and economic progress within and between countries.

### Before You Move On
**Summarize** How were colonial borders different from sub-Saharan Africa's traditional borders?

Colonial borders were based on needs for resources and for compromise with other colonial powers while sub-Saharan Africa's traditional borders were based on conflict, agreement, and natural features.

### COOPERATIVE INTERNATIONAL ORGANIZATIONS IN AFRICA

| Organization | Purpose |
|---|---|
| African Union | Peace-keeping; oppose colonization; promote unity; cooperate for economic development |
| Economic Community of West African States (ECOWAS) | Promote economy, industry, transportation, energy resources, agriculture, and natural resources |
| Southern African Development Community | Support local economy, transportation networks, and political interaction |
| Economic Community of Central African States (ECCAS) | Promote industry, transportation, communication, energy, natural resources, economy, tourism, education |
| East African Community (EAC) | Improve cooperation in transport and communication, industry, security, immigration, and economic matters |

### LANGUAGE FAMILIES IN SUB-SAHARAN AFRICA

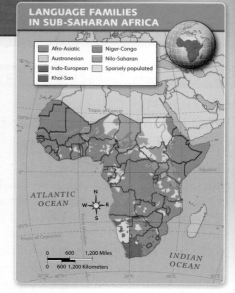

Afro-Asiatic
Austronesian
Indo-European
Khoi-San
Niger-Congo
Nilo-Saharan
Sparsely populated

ATLANTIC OCEAN
INDIAN OCEAN

0   600   1,200 Miles
0   600  1,200 Kilometers

### ONGOING ASSESSMENT
## MAP LAB
GeoJournal

1. **Interpret Maps** Locate country borders near areas with the Nilo-Saharan language group. What can you infer about the location of language groups and the borders that were created during colonization?

2. **Human-Environment Interaction** On the map, identify the oceans that surround Africa. How do natural features such as rivers, lakes, and oceans help countries control territory and methods of transportation?

3. **Make Generalizations** How did colonization lead to conflict between present-day cultures in Africa?

4. **Synthesize** What is one goal that is shared by the organizations shown in the chart?

> **Critical Viewing** Fishermen sun-dry fish caught in a lake near their village in Malawi. What can you infer about this fishing culture from the photo?

It is a rural culture as opposed to an urban culture.

---

## PLAN

### OBJECTIVE Understand the legacy of colonialism and the steps that Africa is taking to form stable countries.

### CRITICAL THINKING SKILLS FOR SECTION 1.1

- Main Idea
- Summarize
- Interpret Maps
- Make Generalizations
- Synthesize
- Analyze Cause and Effect
- Interpret Charts
- Analyze Visuals

### PRINT RESOURCES

*Teacher's Edition* Resource Bank

- Reading and Note-Taking: Analyze Cause and Effect
- Vocabulary Practice: Definition and Details
- **GeoActivity** Analyze Central Africa's Borders

TECHTREK myNGconnect.com

▶ **Fast Forward!**
**Core Content Presentations**
Teach *Africa's Borders and Cultures*

**Interactive Whiteboard**
**GeoActivity** Analyze Central Africa's Borders

**Digital Library**
NG Photo Gallery, Section 1

**Connect to NG**
Research Links

**Also Check Out**
- Charts & Infographics in **Teacher Resources**
- Online World Atlas in **Maps and Graphs**
- GeoJournal in **Student eEdition**

### BACKGROUND FOR THE TEACHER

Most scientists agree that modern humans first lived in Africa around 150,000 years ago and then evolved into the racial, ethnic, and cultural groups that now populate the world. The humans who remained in Africa also evolved into diverse groups. According to recent studies, Africans were further diversified by migrations of Asians back to Africa around 40,000 years ago.

### ESSENTIAL QUESTION

**What historical and geographic factors have influenced the cultures of sub-Saharan Africa?**

Africa's country borders resulted from European powers' division of Africa. Section 1.1 explains the problems caused by borders set during the colonial period and describes cooperative African agencies.

# INTRODUCE & ENGAGE

**Develop a Plan** Have students work in groups. Provide each group with a political map of North America. Explain that, like African countries, North American countries were once colonies. Have students imagine the colonial powers drawing the borders of the North American mainland. Central American borders will not change, but the United States, Canada, and Mexico will become five colonies.

Have students plan how North America should be divided and what factors to take into account. For example, should the continent be divided by language or ethnic groups? Where should the borders be? Have a representative from each group explain how their group would divide the continent. Explain that Africans were not given a voice when their political borders were drawn. `0:30` minutes

# TEACH  Digital Library

## Guided Discussion

1. **Analyze Cause and Effect** How did the colonial legacy affect the cultural characteristics of African countries? *(It made the countries multicultural by bringing together different cultural and language groups within each country.)*

2. **Summarize** Why did the establishment of colonial borders bring about conflict among African groups? *(Colonial borders were established with no recognition of traditional borders, so groups fought over territory.)*

3. **Interpret Charts** Which cooperative international organization in Africa might be called on to send troops to an area where civil war has broken out? How do you know? *(the African Union; peace-keeping is listed as one of its goals)*

**Analyze Visuals** Using the **NG Photo Gallery,** project photos of children boating to school in Botswana and the Zulu hut in South Africa. Ask students what they can tell from the clothing of the students in the photo. Tell them to use the text and the photos to fill out a chart similar to the one below with their observations and inferences. Point out the different physical features and clues to culture, and elicit the conclusion that *where* people live partly determines their culture and how they live. `0:20` minutes

| OBSERVATION | INFERENCE |
|---|---|
| Students are dressed alike. | They wear school uniforms. |
| Huts seem traditional, as though Zulu have built them for years. | These Zulu villagers have preserved at least some established Zulu traditions. |

# DIFFERENTIATE

**English Language Learners** **Teach Word Parts** Point out the words *colony* and *colonial.* Then explain that the suffix *-al* means "relating to or having to do with," as in the words *global* and *governmental.* Tell students that when a suffix is added to a word that ends in *y,* the *y* is changed to *i.* Explain also that when a suffix is added to a word that ends in *e,* the final *e* is often dropped.

**Gifted & Talented** **Explore Ethnic Cultures** Use the Gifted & Talented Strategy 1. Have students research a different indigenous ethnic group from the one they researched before. Suggest that they use a graphic organizer to compare and contrast the two groups they have researched.

# ACTIVE OPTIONS

 **Interactive Whiteboard**
## GeoActivity

**Analyze Central Africa's Borders** Have students analyze the map showing the territories of Central Africa's cultural groups before colonialism and compare those territories with today's political borders. Have them identify groups that are split by political borders. Help students draw conclusions about the impact of European-created borders across various ethnic regions. Guide them to understand that political borders do not always reflect ethnic borders and can therefore lead to cultural conflicts within the political borders. `0:15` minutes

 ## On Your Feet

**Fishbowl** Have students form an inner and outer circle, both facing the center. Use a Fishbowl strategy to have them pose questions and take notes about sub-Saharan Africa's borders. Then have students switch places to pose questions and take notes about the region's cultures. `0:20` minutes

## On Your Feet

**Role-Play** Have students work in pairs and assume the roles of a colonist and an African leader at the time colonial borders were being drawn. The colonist will explain why Europeans want to draw borders and the leader will explain what is wrong with the borders they are drawing. Encourage them to find evidence in the text to help support their arguments. Call on volunteers to role-play their rehearsed discussions in front of the class. `0:25` minutes

## ANSWERS

1. The location of language groups was not considered when colonial borders were created.
2. Atlantic and Indian. Natural water features help countries control their territory by providing clear, sometimes difficult to cross, borders, and they provide a natural method of transportation.
3. The new borders that colonial powers created forced cultural groups to share territory with rivals. The tensions created are still felt today and lead to conflict between contemporary African cultures.
4. One common goal is to promote economic development in various ways.

## 1.2 African Music Goes Global

**TECHTREK**
myNGconnect.com For audio clips of African music and photos of musicians

Digital Library    Magazine Maker

**Main Idea** African music connects the people to their past and communicates their cultures to the world.

Music has always been a way for Africans to celebrate their cultures. Today, African music has become part of many cultures. Experts link African music to the development of jazz, blues, rock-and-roll, and gospel in the United States.

### A Wealth of Music

Each area of sub-Saharan Africa has distinctive music that reaches a wide range of audiences. Advancements in communication and transportation have helped to spread African music.

West African music is influenced by the stories and music of griots. **Griots** (GREE oh) are traditional storytellers. For centuries, they orally passed on the histories of West African cultures. Because they were not written down, these histories are part of the **oral tradition**, the practice of orally passing stories from one generation to the next.

Griots accompany their songs with harps, lutes, and drums. Their influence is **evident**, or clearly present, in West African music today.

Much West African music is a fusion, or blend, of griot music and other African music with global music. Mbalax (uhm BALAKS), for example, is a blend of griot percussion and songs with Afro-Cuban influences. **Youssou N'Dour** is a contemporary griot who plays mbalax music. His popularity has helped spread the music out of West Africa to audiences around the world.

In South Africa, music sometimes focused on politics. One example is protest music. Miriam Makeba and a number of other South African musicians left South Africa to protest government policies in the 1970s and 1980s—gaining global audiences for their music.

### Before You Move On

**Summarize** What are some examples of how African music connects the people to their past and communicates their culture to the world?

African music often directly tells the history of a people, and its popular forms carry that deep cultural connection to the world.

South African singer Lira performs in Soweto, South Africa.

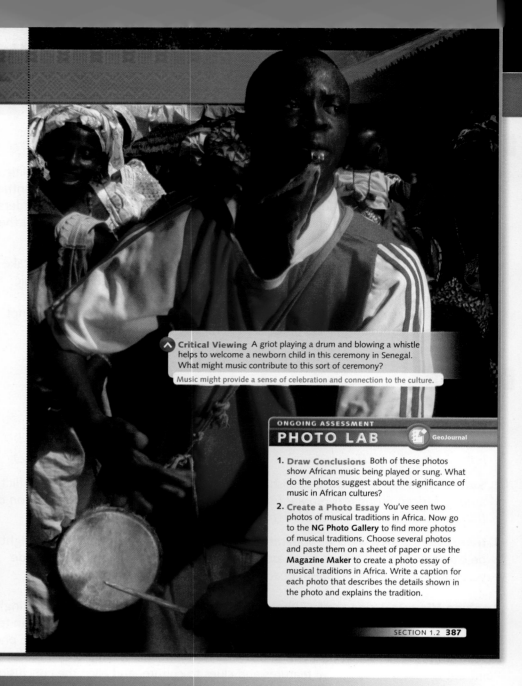

**Critical Viewing** A griot playing a drum and blowing a whistle helps to welcome a newborn child in this ceremony in Senegal. What might music contribute to this sort of ceremony?

Music might provide a sense of celebration and connection to the culture.

**ONGOING ASSESSMENT**

## PHOTO LAB    GeoJournal

1. **Draw Conclusions** Both of these photos show African music being played or sung. What do the photos suggest about the significance of music in African cultures?

2. **Create a Photo Essay** You've seen two photos of musical traditions in Africa. Now go to the **NG Photo Gallery** to find more photos of musical traditions. Choose several photos and paste them on a sheet of paper or use the **Magazine Maker** to create a photo essay of musical traditions in Africa. Write a caption for each photo that describes the details shown in the photo and explains the tradition.

---

## PLAN

**OBJECTIVE** Examine the role of music in Africa's cultures and its influence around the world.

### CRITICAL THINKING SKILLS FOR SECTION 1.2

- Main Idea
- Summarize
- Draw Conclusions
- Analyze Cause and Effect
- Describe
- Analyze Visuals

### PRINT RESOURCES

*Teacher's Edition* Resource Bank

- Reading and Note-Taking: Summarize Information
- Vocabulary Practice: Venn Diagram
- **GeoActivity** Solve a Puzzle About African Music

**TECHTREK**    myNGconnect.com

**Fast Forward!**
**Core Content Presentations**
Teach *African Music Goes Global*

**Digital Library**
- Music Clip, Section 1
- NG Photo Gallery, Section 1

**Magazine Maker**

**Connect to NG**
Research Links

**Interactive Whiteboard**
**GeoActivity** Solve a Puzzle About African Music

**Also Check Out**
GeoJournal in **Student eEdition**

### BACKGROUND FOR THE TEACHER

One influence on Mbalax was rumba, which is music that evolved in Central Africa and East Africa. Most Africans brought to Cuba during the slave trade came from the Congo. These slaves are believed to have carried a Congolese dance and its rhythms and songs to the Americas. When a Cuban rumba craze hit Africa in the 20th century, Congolese musicians recognized it as a descendent of a local dance. A new Congolese rumba evolved and swept across Africa.

### ESSENTIAL QUESTION

**What historical and geographic factors have influenced the cultures of sub-Saharan Africa?**

Music has been a major influence on the cultures of sub-Saharan Africa. Section 1.2 describes some of Africa's cultural traditions and related musical styles.

# INTRODUCE & ENGAGE  Digital Library

**Name That Tune** Play the **Music Clip** of African music. Ask students to describe the music. Then ask them if they can identify specific elements in these samples that they have heard in other musical styles such as rock-and-roll or jazz.

**Activate Prior Knowledge** Have students work in groups and discuss their responses to the music samples, as well as their previous associations with African music. Using the **NG Photo Gallery,** project photos of Youssou N'Dour and Miriam Makeba. Invite students to share their knowledge of or reactions to either musician. Ask them to discuss their knowledge or ideas about the influence of African music on American music. Call on volunteers from each group to report on the discussion for their group. **0:20** minutes

# TEACH  Digital Library

## Guided Discussion

**1. Analyze Cause and Effect** How can transportation influence cultural change such as the spread of musical styles? *(When people travel faster and more easily, musicians can travel globally. People can visit other countries and be exposed to different music.)*

**2. Describe** What is Mbalax? *(a blend of griot percussion and songs with Afro-Cuban and Haitian influences)*

**Analyze Visuals** Using the **NG Photo Gallery,** project the photo of the griot woman posing with the kora instrument. Ask students how griot music has influenced cultures in Africa and globally. *(Griot music is played all over the world and has also been incorporated into other musical forms.)* Have students discuss the Before You Move On question, and then ask how West African culture influenced griot music. *(The lack of a written language and the tradition of oral histories and storytelling led to the emergence of griots and the development of griot music.)* **0:20** minutes

# DIFFERENTIATE

**Striving Readers  Use Sentence Starters** Provide these sentence starters for students to complete after reading:

- The job of a griot is _____.
- One example of a blend between griot music and Afro-Cuban influences is _____.

**English Language Learners  Understand Sequence** Tell students to use the text, the visuals, and the discussion above to create a Sequence Diagram showing how West African oral traditions gradually became a part of popular music in other parts of the world.

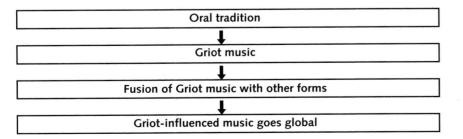

Oral tradition → Griot music → Fusion of Griot music with other forms → Griot-influenced music goes global

# ACTIVE OPTIONS

 **Interactive Whiteboard**
## GeoActivity

**Solve a Puzzle About African Music** To review and reinforce key terms and concepts, project a copy of the crossword puzzle and provide students with a copy. Have students work in pairs to solve the puzzle. When pairs have finished, call on volunteers to supply words for the projected puzzle. **0:15** minutes

 ## On Your Feet

**Team Up** Have students work in small groups to complete the photo essay in the Photo Lab. Students can research photos individually, and then the group selects the photos for the essay. Have members paste the photos up or use the **Magazine Maker.** Use the Round Table strategy to have students take turns writing captions for the photo essay. Then display the photo essays so that each student can view them. **0:20** minutes

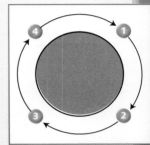

 ## On Your Feet

**Africa's Musical Influences** Post a sign in each corner of the classroom—one for each bullet point below. Have students form four groups according to the posted signs, and ask them to use the **Research Links** to learn more about the influence of African music on:

- American jazz
- Rock-and-roll
- Blues
- Gospel

**ASK:** How did African music contribute to the development of each type of American music? Ask each group to prepare a two-minute presentation of their findings for the rest of the class. **0:15** minutes

---

ONGOING ASSESSMENT
# PHOTO LAB  GeoJournal

## ANSWERS
1. African music is a big part of African culture.
2. Photo essays should include several photos of African musical traditions and a caption for each photo that explains the tradition and how it is a part of modern life.

## 1.3 Kenya Modernizes

TECHTREK
myNGconnect.com For an online
map and photos of Kenya

Maps and Graphs    Digital Library

**Main Idea** Kenya is modernizing its economy and improving its standard of living.

Kenya's geographic features range from beaches, savannas, deserts, and farmland to snow-capped mountains such as Mount Kenya, for which the country is named. Large mammals such as the African elephant, giraffes, and lions roam Kenya's **reserves**, land set aside for the protection of animals. The diverse geography and wildlife are key to Kenya's economic future.

### Cultural Diversity

You can hear many languages and see an array of traditional clothing on a busy street in **Nairobi** (ny ROE bee), Kenya's capital. More than 40 ethnic groups live in Kenya. The largest are the Kikuyu (ki KOO yoo), Luhya, Luo, Kalenjin, and Kamba. This diversity makes Kenya a multicultural society.

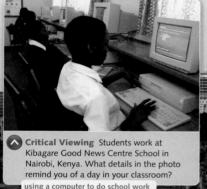
**Critical Viewing** Students work at Kibagare Good News Centre School in Nairobi, Kenya. What details in the photo remind you of a day in your classroom?
using a computer to do school work

As you've learned, cultural diversity has sometimes led to rivalry and conflict in Africa. Even so, diverse groups have been able to work toward common goals.

For example, the people of Kenya united in their struggle for independence from British rule. After independence in 1963, **Jomo Kenyatta**, a Kikuyu, became Kenya's first elected leader. To help all Kenyans pull together, he appointed members from different ethnic groups as his advisors.

### Modernization

Kenyatta and other leaders encouraged **domestic policies**, or government plans within a country, that led to economic growth and modernization. **Modernization** is the development of policies and actions designed to bring a country up to world standards in technology and other areas.

Education is an important factor in modernization for Kenya. Most children there attend free elementary schools. The adult **literacy rate**, or percentage of people who can read, soared from 32 percent in 1970 to 85 percent in 2003.

Nairobi, Kenya

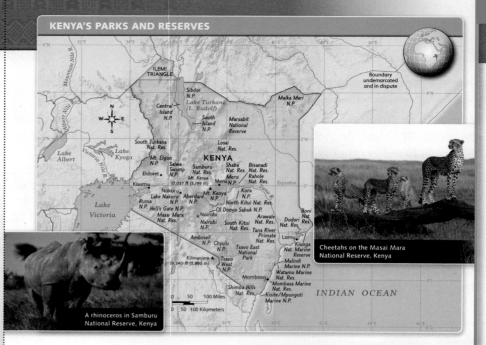
KENYA'S PARKS AND RESERVES

A rhinoceros in Samburu National Reserve, Kenya

Cheetahs on the Masai Mara National Reserve, Kenya

INDIAN OCEAN

Kenya's modernization is also evident in its growing tourist industry. The scenic beauty and unique wildlife found in Kenya's national parks and reserves attracts tourists. The government is determined to protect the parks and reserves because of the jobs and money they bring into the country.

In 2000, Kenya, Uganda and Tanzania formed the East African Community in order to improve trade and industry in the region. These efforts to expand the economy should further improve the standard of living for Kenya's citizens.

**Before You Move On**
**Summarize** What steps has Kenya taken to modernize? economic and domestic policies; improving the literacy rate; promoting tourism

### ONGOING ASSESSMENT

## MAP LAB
GeoJournal

1. **Interpret Maps** What does the number of national parks and reserves shown on the map indicate about their importance in Kenya?

2. **Place** In what ways are the national parks and reserves shown on the map part of the economic modernization of Kenya?

3. **Form and Support Opinions** What makes Kenya diverse? Explain an advantage or disadvantage of diversity in Kenya. Support your opinion with details from the map and from what you have read about Kenya.

4. **Turn and Talk** Think about Jomo Kenyatta's decision to include different ethnic groups in his council. Talk to a partner and discuss effective ways of bringing people together.

---

## PLAN

**OBJECTIVE** Analyze the challenges Kenya has faced and the progress it has made.

### CRITICAL THINKING SKILLS FOR SECTION 1.3

- Main Idea
- Summarize
- Interpret Maps
- Form and Support Opinions
- Make Predictions
- Monitor Comprehension
- Evaluate
- Identify and Explain
- Analyze Visuals

### PRINT RESOURCES

*Teacher's Edition* Resource Bank

- Reading and Note-Taking: Identify Goals and Outcomes
- Vocabulary Practice: Definition Clues
- **GeoActivity** Graph Kenya's Economic Indicators

### TECHTREK    myNGconnect.com

>> Fast Forward!
**Core Content Presentations**
Teach *Kenya Modernizes*

**Digital Library**
NG Photo Gallery, Section 1

**Connect to NG**
Research Links

**Maps and Graphs**
**Interactive Map Tool**
Analyze Patterns of Population

**Also Check Out**
- Online World Atlas in **Maps and Graphs**
- Graphic Organizers in **Teacher Resources**
- GeoJournal in **Student eEdition**

### BACKGROUND FOR THE TEACHER

Lacking mineral resources, Kenya's economy has relied on agricultural products as exports. Unlike many African countries, Kenya has good roads and railways connecting agricultural areas to coastal ports. Agriculture, however, has been devastated at times by droughts and floods. In addition, population growth has led to unemployment, housing shortages, an overloaded education system, and challenges in feeding Kenya's people.

### ESSENTIAL QUESTION

**What historical and geographic factors have influenced the cultures of sub-Saharan Africa?**

In struggling to modernize, Kenya has had to overcome a number of factors. Section 1.3 describes both the challenges Kenya faces and its progress in modernizing.

## INTRODUCE & ENGAGE  Digital Library

**Make Predictions** Have students study the photos and maps in the lesson. **ASK:** Based on the photos and the map, what are some characteristics of Kenya? Record students' responses on an Idea Web such as the one shown. After students have read the lesson, revisit the Idea Web and add to it or correct any misconceptions students may have had.

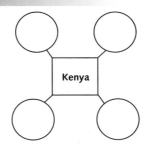

**0:10 minutes**

## TEACH  Digital Library

### Guided Discussion

1. **Monitor Comprehension** Give an example of cooperation among Kenya's cultures that occurred before independence. *(Different cultural groups united to work for independence from British rule.)*

2. **Evaluate** In what way does Kenya's literacy rate demonstrate modernization since independence? *(The literacy rate increased by nearly 50 percent from 1970 to 2003. This increase demonstrates a commitment to educating all Kenyans and improving the overall standard of living in the country.)*

3. **Identify and Explain** What is a reserve, and how does it affect Kenya's economy? *(A reserve is land set aside for protected animals. Reserves provide jobs for people and attract tourists.)*

**Analyze Visuals** Show the photo of students in school and the photo of Nairobi in the **NG Photo Gallery. ASK:** How do the students in the school seem to feel about being there? *(They are serious and attentive.)* What evidence of modernization in Kenya can be seen in the photo? *(Students are wearing modern western clothing. There are skyscrapers and parks and roads.)* **0:15 minutes**

## DIFFERENTIATE  Connect to NG

**Inclusion** **Analyze Visuals** Provide questions to help students describe the photographs in the text. For example, what is the room shown in the picture? Who are the people sitting at the desks? What are they doing? What do you notice about the students? What do you notice about their clothing?

**Pre-AP Research Tourism Statistics** Have students use the **Research Links** to research tourism in Kenya for the past ten years. Ask them to create a graph showing the number of tourists to Kenya for each year. In addition, students should write a description of the most common types of tourism in Kenya. Finally, have them write an analysis of factors that affect tourism as supported by the statistics in their graphs and their research.

## ACTIVE OPTIONS

 **Interactive Map Tool**

### Analyze Patterns of Population

**PURPOSE** Understand patterns of population density in Kenya

**SET-UP**

1. Open the **Interactive Map Tool,** set the "Map Mode" to National Geographic, and zoom in on Kenya and its neighbors.

2. Under "Human Systems—Populations & Culture," turn on the Population Density layer. Move the transparency slider back and forth to alternately show and hide the population density.

**ACTIVITY**

1. Tell students that population growth has created problems in Kenya.

2. Ask how Kenya's population density compares to other countries in East Africa. *(Parts of it are more densely populated than much of East Africa.)*

3. Have students point out areas on the population density layer that are very dark. *(areas near Lake Victoria and the coastal ports)*

4. What problems might result from dense population in these areas? *(deforestation, threats to wildlife habitats, overcrowding in cities)* **0:15 minutes**

### On Your Feet

**Numbered Heads** Have students form groups of four and number off within each group. Assign Map Lab Question 3. Have students write down the facts from the text and their prior knowledge that form the basis of their responses. Then call a number and the student from each group with that number reports for the group. **0:10 minutes**

**ONGOING ASSESSMENT**
## MAP LAB  GeoJournal

### ANSWERS

1. that they are very important in Kenya
2. The parks and reserves encourage tourism, which in turn generates income for Kenya.
3. Responses will vary. The large number of ethnic groups in Kenya provides diversity. Advantages of diversity might be cultural richness and multiple viewpoints. A disadvantage might be conflict.
4. Discussions will vary. Encourage students to think about their answers to Question 3 during their discussions.

SECTION 1 GEOGRAPHY

## NATIONAL GEOGRAPHIC

TECHTREK
myNGconnect.com For photos of Explorers at work and an Explorer Video Clip

Digital Library

Exploring
# Traditional Cultures
with Grace Gobbo and Wade Davis

**Main Idea** Preserving indigenous cultures and traditional ways of life benefits modern societies around the world.

### Cures in the Forest

When Emerging Explorer Grace Gobbo walks through a Tanzanian rain forest, she sees more than trees, flowers, and vines. She sees possible cures. As an **ethnobotanist**, she studies the relationship between cultures and plants.

Tanzanians have relied on traditional healers for centuries. Gobbo interviewed more than 80 traditional healers who rely on **medicinal plants**, or plants used to treat illnesses. Scientific research has confirmed that many of the plants these healers use do help treat illnesses. In fact, large drug companies are now using the same plants in many medicines.

However, many of the forests where these plants grow are at risk from logging and clear-cut farming. By teaching the value of medicinal plants, Gobbo hopes to inspire people to preserve their forests and maintain their traditional healing methods. "Nothing was written down," she explains. "The knowledge is literally dying out with the elders."

myNGconnect.com
For more on Grace Gobbo and Wade Davis in the field today

### AFRICAN PLANTS AND USES

| Plant Latin name | Location | Medicinal Use |
|---|---|---|
| Tulbaghia violacea | Southern Africa | lowers blood pressure |
| Catharanthus roseus | Madagascar | treats rheumatism (joint or muscle disorder) |
| Peltophorum africanum | Southern Africa | relieves stomach problems |
| Strychnos madagascariensis | Southern Africa | relieves stomach problems |
| Harpagophytum procumbens | Southern Africa and Madagascar | reduces swelling |
| Sutherlandia frutescens | Southern Africa | treats cancer |
| Agapanthus praecox | Southern Africa | treats heart disease and chest pain |

### Preserving Culture

Like Gobbo, National Geographic Explorer-in-Residence Wade Davis is an ethnobotanist who has studied the use of native plants around the world. His current focus, however, is indigenous cultures around the globe—the customs and practices of people in their daily lives. Davis has lived among 15 cultural groups in the Americas, Asia, Africa, and the Arctic.

Davis has proposed that there is a cultural web of life, just as there is a biological connection between all forms of life. He believes that every culture is connected and that all indigenous cultures have contributed to the cultural web. Davis hopes to preserve this cultural diversity, just as Gobbo works to protect medicinal plants and knowledge of traditional healing in Tanzania.

Davis believes that the development of modern industry and technology has contributed to a decline in the number of indigenous cultures. As a result, the entire cultural web suffers from the loss of each culture. Davis further believes that, like the world's plants and animals, human cultures should be protected so that they can continue to contribute to humanity.

### Before You Move On
**Monitor Comprehension** Why are Gobbo and Davis working to preserve traditional cultures?
in order to preserve knowledge and cultural contributions that may otherwise be lost

ONGOING ASSESSMENT
## VIEWING LAB
  GeoJournal

1. **Analyze Visuals** Go to the **Digital Library** to watch the Explorer Video Clip of Wade Davis. How are his contributions similar to and different from those of Grace Gobbo?

2. **Summarize** According to Wade Davis, why is preserving indigenous cultures important for humanity?

3. **Make Predictions** What image or idea from the video clip was most surprising to you? Write down two questions you still have.

National Geographic Explorer-in-Residence Wade Davis

---

# PLAN

### OBJECTIVE Understand the scientific value of traditional healing methods and the need to preserve traditional cultures.

### CRITICAL THINKING SKILLS FOR SECTION 1.4

- Main Idea
- Monitor Comprehension
- Analyze Visuals
- Summarize
- Make Predictions
- Analyze Primary Sources
- Analyze Cause and Effect

### PRINT RESOURCES

*Teacher's Edition* Resource Bank

- Reading and Note-Taking: Make Generalizations
- Vocabulary Practice: Vocabulary T-Chart
- **GeoActivity** Research Vanishing Cultures

  **TECHTREK** myNGconnect.com

>> Fast Forward!
**Core Content Presentations**
Teach *Exploring Traditional Cultures*

**Digital Library**
Explorer Video Clips: Grace Gobbo and Wade Davis

**Connect to NG**
Research Links

**Maps and Graphs**
**Interactive Map Tool**
Analyze Land Use

Also Check Out
- Charts & Infographics in **Teacher Resources**
- NG Photo Gallery in **Digital Library**
- GeoJournal in **Student eEdition**

### BACKGROUND FOR THE TEACHER

Today, many Tanzanians, including 80 percent of people in rural villages, still rely on traditional healers and medicinal plants. They follow a long-established tradition. Medical centers are few and located at a distance from many villages. Often they are not well-stocked with basic medicines. In addition, some medications are costly. By contrast, traditional healers are everywhere, and the surrounding forest offers about 10,000 species of diverse plants used for medicine.

### ESSENTIAL QUESTION

### What historical and geographic factors have influenced the cultures of sub-Saharan Africa?

Traditional cultures in Africa have used local cures for thousands of years, and scientists are studying the value and effectiveness of those cures. Section 1.4 describes the work of ethnobotanists.

## INTRODUCE & ENGAGE  Digital Library

**Explorer Video Clips** Show the video clips on Grace Gobbo and Wade Davis. **ASK:** What did you find to be the most interesting parts of the video clips? Explain your reactions. *(Responses will vary.)*

**Activate Prior Knowledge** Call attention to the chart of plants and their uses. Ask students what they know about herbs or plant parts used in common medications, such as senna and echinacea. Then record on a chart the herbs with which they are familiar and how they are used. You might wish to display ads for a number of commercial remedies that contain plant parts and herbal remedies. Tell students that plants have been used by traditional healers for thousands of years, and drug companies have begun to add medicinal plants to their medicines. `0:15` minutes

| Plant or Herb | Uses |
|---|---|
|  |  |

## TEACH

### Guided Discussion

1. **Analyze Primary Sources** In the last paragraph on the left-hand page, which of Gobbo's words explain and support her statement that, "The knowledge is literally dying out with the elders." *(Gobbo explained and supported this by also saying, "Nothing was written down.")*

2. **Analyze Cause and Effect** In what ways might the development of modern industry and technology have contributed to a decline in the number of indigenous cultures? *(Possible response: As people learn about and adopt modern ways of life, they stop following and forget about traditional ways of life.)*

### MORE INFORMATION

**Valuable Plants** The daughter of a medical doctor, Grace Gobbo did not believe that traditional medicinal plants worked until she saw the laboratory evidence. In fact, about 25 percent of the prescriptions in the United States are for drugs with active ingredients taken from plants. Today, at least 120 substances extracted or derived from plants are used as drugs in some countries. For example, the heart medications Digitalin, Digitoxin, and Digoxin have been made from the plant *Digitalis purpurea*. The motion-sickness drug Scopolamine has been made from *Datura* plants.

Digitalis purpurea

## DIFFERENTIATE

**English Language Learners Create an Oral History** Ask students to think of one tradition in their family or in their local community that they would like to see preserved for future generations. Pair each student with a proficient speaker and have the proficient speaker listen as the student explains the tradition and why it is so important to him or her. The proficient speaker should ask questions to clarify meaning and correct any errors in grammar or usage.

## ACTIVE OPTIONS

### Interactive Map Tool

**Analyze Land Use**

**PURPOSE** Predict where medicinal plants may grow

**SET-UP**

1. Open the **Interactive Map Tool** and set the "Map Mode" to Topographic.

2. Under "Environment and Society," turn on the Land Cover layer. Adjust the transparency so that both the land cover regions and political borders are visible. Then zoom in on Tanzania.

**ACTIVITY** Have students examine the land cover within Tanzania. **ASK:** In which parts of Tanzania are medicinal plants most likely to grow? *(the parts with forests or woodlands)* Have students note that Tanzania is close to the equator. Then switch to the Climate Zones layer under "Physical Systems—Climate." Help students relate the growth of rain forests and rain forest plants to warm, humid areas. `0:20` minutes

### On Your Feet

**Think, Pair, Share** Have students use the Think, Pair, Share strategy to discuss the Before You Move On question. Then have them switch partners and share their answers. Finally, allow them to share their answers with the class. See "Best Practices for Active Teaching" for a review of this strategy. `0:15` minutes

### Performance Assessment

**Create a Visual Aid** Have students create a Cause-and-Effect diagram showing the effects of colonialism and the slave trade on African music, Kenya's economy, and Africa's indigenous cultures. Students should draw on information in Section 1 but may also use the **Research Links** for information. Go to **myNGconnect.com** for the rubric.

### ONGOING ASSESSMENT

## VIEWING LAB  GeoJournal

### ANSWERS

1. Davis's contributions are similar to Gobbo's in that he is trying to preserve cultures, but different in that his focus is preserving and recognizing human contributions to culture.

2. The loss of any culture is a loss for all of humanity, so the preservation of all cultures benefits everyone.

3. Responses will vary.

# 2.1 Prizes Mineral Resources

TECHTREK
myNGconnect.com For an online map
and photos of mining in sub-Saharan Africa

Maps and Graphs    Digital Library

**Main Idea** Sub-Saharan Africa has mineral resources that could improve life for its people.

The mineral resources of sub-Saharan Africa have the potential to lift the economies of sub-Saharan countries. However, careful management is needed to maximize benefits for the African people.

## Mineral Riches

Sub-Saharan Africa has large deposits of gold, diamonds, and other **minerals**, which are inorganic solid substances formed through geological processes. Many of these minerals are exported to Europe, North America, and Asia where they are used to make automotive and electronic products.

Many sub-Saharan countries use mineral resources as **commodities**, which are materials or goods that can be bought, sold, or traded. These commodities can bring in enormous wealth, but economic progress has been slow. Over time, government corruption has taken much of the profits from mineral mining.

### SELECTED OIL AND DIAMOND EXPORTS SUB-SAHARAN AFRICA, 2005–2006

| Oil | | |
|---|---|---|
| Country | World Rank | Percentage of Country's Total Exports |
| Nigeria | 6 | 91.9 |
| Angola | 12 | 96.6 |
| Equatorial Guinea | 21 | 92.7 |
| Democratic Republic of the Congo | 22 | 89.6 |
| Sudan | 29 | 88.0 |
| Chad | 37 | 94.6 |

| Diamonds | | |
|---|---|---|
| Country | World Rank | Percentage of Country's Total Exports |
| South Africa | 5 | 6.9 |
| Botswana | 9 | 83.5 |
| Namibia | 14 | 43.5 |
| Angola | 16 | 2.4 |
| Democratic Republic of the Congo | 17 | 41.5 |
| Central African Republic | 32 | 36.8 |

**Source:** The World Bank

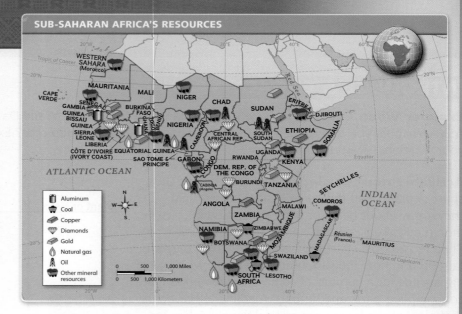

### SUB-SAHARAN AFRICA'S RESOURCES

Aluminum
Coal
Copper
Diamonds
Gold
Natural gas
Oil
Other mineral resources

> **Critical Viewing** Gold miners dig in the Chudja mine near the village of Kobu in northeastern Congo. What does the photo suggest about working conditions in the mines? Working conditions are dirty and possibly dangerous.

## Economic Improvement

Today, unstable governments continue to challenge many sub-Saharan countries. For example, the Central African Republic has significant diamond resources as the chart shows, but a lack of infrastructure, smuggling, and political unrest have limited the development of its diamond mining industry. As a result, the country remains one of the poorest in the world.

Some countries such as South Africa, Namibia, and Tanzania have successfully used their mineral profits to build their economies. In Botswana, the government is a partner in the country's largest diamond mining company. It has invested the profits in education, infrastructure, and health care. Countries with resources

Mineral resources in sub-Saharan African countries improve life for people by providing money that can be invested in the country.

that follow Botswana's example can improve the stability of their economies and improve the lives of their citizens.

### Before You Move On
**Monitor Comprehension** In what ways do sub-Saharan countries' mineral resources improve life for their people?

**ONGOING ASSESSMENT**

## MAP LAB
GeoJournal

1. **Place** Based on the map, what mineral resources can be found in Tanzania?

2. **Compare and Contrast** Pick two countries on the map and compare their resources. What can you infer about their economies based on their resources?

3. **Interpret Charts** Based on the chart, what would happen to Angola's economy if its oil exports were disrupted?

---

# PLAN

## OBJECTIVE Learn about the mineral resources of Sub-Saharan Africa, their economic potential, and the challenges in extracting them.

### CRITICAL THINKING SKILLS FOR SECTION 2.1

- Main Idea
- Monitor Comprehension
- Compare and Contrast
- Interpret Charts
- Categorize
- Identify
- Interpret Maps

## PRINT RESOURCES

*Teacher's Edition* Resource Bank

- Reading and Note-Taking: Outline and Take Notes
- Vocabulary Practice: Word Map
- **GeoActivity** Evaluate Diamond Practices

### TECHTREK myNGconnect.com

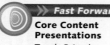

**Fast Forward!**
**Core Content Presentations**
Teach *Prized Mineral Resources*

**Teacher Resources**
Chart: Selected Oil and Diamond Exports

**Connect to NG**
Research Links

**Maps and Graphs**
- **Interactive Map Tool** Analyze the Human Footprint in Sub-Saharan Africa
- Online World Atlas: Sub-Saharan Africa's Resources

**Also Check Out**
- NG Photo Gallery in **Digital Library**
- GeoJournal in **Student eEdition**

## BACKGROUND FOR THE TEACHER

In 2010, soaring prices for gold prompted mine owners to dig even deeper into the earth, making working conditions that much more dangerous. Working conditions and compensation for mine workers vary greatly across Africa. For example, in South Africa, unionized mine workers have some protection and guarantees. Contract workers do not enjoy these benefits, even in South Africa. Abuses are greatest in Sierra Leone, where children have been widely exploited as diamond mine workers.

## ESSENTIAL QUESTION

### How have conflict and government instability slowed economic development in sub-Saharan Africa?

Section 1.5 describes minerals, their distribution, and the challenges and successes in using mineral resources to raise the standard of living for Africans.

# INTRODUCE & ENGAGE  Teacher Resources

**Preview by Analyzing Charts** Tell students that in this lesson they will learn about the importance of sub-Saharan Africa's mineral resources. One way to gauge how dependent a country might be on its mineral resources is to analyze its exports. Project the chart Selected Oil and Diamond Exports, Sub-Saharan Africa, 2005–2006 from **Charts & Infographics** or direct students' attention to the chart in their textbook. **ASK:** What percentage of Chad's total exports is based on oil? *(94.6 percent)* What percentage of Botswana's total exports is based on diamonds? *(83.5 percent)* After reading, discuss how Botswana has managed its dependence on diamonds.

`0:15` minutes

# TEACH  Maps and Graphs

## Guided Discussion

1. **Categorize** Is wood a mineral? Explain your response. *(No. A mineral is a nonliving thing found in nature. Wood comes from a living tree.)*

2. **Identify** What are commodities? *(materials or goods that can be bought, sold, or traded)* Why would commodities be important to the economies of sub-Saharan African countries? *(These countries need to build their economies, and having goods that can be traded globally is an important step toward that goal.)*

3. **Interpret Charts** Based on the chart, which countries are rich in both oil and diamonds? *(Angola and Democratic Republic of the Congo)*

**Interpret Maps** Show the Sub-Saharan Africa's Resources map from the **Online World Atlas.** Direct students' attention to the map legend, which identifies the different types of mineral resources with a unique icon on the map. Call on a volunteer to identify the most common resource shown on the map. *(other mineral resources)* **ASK:** What can you infer from the fact there are so many other mineral resources on the map? *(that sub-Saharan Africa has a variety of mineral resources beyond diamonds and gold)* `0:20` minutes

# DIFFERENTIATE  Connect to NG

**English Language Learners** **True and False** Have students work in pairs to review the text and decide if the following statements are true or false:

- Minerals are inorganic, or nonliving, substances. *(true)*
- Minerals such as gold and diamonds are not very valuable. *(false)*
- Countries with large reserves of minerals are always wealthy. *(false)*
- Botswana has managed its mineral resources effectively. *(true)*

**Gifted & Talented** **Research Products** Have students choose a mineral mined in Africa and use the **Research Links** to learn about its uses and products made from it. Have them write a report of their findings. Their reports should include information about the properties of the mineral that make it suitable for its uses, such as the hardness of diamonds, the flexibility and conductivity of copper, or the light weight of aluminum. Encourage students to find photos or drawings to illustrate their reports. Make the reports available for other students to read.

# ACTIVE OPTIONS

## Interactive Map Tool

### Analyze the Human Footprint in Sub-Saharan Africa

**PURPOSE** Understand the environmental impact of mining

**SET-UP**

1. Open the **Interactive Map Tool** and set the "Map Mode" to National Geographic.

2. Under "Environment and Society," turn on the Human Footprint layer. Adjust the transparency so that both the human footprint and the political borders are visible. Then zoom in on sub-Saharan Africa.

**ACTIVITY** Refer students to the map of mineral resources in their textbook. Have them compare the locations of the mineral resources with the locations of the heaviest human footprints shown on the map. Have students discuss whether or not they see a connection between mining and the human footprint. **ASK:** Why might the human footprint be heavier in areas near mines? *(Mining tears up the earth and pollutes the land, air, and water. Sometimes settlements grow up near mines to house workers or process mined materials. Mined minerals need to be transported, which creates an additional footprint.)* `0:20` minutes

## On Your Feet

**Botswana's Mineral Success** Place students in three groups and have each group focus on Botswana's use of its mineral revenue for education, infrastructure improvements, or health care. Have students use the **Research Links** to find details about each of those categories. Encourage them to find a visual method to share their findings. `0:20` minutes

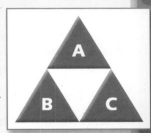

### ONGOING ASSESSMENT

# MAP LAB  GeoJournal

## ANSWERS

1. diamonds and gold
2. Responses will vary. Students should recognize that countries such as South Africa have a variety of resources and countries such as Malawi have none. Students should also infer that the economies of countries with a variety of resources would be stronger than those without resources.
3. The economy would be damaged because of Angola's economic dependence on oil.

## 2.2 Nigeria and Oil

TECHTREK
myNGconnect.com For an online map
of oil production and oil industry photos

Maps and Graphs    Digital Library

**Main Idea** Nigeria's people have received little benefit from the country's oil wealth.

Nigeria has a population of more than 150 million people, the largest in Africa. Its coastline has major ports, and its river system and delta are among the world's largest. Nigeria also produces more oil than any other African country.

### Ethnic Conflict

When oil was discovered in Nigeria in the 1950s, it became the focus of the country's economy. However, Nigeria has faced many obstacles in attempting to use its oil riches. The most difficult challenge has been ethnic conflict.

British colonialism left Nigeria divided among three major ethnic groups—the Hausa-Fulani, the Igbo, and the Yoruba. There were also 250 smaller groups and at least two major religions. When Nigeria gained independence in 1960, these groups struggled for control.

Not long after independence, the new government was overthrown in a **coup**, or an illegal takeover by force. In a series of coups, rival ethnic groups replaced existing governments—often putting military leaders in charge. After Muslims in the north adopted *sharia*, or Islamic law, Christians in the area began moving south. This movement further divided the country, this time along religious lines.

### Challenges of Oil Wealth

In the early 1970s, world oil prices increased and the Nigerian economy grew. Cities expanded and farmers left their rural land for better paying jobs in the cities. As a result, agricultural production declined and Nigeria was forced to import food to feed its people.

The oil industry has added to the ethnic tension. Different groups struggle to control the oil and its profits. Conflict and corruption have prevented Nigerians from sharing in the oil wealth. Most people living in the Niger River delta, where oil production is **concentrated**, or centered, live in poverty.

The delta region is also heavily polluted from oil spills. People in the delta have protested against the pollution and demanded that more of the oil profits be used to improve the area.

### Nigeria's Progress

Between 2007 and 2009, Nigeria made economic gains. Its leaders received favorable loans to repay the country's debt to other countries. Officials began putting in place economic reforms designed to improve Nigeria's infrastructure. Maintaining these improvements while resolving ethnic conflicts will be a challenge for Nigeria's future.

#### Before You Move On
**Summarize** Why have Nigeria's people benefited so little from the country's oil wealth?
*because of division and conflict among ethnic groups and political corruption*

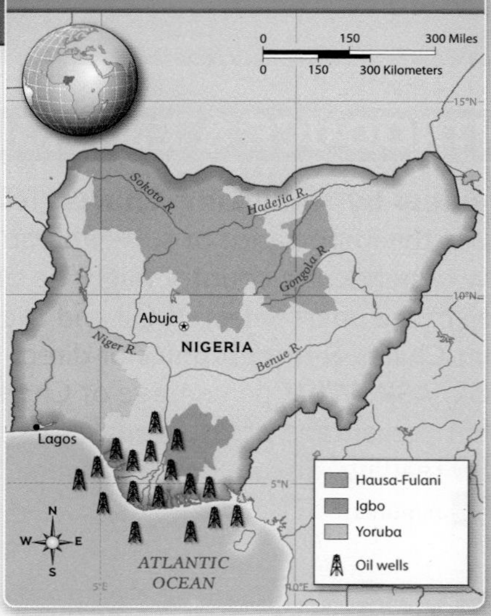

### ETHNIC GROUPS AND OIL

Legend:
- Hausa-Fulani
- Igbo
- Yoruba
- Oil wells

(Map labels: Sokoto R., Hadejia R., Gongola R., Abuja, NIGERIA, Niger R., Benue R., Lagos, ATLANTIC OCEAN)

### ONGOING ASSESSMENT
#### MAP LAB                    GeoJournal

1. **Location** What ethnic group appears to have the most access to the country's oil industry?

2. **Interpret Maps** Identify the delta region on the map. What are some possible consequences of polluting this region?

3. **Analyze Cause and Effect** Use a chart similar to the one below to list effects related to Nigeria's oil industry.

| CAUSE | EFFECTS |
|-------|---------|
| Nigeria's oil industry | 1. |
| | 2. |
| | 3. |

> **Critical Viewing** Fishermen cast a net near an oil refinery in the Niger River delta. Think about the oil industry and the simple fishing shown in the photo. In what ways are they connected?
>
> Possible response: Pollution from the refinery might harm fish and lead to a reduced fish supply.

---

## PLAN

### OBJECTIVE Understand the challenges in unifying Nigeria and in harnessing its oil wealth to modernize its economy.

### CRITICAL THINKING SKILLS FOR SECTION 2.2

- Main Idea
- Summarize
- Interpret Maps
- Analyze Cause and Effect
- Make Predictions
- Make Inferences
- Draw Conclusions

### PRINT RESOURCES

*Teacher's Edition* Resource Bank

- Reading and Note-Taking: Analyze Cause and Effect
- Vocabulary Practice: Vocabulary Cluster
- **GeoActivity** Compare Oil Revenue and Incomes

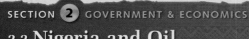

TECHTREK    myNGconnect.com

**Fast Forward!**
**Core Content Presentations**
Teach *Nigeria and Oil*

**Digital Library**
NG Photo Gallery, Section 2

**Connect to NG**
Research Links

**Maps and Graphs**
- **Interactive Map Tool** Population and Oil
- Online World Atlas: Ethnic Groups and Oil

**Also Check Out**
GeoJournal in **Student eEdition**

### BACKGROUND FOR THE TEACHER

One reason people living in the Niger River delta live in poverty is that oil jobs rarely go to local workers. In addition, the local fishing economy has been disrupted by oil pollution. Between 9 and 13 million barrels of oil have been spilled, more than was spilled into the Gulf of Mexico in 2010. Moreover, neglecting other resources has left the economy dependent on oil exports.

### ESSENTIAL QUESTION

### How have conflict and government instability slowed economic development in sub-Saharan Africa?

Nigeria's diverse ethnic groups and religions have been obstacles to forming a unified nation. Section 2.2 describes the challenges of managing oil wealth and the distribution of minerals amidst ethnic conflict.

## INTRODUCE & ENGAGE  Digital Library

**Make Predictions** Project the photos of the oil rig and the oil tanks from the **NG Photo Gallery**. Encourage students to discuss what the photos suggest about the major industry in Nigeria. Point out the main oil resources on the Ethnic Groups and Oil map. Have students predict the economic effects of the oil resources on the national economy, the oil field owners, and ordinary Nigerians. Tell them to show their predictions in the chart shown here. Tell students they will have a chance to verify or modify their predictions as they work through this lesson and the GeoActivity. `0:15` minutes

### EFFECTS OF NIGERIA'S OIL RESOURCES

| ON COUNTRY'S ECONOMY | ON OIL FIELD OWNER | ON ORDINARY NIGERIANS |
| --- | --- | --- |
| | | |

## TEACH  Maps and Graphs

### Guided Discussion

**1. Make Inferences** How do Nigeria's oil exporters benefit from Nigeria's location and the location of its oil resources? (*Nigeria is on the coast with major ports for shipping and contains a major river system and delta. A port is very near its oil fields. The oil fields are located along the river and its tributaries, which lead to a port.*)

**2. Draw Conclusions** In the last paragraph, what evidence suggests that Nigeria had some economic difficulties before 2007? (*The paragraph says that between 2007 and 2009, Nigeria made economic gains, suggesting that it was not making them before. Its leaders worked out new, more favorable loans to pay off its debt. The debt suggests prior economic difficulty.*)

**Interpret Maps** Point out the Ethnic Groups and Oil map in the **Online World Atlas**. Explain how to use the legend to locate the oil resources and the territories of the ethnic groups. **ASK:** How do the map and the text help explain Nigeria's challenges in forming a stable government and using its oil resources to benefit its people? (*Rival ethnic groups live within Nigeria's borders and struggle for control. By destabilizing the government and engaging in armed conflict, they create an unfavorable climate for economic development. In addition, only one major ethnic group lives near the oil fields.*) `0:20` minutes

## DIFFERENTIATE  Connect to NG

**Striving Readers** **Summarize** Assign pairs of students to read each section of the lesson (introductory paragraph plus "Ethnic Conflict," "Challenges of Oil Wealth," "Nigeria's Progress," and the Ethnic Groups and Oil map). Encourage students to use context clues or a dictionary to help them understand unfamiliar words. Have each pair summarize its section for the group.

**Gifted & Talented** **Explore Ethnic Cultures** Have students research and report on one of Nigeria's cultures, such as the Hausa-Fulani, the Yoruba, the Igbo, the Ogoni, or the Ijaw. Have them include information about the culture, its dominant religion, and any conflicts with other cultural groups. Suggest that students use the **Research Links** to conduct their research.

# ACTIVE OPTIONS

 **Interactive Map Tool**

### Population and Oil

**PURPOSE** Examine the relationship between population density and oil resources

**SET-UP**

1. Open the **Interactive Map Tool,** set the "Map Mode" to National Geographic, and zoom in on Nigeria.

2. Under "Human Systems—Populations & Culture," turn on the Population Density layer. Adjust the transparency to alternately show and hide the population density.

**ACTIVITY**

1. Point out areas on the map with the most dots or the largest patches of darkness.

2. Have students note that some of the most populated areas are near ports, on the coast, or along waterways near oil resources.

3. Ask students to explain this relationship. (*Drilling for oil creates a need for places to live and businesses to supply the drillers. Cities grow because of transportation and trade.*) `0:20` minutes

**EXTENSION** Under "Environment and Society," turn on the Lights at Night layer. **ASK:** Why is the greatest concentration of light around the port cities? (*The oil rigs are probably lit at night, as are the businesses that supply them. The lights in and near the port cities are on at night.*) `0:15` minutes

### On Your Feet

**Create a Living Map** Explain that the classroom represents Nigeria, with the area near the door symbolizing the Niger River delta. Place the main classroom resources (books, a computer, supplies) in the delta area along with a trashcan. Divide the class into three groups to represent the main ethnic groups in the country. Have each group go to the part of the classroom that represents where it primarily lives. With students, discuss how the distribution of people, resources, and pollution could lead to conflict. `0:15` minutes

---

**ONGOING ASSESSMENT**

# MAP LAB  GeoJournal

### ANSWERS

1. the Igbo

2. Possible consequences: harm to the fishing industry, to the environment generally, and to the water supply

3. ethnic conflict; corruption; pollution

## 2.3 Agriculture and Food Supply

TECHTREK
myNGconnect.com For photos of agriculture and Guided Writing

Student Resources
Digital Library

**Main Idea** Africa is improving its ability to feed its growing population.

Images of African children in need are all too common. Their hunger is real and often the result of famine. **Famine** is a widespread and sustained shortage of food. Natural disasters, such as droughts and floods, and armed conflicts can all disrupt the availability of food and contribute to a famine. Widely reported famines occurred in Sudan in 1998, Ethiopia in 2000, 2002, and 2003, Malawi in 2002, and Niger in 2005. Famine is a constant danger in Africa and threatens the health of millions of people.

### A Threatened Food Supply

Population growth has been rapid in some parts of Africa, but food production has not increased as rapidly. The average African eats 10 percent fewer calories today than he or she did 20 years ago. The number of undernourished people in sub-Saharan Africa increased from

**Critical Viewing** Women harvest cotton in Mali. Based on the photo, how would you describe this Mali cotton farm?

The women are picking cotton by hand and the field appears to have a lot of cotton.

about 90 million in 1970 to 225 million in 2008. Many African children suffer from malnutrition, which is a lack of nutrients essential to good health. Because of hunger and malnutrition, African children typically have shorter life expectancies than other children around the world.

African food crops include corn, yams, and sorghum, which is a type of grain. Before colonization, Africans grew these crops with the goal of feeding everyone. After colonization, European settlers took the most fertile land, and farming shifted from food crops to cash crops for export. Cash crops such as coffee and cotton are grown because they can be sold for more money than food crops. The income from cash crops allows farmers to purchase more, but less food is grown to feed the African people.

Since independence, some land has been returned to Africans. However, African land can be easily overworked and overgrazed, exhausting the soil. Farmers also struggle with droughts, soil erosion, and desertification.

### New and Better Farming

Africans are working to improve agricultural practices. For example, farmers are moving animals from place to place to avoid overgrazing. They are also growing different crops on the same plot to avoid exhausting the soil. More **legumes**, which are peas or beans, are being planted. These add to the food supply and release helpful nutrients into the soil. Farmers are also enriching the soil by using fertilizer with animal and plant waste instead of chemicals.

**Microcredit**, or small loans, has helped poor farmers invest in land, tools, and seeds. Relief agencies have begun to provide free seeds and tools to farmers. Scientists hope to develop seeds that are more productive and drought resistant. These seeds could help farmers grow more food crops for their own use as well as cash crops for export. If successful, these efforts will feed Africans, extend life expectancies, and improve economies.

**Before You Move On**
**Summarize** What is Africa doing to improve its agriculture? moving animals; rotating crops; planting legumes; fertilizing with plant and animal waste

**Visual Vocabulary** **Erosion** is the wearing away of Earth's surface by natural forces. The grid-like structures in the photo are fences made from branches. The fences keep sand from eroding onto land used for crops and grazing.

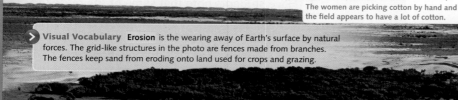

ONGOING ASSESSMENT
### WRITING LAB
GeoJournal

1. **Summarize** What is the difference between food crops and cash crops?

2. **Analyze Cause and Effect** What is the relationship between reduced food production and life expectancy?

3. **Write Comparisons** Write a paragraph comparing African food crops and cash crops. Describe why is it important for African farmers to balance growing food crops with cash crops. Then work in groups and share your paragraphs. Go to **Student Resources** for Guided Writing support.

---

## PLAN

**OBJECTIVE** Identify and describe the challenges of improving agriculture and increasing food output for Africa's growing population.

### CRITICAL THINKING SKILLS FOR SECTION 2.3

- Main Idea
- Summarize
- Analyze Cause and Effect
- Compare and Contrast
- Describe
- Analyze Visuals

### PRINT RESOURCES

*Teacher's Edition* Resource Bank

- Reading and Note-Taking: Find Main Idea and Details
- Vocabulary Practice: Descriptive Paragraph
- **GeoActivity** Compare Zimbabwe's Crop Production

TECHTREK myNGconnect.com

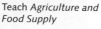
Fast Forward!
**Core Content Presentations**
Teach *Agriculture and Food Supply*

**Digital Library**
- GeoVideo: *Introduce Sub-Saharan Africa*
- NG Photo Gallery, Section 2

**Maps and Graphs**
Interactive Map Tool
Analyze Agriculture and Land

**Also Check Out**
- Graphic Organizers in **Teacher Resources**
- GeoJournal in **Student eEdition**

### BACKGROUND FOR THE TEACHER

The International Food Policy Research Institute (IFPRI) created a Global Hunger Index (GHI) based on three indicators: 1) the percentage of people who consume too few calories for health; 2) how many children under the age of five are underweight; and 3) the proportion of child deaths that are mainly caused by malnutrition and disease. In 2009, the countries with the highest 2009 GHI scores were all in sub-Saharan Africa.

### ESSENTIAL QUESTION

**How have conflict and government instability slowed economic development in sub-Saharan Africa?**

Section 2.3 shows that the effort to address Africa's slow economic development led to the increase of cash crops over food crops. This practice worsened famine and malnutrition in Africa.

# INTRODUCE & ENGAGE

**Compare and Contrast Calorie Intake** Explain that in the United States, many diseases are caused by dietary excess. Tell students that for most of the world's people, diseases are more likely caused by insufficient food. Display labels of prepared foods that frequently constitute breakfast, lunch, and dinner for Americans. Choose foods for which the calories add up to at least 2,000 per day. Have students list on a chart similar to the one here the number of calories per serving from each food. Have students add up the number of calories supplied by these foods. Add in a few calories for typical snacks to make at least 2,200 calories. Explain that experts say for adults with light activity, the average requirement is 2,200 calories a day. In some African refugee camps, adult refugees are fed only 1,400 calories per day. `0:20` minutes

| Food | Calories |
| --- | --- |
|  |  |

# TEACH  Digital Library

## Guided Discussion

1. **Analyze Cause and Effect** What factors make it hard for Africa to feed its people? *(colonial disruption of traditional land ownership and management, shift to cash crops, population growth, soil exhaustion, desertification)*

2. **Describe** What steps are farmers in Africa taking to improve soil and farming conditions? *(Farmers are rotating crops and grazing areas so that the soil does not become depleted of nutrients. Farmers are planting more legumes and using natural fertilizers to further enrich the soil.)*

**Analyze Visuals** Show the GeoVideo: *Introduce Sub-Saharan Africa* and point out the part of the video that displays agricultural land in Africa. Then, using the **NG Photo Gallery,** project the photo of the large cash farm and the small farm. Name specific crops from the text and ask if this crop would be more likely to be grown on the large farm or the small farm and explain why. *(In general, the cash crops will be grown on the large farm to take advantage of economies of scale and the subsistence crops on the small farm because these farmers have limited resources.)* **ASK:** Which farm would be more likely to grow coffee? *(the large farm)* Why? *(Coffee is not usually grown on a small scale for family use. It is grown to sell.)* `0:20` minutes

# DIFFERENTIATE

**Striving Readers Summarize** Read the lesson aloud while students follow along in their textbooks. At the end of each paragraph, ask students to summarize what you read in a sentence. Allow them time to write the summary on their own paper.

**Gifted & Talented Conduct a Meeting** Have a group of students assume the roles of officers in an organization that addresses global hunger. Tell them to discuss as a panel the various causes of food shortage in sub-Saharan Africa and some possible steps that can be taken to feed Africans.

# ACTIVE OPTIONS

 **Interactive Map Tool**

## Analyze Agriculture and Land

**PURPOSE** Predict where the food supply in sub-Saharan Africa is low

**SET-UP**

1. Open the **Interactive Map Tool** and set the "Map Mode" to National Geographic.

2. Under "Environment and Society," turn on the Land Cover layer. Adjust the transparency so that both the land cover regions and political borders are visible. Then zoom in on Africa.

**ACTIVITY**

Have students note where cropland is located in Africa. Point out the lack or scarcity of cropland in Burundi, Chad, the Democratic Republic of Congo, Eritrea, and Sierra Leone. Have students predict how this affects food supply in these countries. Tell students that these are among the countries in which hunger is the greatest problem. `0:20` minutes

## On Your Feet

**Plan a Garden** Have students work in small groups to create a plan for a 100-square-foot garden that will provide a balance of cash crops and food crops and will be sustainable over time. Students can refer to the lesson to identify which crops to plant and which methods to use to ensure that they don't exhaust the soil. Have groups create a diagram or model of their garden and present their plan to the rest of the class. Students can then discuss which plan is the best in terms of food production and sustainability. `0:25` minutes

## 2.4 Improving Public Health

TECHTREK
myNGconnect.com For data and
current news about public health in Africa

Connect to NG    Global Issues

Inspiring people to care about the planet
National Geographic Society Mission

**Main Idea** National governments and international agencies are committed to improving health care in Africa by reducing the impact of diseases.

Nearly one million people die of malaria each year, and 9 out of 10 of them are in Africa. Eighty-five percent of the victims are children under the age of five. Malaria is one of many chronic diseases that plague the continent.

### Climate, Poverty, and Disease

In 2008, the average life expectancy for a woman in sub-Saharan Africa was 49 years. That is 32 years shorter than the average in North America. One cause is the deadly toll taken by diseases such as malaria, sleeping sickness, and yellow fever.

Only 15 percent of the world's people live in Africa, but 90 percent of tropical disease cases occur there. The organisms that cause disease thrive in its tropical climates, as do the insects that carry the diseases.

For example, malaria is carried by a mosquito and causes flu-like symptoms. Severe forms can cause brain and nerve damage and death. Malaria probably began in ancient times as an **epidemic**—an outbreak limited to a particular community. Later, it became a **pandemic**, meaning it spread over a large area, in this case, across much of the world. Malaria can be prevented by draining or treating water where insects breed and by sleeping under mosquito nets treated with chemicals to kill insects.

In addition to the tropical climate, poverty contributes to the spread of disease. Poor Africans may lack mosquito nets, screened windows, and technology for draining insect breeding grounds. Poverty also raises the rates of other infections because of overcrowding, poor sanitation, and contaminated water.

#### Before You Move On
**Summarize** What are some factors that contribute to the spread of disease in Africa? tropical climate; poverty; overcrowding; poor sanitation; contaminated water

### KEY VOCABULARY

**epidemic,** n., an outbreak of disease affecting a large number of people within a community at the same time

**pandemic,** n., an outbreak of disease occurring over a wide geographic area

**vaccine,** n., treatments to increase immunity to a particular disease

**infectious,** adj., capable of spreading rapidly to others

Students in Ethiopia read before school under the protection of a mosquito net.

### COMPARE ACROSS REGIONS

#### The Fight Against Disease

The fight against diseases such as malaria, HIV/AIDs, and yellow fever has become a global commitment. Many agencies offer medication to treat diseases and vaccines to prevent them. Vaccines are treatments designed to increase immunity, or resistance, to a particular disease. Scientists are trying to find new vaccines and cures for infectious diseases, or diseases that can spread rapidly.

Eliminating malaria is a global goal for the 21st century. Worldwide, there are an estimated 250 million cases every year. A non-governmental organization (NGO) called Malaria No More works to fight malaria in Africa. An NGO is a nonprofit volunteer group founded by citizens. Malaria No More hands out mosquito nets to protect people.

The World Health Organization (WHO) battles malaria around the world. The group's Mekong Malaria Program in Southeast Asia works with governments and NGOs to monitor disease outbreaks and treatment programs in the region.

A major source of funding for malaria treatment programs is the Bill and Melinda Gates Foundation. The foundation funds research for a vaccine and more effective anti-malarial drugs for people who have already been infected.

All of these programs reflect a renewed commitment on the part of national governments, private foundations, and NGOs to fight malaria and other diseases around the world.

### MALARIA BY THE NUMBERS

**38**
Countries worldwide that reduced cases of malaria by over 50 percent between 2000 and 2008

**45**
Number of seconds between each death of an African child due to malaria

**109**
Countries worldwide reporting malaria cases in 2009

**2,414**
Estimated number of people worldwide who die every day from malaria

**801,000**
Estimated number of Africans who die every year from malaria

**Source:** World Health Organization, United Nations Children's Fund

#### Before You Move On
**Monitor Comprehension** What are the main tools in the global fight against disease?

ONGOING ASSESSMENT
### READING LAB    GeoJournal

1. **Analyze Cause and Effect** What is one cause of the short life expectancy among sub-Saharan Africans?
2. **Make Predictions** How might development of a vaccine against malaria affect the life expectancy in Africa?
3. **Make Inferences** How might you expect malaria to impact the economies of countries with large numbers of cases?

organizations researching vaccines and more effective anti-malarial drugs, distributing preventive measures like mosquito nets, and tracking outbreaks and treatment in high-risk areas of the world

SECTION 2.4  **399**

---

## PLAN

### OBJECTIVE Examine the steps Africa is taking to fight disease and improve public health.

### CRITICAL THINKING SKILLS FOR SECTION 2.4

- Main Idea
- Summarize
- Monitor Comprehension
- Analyze Cause and Effect
- Make Predictions
- Make Inferences
- Compare and Contrast

### PRINT RESOURCES

*Teacher's Edition* Resource Bank

- Reading and Note-Taking: Identify Problems and Solutions
- Vocabulary Practice: Definition Tree
- **GeoActivity** Interpret a Map of Malaria Outbreaks

 myNGconnect.com

 Fast Forward!
**Core Content Presentations**
Teach *Improving Public Health*

**Connect to NG**
Research Links

 **Interactive Whiteboard**
**GeoActivity** Interpret a Map of Malaria Outbreaks

**Also Check Out**
- NG Photo Gallery in **Digital Library**
- Charts & Infographics in **Teacher Resources**
- GeoJournal in **Student eEdition**

### BACKGROUND FOR THE TEACHER

Malaria symptoms can be treated, but drug resistance is a challenge. The parasite that causes malaria mutates, becoming resistant to malaria drugs. Traditional healers have used medicinal plants to treat malaria symptoms. Laboratory evidence has shown the following African medicinal plants to be effective: *Maytenus senegalensis, Cyperus rotundus (Cyperaceae), Hoslundia opposita Vahl, (Labiatae), and Lantana camara L. (Verbenaceae).*

### ESSENTIAL QUESTION

#### How have conflict and government instability slowed economic development in sub-Saharan Africa?

Section 2.4 centers on the factors that make Africa vulnerable to severe diseases, as well as what governments and other agencies are doing to solve the problems.

# INTRODUCE & ENGAGE

**Activate Prior Knowledge** Explain to students that this lesson will discuss the impact of disease in Africa. Have students work in groups and list common but dangerous diseases that they already know about such as measles, influenza, and cancer. Tell them to use a chart like the one below to list the diseases, prevention strategies, and treatment options. Discuss the fact that some diseases cannot be prevented with vaccines or cured with drugs. Have students examine evidence from the Malaria By the Numbers chart that shows malaria is widespread *(the number of countries reporting cases)* and serious *(the statistics about malaria deaths)*. Explain that they will add to their knowledge about malaria during the lesson. `0:20` minutes

| DISEASE | PREVENTION | TREATMENT |
|---------|-----------|-----------|
|         |           |           |

# TEACH

## Guided Discussion

**1. Analyze Cause and Effect** How does poverty contribute to the spread of disease in Africa? *(Poor rural Africans may lack insect traps, mosquito nets, screened windows, and technology for draining or managing breeding grounds of insects that carry diseases. They may also lack vaccines that could prevent some diseases. Poverty also raises rates of other infections. Overcrowding, poor sanitation, and contaminated water spread diseases.)*

**2. Make Inferences** How might widespread disease become a cause of poverty? *(If people are ill, they cannot work productively. If the primary earners in the family die, the family can slide into poverty. Time, money, and resources may be used to fight disease rather than to build economies.)*

**3. Compare and Contrast** How are an epidemic and a pandemic similar and different? *(Both refer to the spread of a disease. An epidemic affects only one region, whereas a pandemic is worldwide.)*

### MORE INFORMATION

**Sleeping Sickness** Sleeping sickness is another widespread, serious, and often fatal disease in Africa. It attacks the nervous system, causing fever, aches, seizures, and sometimes death. The disease is spread by the bite of the tsetse fly. The same parasite causes a similar disease in livestock and can be spread from livestock to humans. The insect is widespread in the savannas where land is otherwise suitable for farming and grazing. Its presence discourages the keeping of livestock, leaving farmers without manure for the soil and draft animals for labor.

# DIFFERENTIATE  Connect to NG

**Pre-AP Compare and Contrast** Have students use the **Research Links** to research the effects of malaria in other parts of the world. Ask students to write a blog that compares and contrasts prevention and treatment efforts in other parts of the world with those in Africa. Remind them to include statistics on incidence of disease in their blog as well as international success rates.

 Interactive Whiteboard
## GeoActivity

**Interpret a Map of Malaria Outbreaks**
Project the map and supply students with copies. Discuss the factors that would enable large populations of mosquitoes to thrive. Have students discuss the questions in groups and record their responses. Then have representatives from each group share responses. `0:15` minutes

**EXTENSION** Have interested students do research on the science of epidemiology as applied in the United States. Suggest that they use presentation software to put together a multimedia presentation for the class in which they identify common diseases that the Centers for Disease Control and Prevention monitors in this country. Ask them to provide recent statistics on their incidence in different parts of the United States and at different seasons. Remind them that they may also look for statistics that deal with the eradication of various diseases that used to afflict large numbers of people—and in some cases, the resurgence of those diseases. `0:20` minutes

 ## On Your Feet

**Jigsaw** Use the Jigsaw strategy to have students answer the Before You Move On question. Have each group become an expert on a different strategy in the fight against malaria, such as mosquito nets, vaccines and drugs, draining insect breeding grounds, or screened windows. Encourage them to use the **Research Links** if needed. Then use the Jigsaw strategy to have experts report their findings to different groups. See "Best Practices for Active Teaching" for a review of this strategy. `0:25` minutes

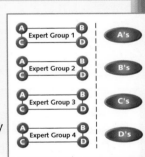

## ANSWERS
1. disease
2. Life expectancy might go up because fewer people would die from malaria.
3. The economies of countries with a high incidence of malaria suffer.

## 2.5 Sudan and Somalia

TECHTREK
myNGconnect.com For online maps
and current events in Sudan and Somalia

Maps and
Graphs

Connect
to NG

**Main Idea** Civil wars involving ethnic and religious groups in Sudan and Somalia have limited progress in these countries.

For years, Sudan and Somalia have been plagued by war, famine, and disease. Many people survived conflict only to die of starvation. In both countries, climate, history, and culture all combined to help create this difficult situation.

As you've learned, colonial rule in Africa left countries divided among different ethnic and religious groups. Sudan and Somalia also face a geographic division: The Sahel runs through both of these countries, dividing them between northern Africa and sub-Saharan Africa.

### Conflict in Sudan

Sudan is mostly desert in the north. Nomadic Muslim herders of Arabic descent live there. The south is swamp and savanna that was settled by farmers of African descent. Northerners are mainly Muslim, while southerners practice mainly Christianity or indigenous religions. Both north and south include a mix of ethnic groups.

These religious and ethnic differences have led to conflict. Since Sudan's independence in 1956, the government has oppressed Christians in the country. In Darfur, the government created a largely Arab militia in 2003. The militia attacked government protestors, but also attacked militia members' personal enemies. Almost 400,000 people were killed, and about 2.5 million people became **refugees**, or people who flee a place to find safety.

Neighboring countries such as Chad set up refugee camps for people fleeing Sudan. One camp housed more than 250,000 people in 2010. The camps have no permanent shelter or sewer system, often suffer food shortages, and rely on the host countries and relief agencies for help.

The refugees included a group known as the **Lost Boys of Sudan**. These young men were orphaned by the civil war and stuck together to escape the violence. They traveled to Ethiopia, then back to Sudan, and then to camps in Kenya. In 2001, the United States took in more than 3,500 of these young men. Many attended high school and college in the United States.

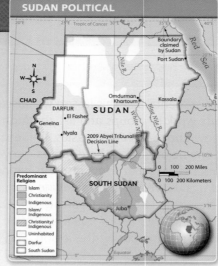

SUDAN POLITICAL

SOMALIA POLITICAL

**Critical Viewing** Eyl (AY uhl), shown here, is a town in Somalia's Puntland state. What might you infer from this photo about economic conditions in Eyl? *Eyl, or at least the area shown, does not appear to be wealthy.*

### Somalia

Somalians have suffered through conflict among five major **clans**, or large, family-based units with loyalty to the group. Even within the clan, sub-clans may clash. As a result, Somalians have never united to form a single nation.

In 1991, clan-based groups overthrew a crumbling military government and battles raged between rival clans. This conflict disrupted farms that were already threatened by flood and drought. With no central government, some clans turned to piracy, which continues today. They attack and rob foreign ships or hold the ships and their crews for ransom.

Somalia is considered by many to be a **failed state**, a country in which government, economic institutions, and civil order have broken down. The regions of Somaliland and Puntland have claimed

independence but have not received international recognition. In the 21st century, forces from the United Nations and the African Union have been trying to keep peace in the region.

**Before You Move On**
Summarize How have conflicts limited progress in Sudan and Somalia? *Conflicts have destabilized the countries and created large numbers of refugees.*

**ONGOING ASSESSMENT**
## MAP LAB
GeoJournal

1. **Interpret Maps** Using the map of Sudan, describe the geographic distribution of the main religions.
2. **Region** Using the map of Somalia, describe how it is divided. Based on your description, what challenges might Somalia face?
3. **Draw Conclusions** What is a failed state, and why might Sudan and Somalia both be considered failed states?

---

## PLAN

**OBJECTIVE** Compare and contrast the problems in Sudan and Somalia.

### CRITICAL THINKING SKILLS FOR SECTION 2.5

- Main Idea
- Summarize
- Interpret Maps
- Draw Conclusions
- Compare and Contrast
- Analyze Cause and Effect
- Identify

### PRINT RESOURCES

*Teacher's Edition* Resource Bank

- Reading and Note-Taking: Compare and Contrast
- Vocabulary Practice: Four-Column Chart
- **GeoActivity** Build a Time Line of Events

### TECHTREK myNGconnect.com

**Fast Forward!**
**Core Content Presentations**
Teach *Sudan and Somalia*

**Maps and Graphs**
- **Interactive Map Tool** Analyze Borders and Language Diversity
- Online World Atlas: Sudan Political; Somalia Political

**Also Check Out**
- NG Photo Gallery in **Digital Library**
- GeoJournal in **Student eEdition**

### BACKGROUND FOR THE TEACHER

In 2010, Minority Rights Group International (MRG) ranked Somalia and Sudan first and second among countries where minority ethnic groups face the greatest risk of violence and displacement. According to MRG, it was the absence of effective state authority and accepted rule of law that put minorities at risk in Somalia. At particular risk of persecution are minority ethnic groups, such as the Bantu, that are not part of the clan system.

### ESSENTIAL QUESTION

**How have conflict and government instability slowed economic development in sub-Saharan Africa?**

Historical and geographic factors have both been at the source of instability in Sudan and Somalia. Section 2.5 describes these factors and the struggles of these two countries.

# INTRODUCE & ENGAGE

**K-W-L Chart** Provide each student with a K-W-L chart like the one below. Have students brainstorm what they know about Somalia and Sudan from the news or from the previous chapter. Then ask them to write questions that they would like to have answered as they study the lesson. Allow time at the end of the lesson for students to fill in what they have learned. `0:20` minutes

| WHAT DO<br>I KNOW? | WHAT DO I<br>WANT TO LEARN? | WHAT DID<br>I LEARN? |
|---|---|---|
| | | |

# TEACH  Maps and Graphs

## Guided Discussion

**1. Compare and Contrast** What do the armed conflicts between groups in Sudan and Somalia have in common? How are they different? *(They both involve conflict among different ethnic groups. In Sudan, religious tensions cause much of the conflict.)*

**2. Analyze Cause and Effect** How have geographic differences between northern and southern Sudan created different economies and cultures? *(Lacking enough water for farming in Sudan's dry north, northerners are nomadic herders. The swamps and savannas of the south are settled by farmers.)*

**3. Identify** What were the conditions that led to the rise of piracy off the Somalian coast? *(the collapse of the central government due to drought, famine, and clan warfare)*

**Interpret Maps** Project the Sudan Political map from the **Online World Atlas**. Explain that in January 2011, Sudan held a referendum, or vote, on whether southern Sudan should become a separate country. **ASK:** Based on the map and what you've read, why might southern Sudan want to become a separate country? *(because the people there are primarily Christian and have been persecuted by the Sudanese government)* What characteristics of southern Sudan's physical geography might encourage Sudan's government to want to retain southern Sudan? *(Southern Sudan includes most of the country's valuable farmland.)* `0:15` minutes

# DIFFERENTIATE  Maps and Graphs

**Inclusion Monitor Comprehension** Have students write the letters A, B, and C on three separate index cards. Then check students' understanding of the lesson by asking them questions that have three possible answer choices, labeled A, B, and C. Instruct students to hold up the card with the letter that corresponds to the correct answer. Help students find the answers for any questions that cause them difficulty.

**English Language Learners Teach Word Parts** List these words on the whiteboard: *geographic, Arabic, economic.* Have students copy them and identify the suffix they share in common. Explain that the suffix *-ic* means "of, characteristic of, or having to do with." Tell them that adding the suffix *-ic* changes a noun to an adjective. Remind students that before a suffix is added, a final letter may be changed or dropped. Then ask them to identify the nouns to which the suffix *-ic* was added and explain how the meanings are changed. Ask students for other examples of adjectives that are formed by adding *-ic* to a noun.

# ACTIVE OPTIONS

 **Interactive Map Tool**

**Analyze Borders and Language Diversity**
PURPOSE Explore how language regions cross sub-Saharan Africa's country borders

**SET-UP**

**1.** Open the **Interactive Map Tool,** set the "Map Mode" to National Geographic, and set the "Region" to Africa.

**2.** Under "Human Systems—Populations & Culture," turn on the Language Diversity layer. Set the transparency level to 40 percent.

**ACTIVITY** Under "Country," select, in turn, Sudan and Somalia. **ASK:** What does the language diversity suggest about the ethnic groups within each country's borders? *(Sudan has more ethnic diversity than Somalia.)* `0:10` minutes

**EXTENSION** Under "Human Systems—Populations & Culture," turn on the Major Religions layer. **ASK:** How are the two countries alike and different? *(They both have significant Sunni Muslim populations. Sudan has different dominant religions in the southern and northern regions. Somalia has only one dominant religion.)* `0:10` minutes

## On Your Feet

**Tell Me More** Have students form two teams and assign each team one of the following topics: Sudan or Somalia. Each group should write down as many facts about their topic as they can. Have the class reconvene and have each group stand up, one at a time. The sitting group calls out, "Tell me more about [Sudan or Somalia]!" The standing group recites one fact. The sitting group again calls, "Tell me more!" until the standing group runs out of facts to share. Then the groups switch places. `0:15` minutes

## ONGOING ASSESSMENT
# MAP LAB  GeoJournal

### ANSWERS

**1.** Islam is practiced mainly in the north, and Christianity and indigenous religions are practiced mainly in the south.

**2.** Responses will vary but should include references to the states of Somaliland and Puntland. Students should recognize the challenges to stability a country faces when areas claim independence.

**3.** A failed state is a nation in which government, economic institutions, and order have broken down. Although Somalia is used as the example, Sudan's conflicts also exhibit a breakdown in state order.

## 2.6 Ending Apartheid

TECHTREK
myNGconnect.com For photos of South Africa

Digital Library

Nelson Mandela gestures to the crowd at a rally shortly after his release from prison.

**Main Idea** In 1994, South Africa moved from a minority, racist government to a democratically elected government.

In 1994, long lines of South Africans of all races stood for hours under a blazing hot sun. The majority of them waited to vote for the first time in their lives. This day marked the end of racial **segregation**, or separation by race, and the birth of a new democracy.

### Rich Resources Lure Colonists

South Africa stretches from warm tropics in the north to chilly waters in the south. Its geography and climate support a variety of crops, and it has large deposits of diamonds, gold, and other minerals.

In the 19th century, both Dutch and British colonists laid claim to these lands. The Dutch settlers, known as Boers or Afrikaners, formed their own republics. Boers had enslaved Africans and imported other people as laborers from Asia. Both the British and the Boers seized lands from Zulus, Xhosa, and

other Africans. Even more Africans were forced to work for Boer and British colonists after the discovery of large gold and diamond deposits around 1870.

### The Beginning of Apartheid

In 1902, after a series of wars, the Boer territories became British colonies known as the Union of South Africa. The British colonial government divided South Africa into white and black areas. Only white Africans could vote. Most of the land, and all of the best land, was reserved for the white minority. Black Africans were left with the land that was less useful or productive. Cities were declared white, and black Africans could enter them only to work.

▼ **Critical Viewing** A crowd in South Africa celebrates at a soccer match. What can you infer from the photo about how a sporting event might help bring people together?

A sporting event provides a common ground for people who might have other differences. It may help them see that they are not so different from each other.

In 1948, new laws created **apartheid** (uh PART hite), or the legal separation of races. In addition to being divided by race, South Africans could only own land in areas assigned to them. Black South Africans were required to carry identification papers at all times.

In 1970, the government made all black South Africans citizens of a homeland instead of citizens of South Africa. **Homelands** were supposed to be self-governing areas, but the national government actually controlled them. The homelands separated the races even more.

### The End of Apartheid

In the early 20th century, black Africans formed the **African National Congress** (ANC) to protest their treatment. Later, South Africa outlawed the ANC and imprisoned its leaders, including **Nelson Mandela**. In 1977, **Stephen Biko**, president of a student protest organization, was arrested and beaten to death. He and Mandela became symbols for the protest movement in South Africa.

In 1989, a new white president, F. W. de Klerk, began to change apartheid laws. He legalized the ANC and released its leaders, including Mandela. In 1994, voting rights were extended to all South Africans, and the people elected Mandela president.

Decades of apartheid left South Africa far from racial equality. The government has worked to give black South Africans access to better jobs and farmland, but a large economic gap remains between most blacks and whites in the country. In 2002, the government took control of

the country's mineral resources, in part to make sure that black South Africans profited fairly. Progress is slow, but South Africa's ability to harness its resources has allowed it to develop the most prosperous economy in Africa.

**Before You Move On**
Summarize How did South Africa change from minority rule to a more democratically elected government?

It changed through the protests of the African National Congress and the news laws passed by F.W. de Klerk.

ONGOING ASSESSMENT
## READING LAB
GeoJournal

1. **Monitor Comprehension** What was apartheid and how did it begin?
2. **Movement** In what ways did colonization and apartheid remove Africans from their homes?
3. **Compare and Contrast** Give an example of how the government under apartheid limited peoples' rights and an example of how the government expanded rights after apartheid.

SECTION 2.6 **403**

---

## PLAN

### OBJECTIVE Explain how apartheid came to an end and how democratic government was founded in South Africa.

### CRITICAL THINKING SKILLS FOR SECTION 2.6

- Main Idea
- Summarize
- Monitor Comprehension
- Compare and Contrast
- Analyze Cause and Effect
- Find Main Idea and Details
- Analyze Visuals

### PRINT RESOURCES

*Teacher's Edition* Resource Bank

- Reading and Note-Taking: Sequence Events
- Vocabulary Practice: Definition Chart
- **GeoActivity** Analyze Primary Sources: Apartheid and Segregation

 TECHTREK  myNGconnect.com

 ▶▶ *Fast Forward!*
**Core Content Presentations**
Teach *Ending Apartheid*

 **Digital Library**
NG Photo Gallery, Section 2

**Connect to NG**
Research Links

**Interactive Whiteboard**
**GeoActivity** Analyze Primary Sources: Apartheid and Segregation

**Also Check Out**
- Graphic Organizers in **Teacher Resources**
- GeoJournal in **Student eEdition**

### BACKGROUND FOR THE TEACHER

South Africa hosted the 1995 Rugby World Cup—one year after Nelson Mandela was elected president. Racial tension was very much still a part of life in South Africa, and Mandela saw the tournament as an opportunity to help unite white and black South Africans. Inspired by Mandela, the captain of the South African national rugby team led the "Springboks," as they are known, to a wildly improbable victory in the 1995 World Cup. These events were depicted in the 2009 movie *Invictus*.

### ESSENTIAL QUESTION

### How have conflict and government instability slowed economic development in sub-Saharan Africa?

Section 2.6 describes the history and end of apartheid, its aftermath, and what is being done to end its continuing legacy.

## INTRODUCE & ENGAGE

**Activate Prior Knowledge** Have students work in groups and brainstorm facts about segregation in the United States and apartheid in South Africa. Have them work individually to list facts about segregation on a Venn diagram like the one at the right. Explain that they will be able to add to the apartheid and middle sections as they work through the lesson. `0:15` minutes

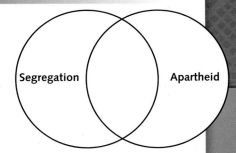

## TEACH

### Guided Discussion

1. **Analyze Cause and Effect** What law ensured that South Africa would be ruled by a white minority? *(the law that determined that only white Africans were allowed to vote)*

2. **Find Main Idea and Details** Besides the ANC, what other group was active in opposing apartheid? *(Stephen Biko's student group)*

3. **Compare and Contrast** Give an example of a white African and a black African who worked to end apartheid. How did their contributions differ? *(President de Klerk and Stephen Biko. The President had power and worked within the government to change the laws. Biko spoke to power from outside the government, protesting its policies.)*

**Analyze Visuals** Refer students to the South African flag shown in this lesson. Point out to students that national flags contain a lot of symbolism. Tell students that in the South African flag the black, yellow, and green are part of the African National Congress flag and the red, white, and blue are part of the flags of Great Britain and the Netherlands. **ASK:** What do you think the "Y" shape symbolizes? *(It symbolizes two different groups merging into one.)* `0:10` minutes

## DIFFERENTIATE  Digital Library

**English Language Learners Teach Closed and Hyphenated Compound Words** Remind students that two words can be put together to make a new word. Write these words and have students copy them.

*homeland    self-governing    poverty-stricken*

Explain that some compound words, such as *homeland,* are closed compound words. Some, such as *poverty-stricken,* are hyphenated compound words. Explain that hyphenated compound words are often adjectives, or describing words. Ask students to circle the two words within each word. Then help them define each of the two smaller words and the resulting compound word.

**Gifted & Talented Write a Biography** Have students research and write a biography of an anti-apartheid activist or government leader. They can research one of the people named in the lesson or a different person. Tell them to include information about the subject's anti-apartheid contributions. Suggest they use the **NG Photo Gallery** or online sources for photos to illustrate their reports. Make the biographies available for other students to read.

# ACTIVE OPTIONS

 **Interactive Whiteboard**
## GeoActivity

**Analyze Primary Sources: Apartheid and Segregation** Project the documents and photographs and supply students with copies. Through questioning and discussion, help students draw comparisons among social policies in different countries. Then discuss the difference between racial separation that results from laws and separation or discrimination that occurs as a result of other factors. Give students time to add to the Venn diagrams they began at the beginning of the lesson. `0:15` minutes

## On Your Feet

**Think, Pair, Share** Have students answer Reading Lab Question 3. One partner gives an example of how the government under apartheid limited rights and the other gives an example of how the government expanded rights after apartheid. Finally, have students use the Think, Pair, Share strategy to share information with the class. `0:10` minutes

 ## Performance Assessment

**Create a Group Presentation** Have students create a presentation assessing economic development in sub-Saharan Africa. It should include the geographic, historical, and cultural factors that work for and against physical and economic health in sub-Saharan Africa. Encourage students to create visuals to illustrate their points. Students should draw on information in Section 2 for support, but may use the **Research Links** for information beyond the text. Go to **myNGconnect.com** for the rubric.

**ONGOING ASSESSMENT**
# READING LAB  GeoJournal

### ANSWERS

1. Apartheid was the government-backed separation of the races. It began with the passage of a set of laws in 1948.
2. Colonization and apartheid stripped people of their rights and limited their participation in the government.
3. Sample responses: The homeland policy was an example of how the government limited peoples' rights. After apartheid, all citizens were given the right to vote.

## VOCABULARY

For each pair of vocabulary words, write one sentence that explains the connection between the two words.

1. ethnic group; transportation corridor

> Bodies of waters can act as transportation corridors between different African ethnic groups.

2. griot; oral tradition
3. ethnobotanist; medicinal plant
4. commodity; mineral
5. famine; erosion
6. epidemic; pandemic

### MAIN IDEAS

7. What factors were ignored when the colonial boundaries of African countries were drawn? (Section 1.1)
8. How has Africa's music influenced music in the United States? (Section 1.2)
9. What challenges has Kenya faced in modernizing its economy? (Section 1.3)
10. How are Grace Gobbo and Wade Davis helping to preserve traditional cultures? (Section 1.4)
11. What circumstances have kept Africans from profiting from mineral resources? (Section 2.1)
12. How has population growth made it harder for Africa to feed its people? (Section 2.3)
13. What is being done to reduce the spread of malaria in Africa? (Section 2.4)
14. What are some of the causes of the conflict in Sudan and Somalia? (Section 2.5)
15. How has life improved in South Africa since the end of apartheid? (Section 2.6)

## CULTURE

### ANALYZE THE ESSENTIAL QUESTION

What historical and geographic factors have influenced the cultures of sub-Saharan Africa?

**Critical Thinking: Draw Conclusions**

16. Without the influence of colonialism, would African countries be as ethnically diverse as they are today? Why or why not?
17. In what ways have sub-Saharan Africa's geography, climate, and resources helped to shape the lifestyles of its people?

### INTERPRET MAPS

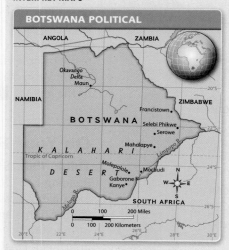

BOTSWANA POLITICAL

18. **Location** Which city can be found near 22°S latitude and 28°E longitude?
19. **Human-Environment Interaction** What type of geographic feature defines the irregular shape of Botswana's southern border?

## GOVERNMENT & ECONOMICS

### ANALYZE THE ESSENTIAL QUESTION

How have conflict and government instability slowed economic development in sub-Saharan Africa?

**Critical Thinking: Analyze Cause and Effect**

20. Describe some specific natural resources that have helped sub-Saharan African countries develop economically.
21. How did colonialism slow down Africa's economic development?
22. What effects did apartheid have on racial equality in South Africa?

### INTERPRET GRAPHS

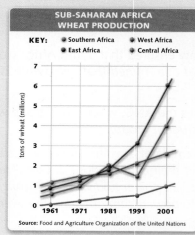

SUB-SAHARAN AFRICA WHEAT PRODUCTION

Source: Food and Agriculture Organization of the United Nations

23. **Analyze Data** In which region of Africa did food production increase the most?
24. **Evaluate** What additional information is needed in order to determine growth in food production per capita?

## ACTIVE OPTIONS

**Synthesize** the Essential Questions by completing the activities below.

25. **Write a Letter** Imagine that you are a member of an aid team working on improving public health in Africa. Pick a specific country and write a letter to donors explaining why your organization and team need money to support your work. **Read your letter aloud to a partner to practice presenting the information.**

**Writing Tips**
- Take notes from the chapter about the health concerns faced by many people in Africa.
- Present clear, strong evidence to support your proposal.
- Make specific suggestions about how the money can best be spent to improve the quality of life for all the country's people.

**TECHTREK** myNGconnect.com For research links on sub-Saharan Africa

26. **Create a Chart** Make a three-column chart showing comparisons among three countries in sub-Saharan Africa. Be sure each country comes from a different area (West, East, Central, or Southern). Use the research links at **Connect to NG** and other online sources to gather the data for the categories shown below. Based on the data, which country has the most people? The fewest?

| | Ghana (West Africa) | Uganda (East Africa) | Lesotho (South Africa) |
|---|---|---|---|
| Year Country Gained Independence | | | |
| Population | | | |
| Square Miles of Land | | | |
| Main Economic Resources | | | |

# CHAPTER Review

## VOCABULARY ANSWERS

1. > Bodies of waters can act as transportation corridors between different African ethnic groups.

2. Following oral tradition, griots recite oral history to pass on their culture to new generations.
3. An ethnobotanist such as Grace Gobbo investigates the medicinal plants used by traditional healers.
4. Valuable minerals such as gold and diamonds are among the commodities that can be bought, sold, or traded by developing economies in Africa.
5. Soil erosion can reduce farming productivity and contribute to a famine.
6. An epidemic is a disease outbreak that is confined to a specific region; if it spreads worldwide it is called a pandemic.

## MAIN IDEAS ANSWERS

7. The boundaries of the homelands of Africa's cultural groups were ignored.
8. Africa's music influenced the development of jazz, blues, rock-and-roll, and gospel in the United States.
9. Kenya has faced the challenges of unifying different ethnic groups and avoiding ethnic tension.
10. Gobbo is recording knowledge of traditional healing practices and Davis is raising awareness of the importance of indigenous cultures.
11. Colonialism allowed profits to be made by the colonizing countries; government corruption kept profits from benefiting the people in the region.
12. Population has increased faster than food production.
13. distributing mosquito nets; spraying; developing treatments and vaccines
14. ethnic and religious strife
15. right to vote, freedom from segregation and discriminatory laws, better lands to farm, better jobs

## CULTURE

### ANALYZE THE ESSENTIAL QUESTION ANSWERS

**16.** Probably not. European colonists settled in Africa and also imported laborers from Asia. They drew borders that included a number of ethnic groups within one colony. Previously, many Africans had lived in isolated villages or within the regions of one cultural group. Only trade and the influence of Islam had introduced multicultural elements.

**17.** People who lived in lands too dry to support farming became nomadic herders. Those who lived in good farmland became settled farmers. When minerals were discovered, many Africans switched from food production to mining, left their homes to work in the mines, created a culture of migrant mine laborers, and brought elements of their culture to a new country.

### INTERPRET MAPS

**18.** Selebi Phikwe

**19.** a river

## GOVERNMENT & ECONOMICS

### ANALYZE THE ESSENTIAL QUESTION ANSWERS

**20.** minerals, oil, animals, and landscapes that attract tourists

**21.** Colonial powers drew borders that left countries ethnically divided and created cultural conflict. They also redistributed land in ways that disrupted traditional land management systems and created negative impacts on African farmers.

**22.** Apartheid legalized the racial inequality that was present for decades in South Africa. Black South Africans could only own land in certain areas, had to carry identification at all times, and eventually faced relocation to homelands.

### INTERPRET GRAPHS

**23.** East Africa

**24.** Statistics are needed that show populations of these regions in each of these years.

## ACTIVE OPTIONS

### WRITE A LETTER

**25.** Letters should
- have a greeting;
- focus on a specific country;
- explain why the organization and team need money;
- contain evidence to support the request for donor support;
- have a concluding section that restates the purpose;
- close with a signature.

### CREATE A CHART

**26.** See the chart at the right for sample information. Uganda has the most people. Lesotho has the fewest people. ──────────→

|  | Ghana (West Africa) | Uganda (East Africa) | Lesotho (South Africa) |
|---|---|---|---|
| Year Country Gained Independence | 1957 | 1962 | 1966 |
| Population | 24,339,838 | 33,398,682 | 1,919,552 |
| Square Miles of Land | 92,098 | 93,065 | 11,720 |
| Main Economic Resources | gold, cocoa, oil, agriculture | agriculture, some copper, gold, oil | remittances from miners, customs duties, small manufacturing, hydropower |

# Deserts of the World

Deserts make up about one fifth of the land on Earth. Geologically speaking, deserts as we know them are relatively young—forming within the last 65 million years. Deserts are dry lands that can lose more water through evaporation than they get from precipitation. Rainfall in deserts is usually less than 10 inches a year. Limited rainfall, low humidity, often high daytime temperatures, and winds all contribute to the desert's dryness.

Deserts sometimes cover large areas and extend beyond country borders. For example, the Sonoran Desert crosses the border between Mexico and the United States. The Kalahari Desert covers parts of three countries—Botswana, Namibia, and South Africa.

## Compare

- Botswana
- China
- Mexico
- Mongolia
- Namibia
- South Africa
- United States

### PHYSICAL CHARACTERISTICS

Many people think of a desert as a hot, sandy wasteland with no water and no life. In fact, there is an amazing diversity among deserts. Some are hot and sandy, but some have rainy seasons and can get very cold. While about one fourth of deserts are made of sand, the rest are composed of dirt, clay, rock, ice, and other materials. For example, Antarctica is a desert. Deserts can be flat or hilly, below sea level or in mountains.

### DESERT PLANTS AND ANIMALS

Deserts are home to a wide array of plants and animals that have adapted to the harsh climates. Desert plants, such as the saguaro cactus (below), can go long periods without water. Some plants have shallow root systems that cover a large area to gather as much water as possible. Many desert animals, such as the elf owl (below), are nocturnal, hunting for food after the sun goes down and the temperatures drop.

Namib Desert, Namibia

Elf owl in a saguaro cactus, Sonoran Desert, United States

## SELECTED DESERTS OF THE WORLD

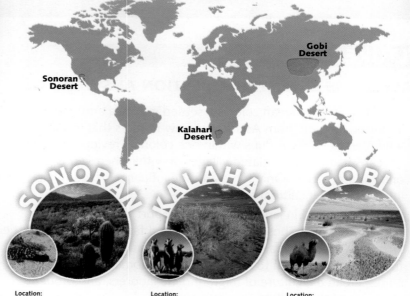

Sonoran Desert

Gobi Desert

Kalahari Desert

### SONORAN

**Location:**
United States, Mexico

**Approximate size:**
100,000 square miles

**Average yearly rainfall:**
4–12 inches

**Interesting animal species:**
Gila monster

**Examples of temperature ranges:**
120°F (summer)
32°F (winter)

### KALAHARI

**Location:**
Botswana, South Africa, Namibia

**Approximate size:**
220,000 square miles

**Average yearly rainfall:**
3–7.5 inches

**Interesting animal species:**
Meerkat

**Examples of temperature ranges:**
113°F (summer)
7°F (winter)

### GOBI

**Location:**
China, Mongolia

**Approximate size:**
500,000 square miles

**Average yearly rainfall:**
2–8 inches

**Interesting animal species:**
Bactrian Camels

**Examples of temperature ranges:**
113°F (summer)
-40°F (winter)

Source: World Wildlife Fund; worldatlas.com; gobidesert.org; Arizona-Sonoran Desert Museum

### ONGOING ASSESSMENT
## RESEARCH LAB  GeoJournal

1. **Analyze Data** Which desert has the widest range in temperatures?
2. **Compare and Contrast** How do the deserts compare in size?

**Research and Create Charts** Locate the Patagonian and Sahara deserts on a map. Do research to compare the deserts and use a chart like the one above to present your findings. Adjust the categories depending on the information you want to compare.

---

# PLAN

## OBJECTIVE Compare deserts in various world regions using data.

## CRITICAL THINKING SKILLS

- Analyze Data
- Compare and Contrast
- Create Charts
- Analyze Visuals
- Summarize
- Make Inferences
- Create Graphs

## PRINT RESOURCES

*Teacher's Edition* Resource Bank

**Review: GeoActivity** Compare Precipitation Across Regions

 **TECHTREK**  myNGconnect.com

**Teacher Resources**
Infographic: Selected Deserts of the World

**Interactive Whiteboard GeoActivity** Compare Precipitation Across Regions

**Also Check Out**
Research Links in **Connect to NG**

## BACKGROUND FOR THE TEACHER

The Gila monster is one of the world's few venomous lizards. Despite its fierce name, however, no Gila monster has ever killed a human. Gila monsters spend most of their time sheltering in underground burrows. Thanks to the fat they store in their tails, they can go months between meals.

Meerkats are sociable animals that survive through cooperation. In a group of meerkats, some will serve as lookouts, standing on their hind legs to survey the surrounding land while others seek food. Sometimes meerkats hunt together, communicating through their distinctive sounds.

Like their Arabian cousins, Bactrian camels store fat in their humps to serve as a source of energy when food and water are scarce. Bactrian camels, however, have two humps instead of just one. Bactrian camels are also the only camels that live in the wild.

## INTRODUCE & ENGAGE

**Analyze Visuals** Gather and display photos of various deserts. Include a variety of locations such as Death Valley in California, the Dry Valleys of Antarctica, the Sahara, the Atacama Desert of Chile, and the Negev in Israel, as well as the deserts mentioned in this lesson. Have students compare and contrast the photos, noting that the deserts vary greatly in features and flora. `0:10` minutes

## TEACH  Teacher Resources

### Guided Discussion

1. **Summarize** What do all deserts have in common? *(They are very dry, receiving little rainfall, and they have flora and fauna that are adapted to life in dry conditions.)*

2. **Analyze Data** Project the infographic Selected Deserts of the World. **ASK:** Looking at the infographic, what can you say about the temperature ranges in the three deserts? *(These deserts experience a very large range of temperatures.)*

3. **Make Inferences** How might winters in the Gobi Desert differ from winters in the Kalahari Desert? *(The Gobi Desert gets much colder. It might get snow and ice in the winter. The low temperature in the Kalahari Desert is around the freezing mark, so it might get some frost.)*

**Create Graphs** Have students work in small groups to create bar graphs or other types of graphs to compare the information in the infographic. For example, students can create graphs that compare the maximum and minimum average annual rainfall, the average high and low temperatures, the temperature range, and desert sizes. Have students present their graphs to the class and make three statements based on the information in their graphs. *(e.g., The Gobi Desert experiences the coldest temperatures.)* `0:20` minutes

## DIFFERENTIATE

**English Language Learners Paired Reading** Have students work in pairs to read the text and the infographic. Have partners read the text and infographic silently once, and then take turns reading aloud. Have students work together to summarize the information in each paragraph. Encourage Spanish-speakers to try using cognates to help them understand unfamiliar words, as the text contains several English cognates for Spanish words (e.g., desert—*desierto*; evaporation—*evaporación*; diversity—*diversidad*; composed—*compuesto*).

**Gifted & Talented Create a Chart** Have students research a desert of their choice, focusing on how plants and animals in the ecosystem interact with each other and how they adapt to the desert's conditions. Students may work individually or in pairs. Once they have completed their research, have students create a poster (either on paper or electronically) illustrating a complex food web that exists in their desert. Tell students they should include detailed captions that explain how the organisms interact and that mention their adaptations to the desert ecosystem.

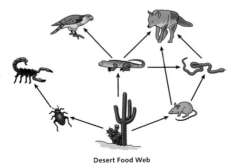

Desert Food Web

### Interactive Whiteboard
### GeoActivity

**Compare Precipitation Across Regions** Review this activity with students, or introduce it if you have not done it with the class before. **ASK:** How do these precipitation numbers compare with the deserts in this section? Which deserts have the greatest amount of precipitation? Which have the smallest amount? `0:15` minutes

### On Your Feet

**Team Word Web** Divide the class into three teams, and give each team a large sheet of paper. Have each team create a Word Web for one of the deserts, with each member contributing at least one word to the web. Then have teams share their webs with the class, and have the class compare and contrast them. `0:20` minutes

### Performance Assessment

**Desert Jeopardy** Have students work in groups to create a quiz about deserts. Each group thinks of three categories for questions and makes up four questions for each category. Questions are worth 10, 20, 30, or 40 points, depending on their level of difficulty. Have students write each question on a separate sheet of paper, with the question on one side and the value on the other. Then have the groups take turns posting their questions on the board, grouped according to category and with the value side facing out.

The group member acting as quizmaster calls on members of the class to choose a question and answer it. If the question is not answered correctly, another student should be called on to answer it. At the end of each round, the student who has most points wins. Go to **myNGconnect. com** for the rubric.

## RESEARCH LAB  GeoJournal

### ANSWERS
1. the Gobi Desert
2. The Gobi Desert is a little more than twice as big as the Kalahari Desert. The Kalahari Desert is about twice as big as the Sonoran Desert.

**Research and Create Charts** Students' charts should reflect accurate research and use the same categories of information for each desert to allow for comparison and contrast.

# Active Options

TECHTREK
myNGconnect.com For photos of endangered species and writing templates

Digital Library    Student eEdition    Magazine Maker

## ACTIVITY 1

**Goal:** Extend your understanding of endangered animals.

### Write a Briefing

Sub-Saharan Africa is famous for the variety of animals that live there. Unfortunately, many of these animals are endangered. Some of these animals are listed below. Choose one or a different threatened animal in the region. Do research and prepare a written briefing about the animal. A briefing is a short summary of important information about a topic. Give your audience facts about the animal and about efforts to protect it.

- African elephant
- addax
- black rhinoceros
- mandrill (shown at right)
- pygmy hippopotamus
- lowland gorilla

mandrill

## ACTIVITY 2

**Goal:** Research sub-Saharan Africa's culture.

### Keep a Travel Journal

Congratulations! You have won a seven-day, all-expenses-paid tour to one of these countries: Kenya, Tanzania, South Africa, Botswana, Zimbabwe, or Zambia. The only condition is that you keep a daily journal describing what you see and do. Choose your country and begin your tour. Use the **Magazine Maker** to share your journal with friends back home.

## ACTIVITY 3

**Goal:** Review sub-Saharan Africa with a game.

### Play a Capital Game

With a group, look at a map and choose 25 countries in sub-Saharan Africa. Write the name of each country on a small card. On another small card, write the capital of each country. Now you're ready to play. Each player draws a country card and tries to identify the capital. If the player misses, the card is put at the bottom of the pile, and it is the next player's turn. If the player names the capital correctly, he or she keeps the card and it is the next player's turn. The one with the most cards wins. Vary the game by choosing a capital card and trying to name the country.

## ASSESS

Use the rubrics to assess each student's participation and performance.

### Project Rubric: Activity 1

| SCORE | Planning / Preparation | Content / Presentation | Participation / Collaboration |
|---|---|---|---|
| **GREAT** 3 | • Uses multiple reliable sources to conduct thorough research about an animal.<br>• Takes plentiful, accurate notes. | • The briefing is concise and clear throughout.<br>• All details are relevant and important.<br>• The writing contains no errors in grammar or mechanics. | • Listens attentively to other students' briefings.<br>• Offers only constructive, respectful feedback. |
| **GOOD** 2 | • Uses at least one reliable source to conduct sufficient research about an animal.<br>• Takes sufficient, accurate notes. | • The briefing is concise and clear much of the time.<br>• Some unnecessary details are present.<br>• There are a few errors in grammar and mechanics. | • Listens somewhat to other students' briefings.<br>• Offers feedback that is often constructive and respectful. |
| **NEEDS WORK** 1 | • Uses just one source that may not be reliable.<br>• Takes few or no notes. | • The briefing is vague and hard to follow.<br>• Many irrelevant, distracting details are present.<br>• Errors in grammar and mechanics make the reading difficult. | • Does not listen to other students' briefings.<br>• Offers no feedback, or addresses other students disrespectfully. |

### Project Rubric: Activity 2

| SCORE | Planning / Preparation | Content / Presentation | Participation / Collaboration |
|---|---|---|---|
| **GREAT** 3 | • Researches the country to find at least four different locations.<br>• Carefully organizes research notes to create an itinerary that makes sense. | • Writing is consistently in the form of a travel journal.<br>• Information is accurate and interesting.<br>• Visuals are effectively incorporated into the text. | • Works well with others.<br>• Assumes a clear role and related responsibilities. |
| **GOOD** 2 | • Researches the country to find at least three different locations.<br>• Organizes research notes with an itinerary in mind. | • Writing sometimes strays from the form of a travel journal.<br>• Most information is accurate.<br>• Some visuals are used. | • Works well with others most of the time.<br>• Sometimes has difficulty sharing decisions and responsibilities. |
| **NEEDS WORK** 1 | • Conducts little or no research, and features two or fewer locations.<br>• Does not organize notes before writing. | • Writing cannot be recognized as a travel journal.<br>• Much of the information is inaccurate and/or dull.<br>• Visuals are absent or irrelevant to the text. | • Cannot work with others in most situations.<br>• Cannot share decisions or responsibilities. |

### Project Rubric: Activity 3

| SCORE | Planning / Preparation | Content / Presentation | Participation / Collaboration |
|---|---|---|---|
| **GREAT** 3 | • Chooses 25 countries and finds the capitals. | • Records all the country names and capitals accurately and legibly. | • Collaborates actively in creating the game.<br>• Plays the game with good sportsmanship.<br>• Shows respect for other participants. |
| **GOOD** 2 | • Chooses at least 20 countries and finds the capitals. | • Records most of the country names and capitals accurately and legibly. | • Collaborates well in creating the game.<br>• Plays the game with good sportsmanship much of the time.<br>• Occasionally lapses in showing respect for other participants. |
| **NEEDS WORK** 1 | • Chooses fewer than 20 countries and does not find all the capitals. | • Makes several mistakes in writing the country names and capitals. | • Does not collaborate with others to create the game.<br>• Displays poor sportsmanship most of the time.<br>• Shows little respect for other participants. |

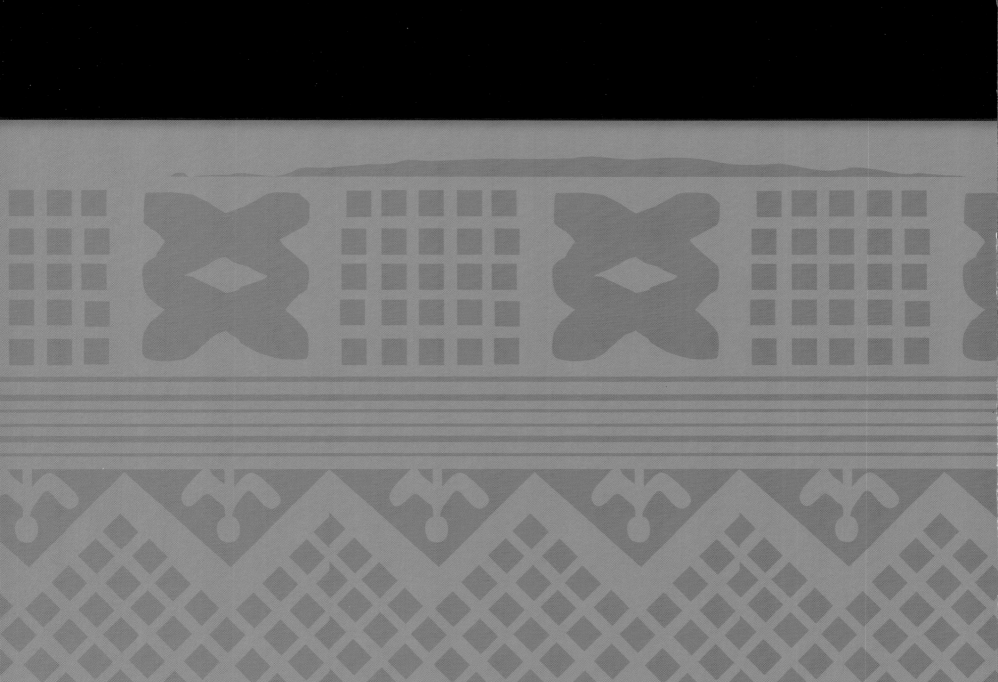

# SUB-SAHARAN AFRICA RESOURCE BANK

## GEOGRAPHY & HISTORY

### SECTION **1** GEOGRAPHY

## SECTION (2) HISTORY

# TODAY

## SECTION (1) CULTURE

# RESOURCE BANK

# FORMAL ASSESSMENT

## GEOGRAPHY & HISTORY

## TODAY

SECTION **1** GEOGRAPHY

## 1.1 Physical Geography

Use with Sub-Saharan Africa Geography & History, Section 1.1, *in your textbook.*

## Reading and Note-Taking Take Notes

As you read Section 1.1, use an Idea Web to take notes about Africa's physical geography.

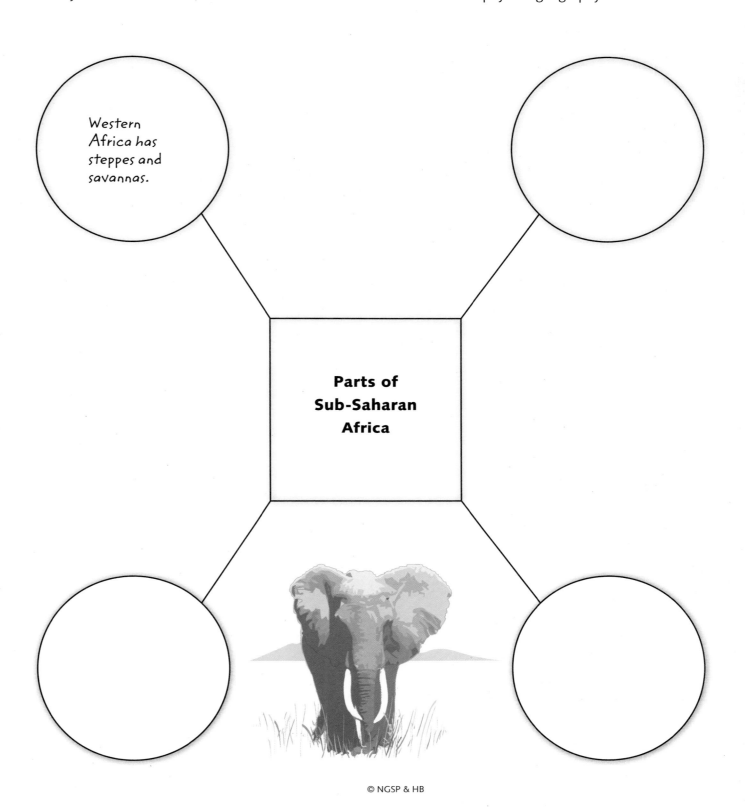

Western Africa has steppes and savannas.

**Parts of Sub-Saharan Africa**

© NGSP & HB

SECTION **1** GEOGRAPHY

*Use with* Sub-Saharan Africa Geography & History,
Section 1.1, *in your textbook.*

## 1.1 Physical Geography

## Vocabulary Practice

**KEY VOCABULARY**

- **basin** (BAY-sihn) n., a region drained by a water system
- **desertification** (deh-ZERT-uh-fih-KAY-shuhn) n., the process in which the soil becomes less fertile
- **rift valley** n., the deep valley that forms when Earth's crust separates and breaks apart
- **savanna** (suh-VAN-uh) n., tropical grasslands

**Definition Chart** Complete a Three-Column Chart for the Key Vocabulary words. Choose one of the words and draw a picture to illustrate it in the space below.

| Word | Definition | In My Own Words |
|------|------------|-----------------|
| basin | region drained by a water system | |

**Vocabulary Illustration**

© NGSP & HB

Name _____  Class _____  Date _____

NATIONAL GEOGRAPHIC
School Publishing

*Use with* Sub-Saharan Africa Geography & History, Section 1.1, *in your textbook.*

*Go to* Interactive Whiteboard GeoActivities at
**myNGconnect.com** *to complete this activity online.*

### 1.1 PHYSICAL GEOGRAPHY

# Compare Precipitation Across Regions

Climate varies widely across sub-Saharan Africa. It greatly influences where and how people live. For example, parts of western Botswana in the Kalahari Desert get less than five inches of rain each year. Such limited precipitation makes farming almost impossible, so few people live there.

Life is different in Rwanda, which has the highest population density in Africa. Each year the country has two rainy seasons, which result in more than 30 inches of annual rainfall. People are able to grow a number of different crops and graze animals on pastureland. The rainy seasons also allow the growth of forests, which are a valuable natural resource.

Rainfall amounts and climate zones vary within some countries. Northern Senegal, on the edge of the Sahara, receives only about 13 inches of annual rainfall, but southern Senegal receives about 50 inches. Because of this difference, parts of the country are made up of dry grasslands and desert areas, while other parts are home to rain forests.

**1. Make Generalizations** Based on the passage, in what way is a country's population density related to its amount of annual precipitation?

_____

_____

_____

**2. Pose and Answer Questions** With a partner, select two areas of sub-Saharan Africa on the map at right. Find other parts of the world with similar annual precipitation. Discuss whether the overall climate in places with similar precipitation would be the same. Be sure to think about the effects of latitude and elevation, too. Explain your reasoning.

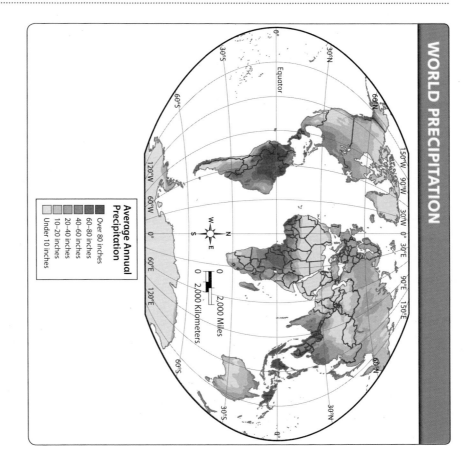

### WORLD PRECIPITATION

**Average Annual Precipitation**

- Over 80 inches
- 60–80 inches
- 40–60 inches
- 20–40 inches
- 10–20 inches
- Under 10 inches

© NGSP & HB

**SECTION 1 GEOGRAPHY**

## 1.2 East Africa and the Rift Valley

*Use with* Sub-Saharan Africa Geography & History, Section 1.2, *in your textbook.*

## Reading and Note-Taking Describe Geographic Information

As you read Section 1.2, use a Region Map to help you describe East Africa's geography.

Great Rift Valley _____

Details: _____

_____

_____

Deep water lakes _____

Details: _____

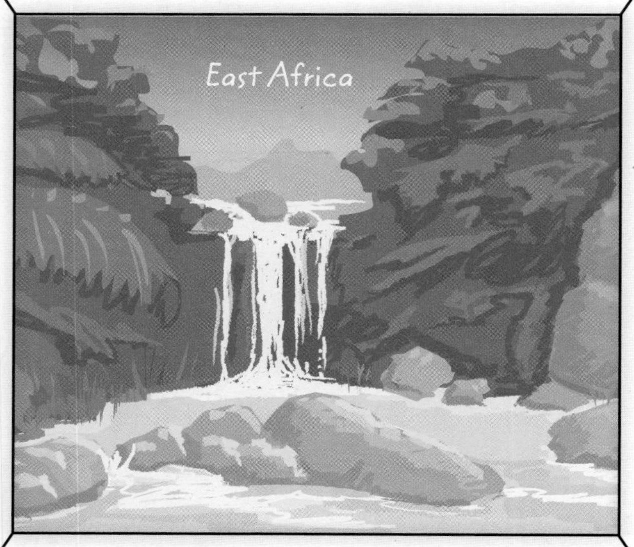

_____

_____

East Africa

_____

Details: _____

_____

_____

_____

Details: _____

_____

_____

© NGSP & HB

Name                                        Class                              Date

SECTION ① GEOGRAPHY                                    *Use with Sub-Saharan Africa Geography & History,*
                                                        *Section 1.2, in your textbook.*

## 1.2 East Africa and the Rift Valley

## Vocabulary Practice

**KEY VOCABULARY**

• **pride** n., a group of lions

**ACADEMIC VOCABULARY**

• **dormant** (DOR-muhnt) adj., inactive

Write a sentence about East Africa's geography using the Academic Vocabulary word *dormant*.

_____

_____

**Compare Vocabulary** Complete a Y-Chart to compare the meanings of the vocabulary words *dormant* and *pride*.

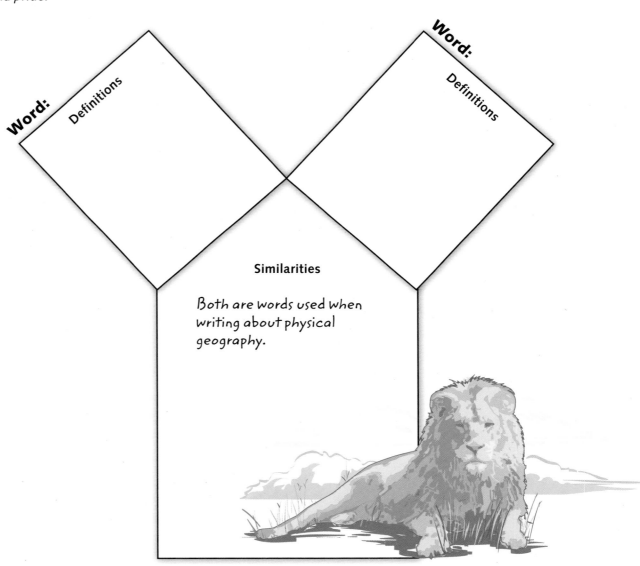

Word:  Definitions

Word:  Definitions

**Similarities**

*Both are words used when writing about physical geography.*

Name _____ Class _____ Date _____

*Use with Sub-Saharan Africa Geography & History, Section 1.2, in your textbook.*

*Go to Interactive Whiteboard GeoActivities at*
**myNGconnect.com** *to complete this activity online.*

☐ **NATIONAL GEOGRAPHIC**
School Publishing

**1.2 EAST AFRICA AND THE RIFT VALLEY**

# Relate Topography and Plate Tectonics

Read the passage on plate tectonics. Then analyze the elevation profile and answer the questions about East Africa's topography.

### Plate Movement Creates Landforms

A *rift* is a crack, break, or separation in the land. Rifts on Earth occur through the process of plate tectonics. Rift valleys form when enormous plates of Earth's crust separate. Over the course of 30 million years, the tectonic plates that form Africa and the Arabian Peninsula have separated, resulting in a huge, flat valley. East Africa's Great Rift Valley is part of this rift, which is thousands of feet below the surrounding plateaus.

Tectonic plate movement also explains the formation of East Africa's tallest mountains. As the plates have separated, hot material, or magma, has risen from deep below Earth's surface and built up volcanic mountains such as Mount Kilimanjaro in Tanzania.

**1. Analyze Visuals** How much higher is Mount Kilimanjaro than the lowest point of the Great Rift Valley?

_____

_____

_____

**2. Make Predictions** Would you expect East Africa's topography to look the same in 50 million years? Why or why not?

_____

_____

_____

## EAST AFRICA ELEVATION

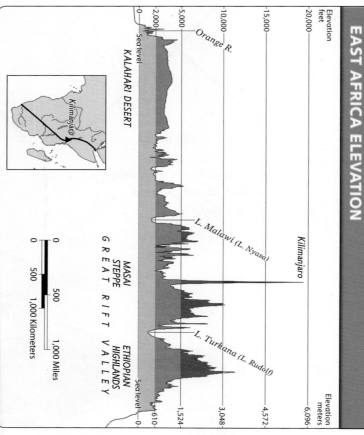

**3. Make Inferences** The Great Rift Valley was formed by the separation of tectonic plates. What might this suggest about the boundaries between tectonic plates elsewhere on Earth?

_____

_____

© NGSP & HB

Name _____  Class _____  Date _____

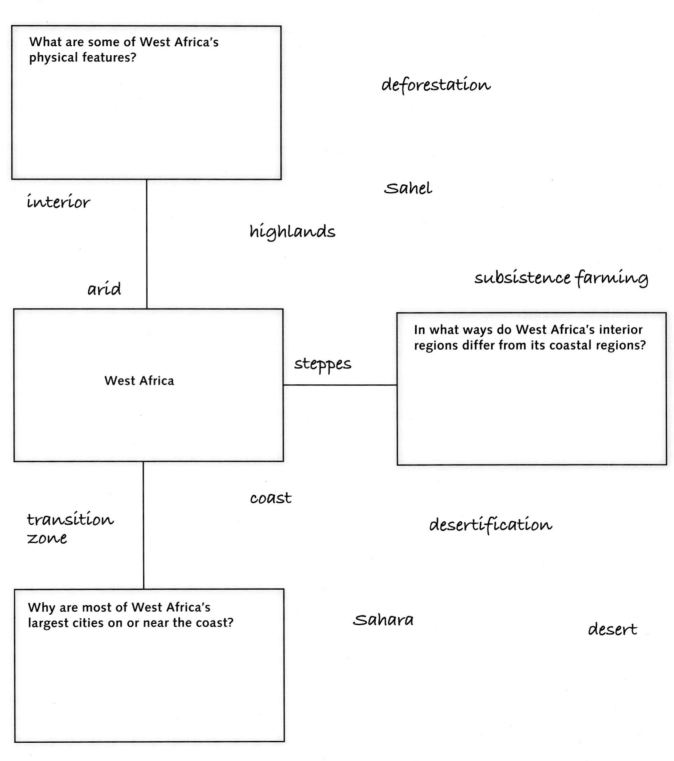

SECTION **1** GEOGRAPHY
## 1.3 West Africa's Steppes

*Use with* Sub-Saharan Africa Geography & History, Section 1.3, *in your textbook.*

## Reading and Note-Taking **Make Connections**

After you read Section 1.3, use the Summary Map to help you summarize the lesson. As you write summary sentences, see how many of the words on this page associated with West Africa you can use.

What are some of West Africa's physical features?

deforestation

interior

Sahel

highlands

arid

subsistence farming

West Africa

steppes

In what ways do West Africa's interior regions differ from its coastal regions?

transition zone

coast

desertification

Why are most of West Africa's largest cities on or near the coast?

Sahara

desert

© NGSP & HB

Name Class Date

SECTION 1 GEOGRAPHY

# 1.3 West Africa's Steppes

*Use with* Sub-Saharan Africa Geography & History, Section 1.3, *in your textbook.*

## Vocabulary Practice

**KEY VOCABULARY**

- **deforestation** (dee-FAWR-ehs-TAY-shuhn) n., the practice of cutting down forests to make way for crops
- **highland** n., an area of higher mountainous land
- **interior** (ihn-TEER-ee-ur) n., the land area away from a coast
- **transition zone** n., an area between two geographic regions that has characteristics of both

**Definition Chart** Complete a Definition Chart for the Key Vocabulary words.

| Word | Definition | In your own words |
|---|---|---|
| interior | land area away from a coast | |
| | | |
| | | |
| | | |



BLACK-AND-WHITE COPY READY

Name _____  Class _____  Date _____

## Graph Water Levels in Lake Chad

Lake Chad was once one of the largest bodies of water in Africa. The lake supported human cultures and wildlife for thousands of years. In recent decades, Lake Chad's water levels have fallen dramatically as a result of drought, desertification, and irrigation projects. In 1963, the lake had a surface area of about 9,650 square miles. By 1972, the lake's area was about 6,500 square miles. In the 1970s and 1980s, periods of severe drought affected the lake, and by 1985, Lake Chad measured only 1,000 square miles. The size of the lake continued to decrease and was only about 580 square miles by 2001. Experts worry that the lake could disappear completely in the next 20 years, causing an enormous crisis for the people in the region.

**1. Calculate to Solve a Problem** What percentage of Lake Chad's surface area disappeared between 1963 and 2001? (To calculate the percentage, first subtract the lake's size in 2001 from the lake's size in 1963. Then divide this number by the size of the lake in 1963. Finally, multiply this result by 100 to get the percentage.)

_____

_____

_____

**2. Analyze Cause and Effect** What is the relationship between the extended periods of drought in the region and use of the lake for irrigation?

_____

_____

_____

_____

**3. Create Graphs** Make a line graph showing Lake Chad's water level over the decades. Use the data from the passage to mark the surface area for each date given. Then connect the points on your graph.

### Water Levels in Lake Chad

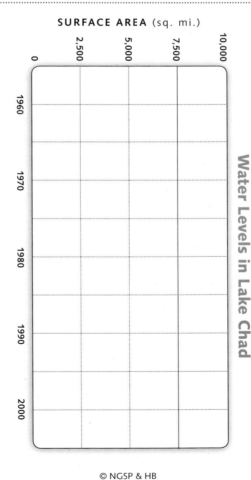

SURFACE AREA (sq. mi.)

10,000

7,500

5,000

2,500

0

1960    1970    1980    1990    2000

**4. Interpret Graphs** Between which years did Lake Chad experience the sharpest decline in surface area?

_____

_____

**5. Compare and Contrast** Central Asia's Aral Sea has also lost a large amount of its surface area. In 1960, the Aral Sea had a surface area of 26,300 square miles, but by 1992 it covered only 13,000 square miles. How does this compare to the disappearance of Lake Chad?

_____

_____

SECTION **1** GEOGRAPHY

## 1.4 Rain Forests and Resources

*Use with* Sub-Saharan Africa Geography & History, Section 1.4, *in your textbook.*

## Reading and Note-Taking Make Generalizations

As you read Section 1.4, use an Idea Diagram to make generalizations about rain forests and resources. Take notes about the introduction and any details you read about. Then make generalizations from the information you gathered.

**Topic:** Rain Forests and Resources

**Introduction:** _____

_____

_____

**Main Heading:** Rain Forest in the Congo Basin

**Main Heading:** Resources of Central Africa

**Details:**

_____    _____

_____    _____

_____    _____

_____    _____

**Details:**

_____    _____

_____    _____

_____    _____

_____    _____

**Generalization:** _____

_____

_____

_____

**BLACK-AND-WHITE COPY READY**

SECTION **1** GEOGRAPHY

## 1.4 Rain Forests and Resources

*Use with* Sub-Saharan Africa Geography & History, Section 1.4, *in your textbook.*

## Vocabulary Practice

**KEY VOCABULARY**

- **hydroelectric** (HY-droh-ee-LEHK-trihk) **power** n., electric power produced by a water source such as a river

- **rain forest** n., a forest with warm temperature, lots of rain, high humidity, and thick vegetation

**Word Web** Complete a Word Web for each Key Vocabulary word.

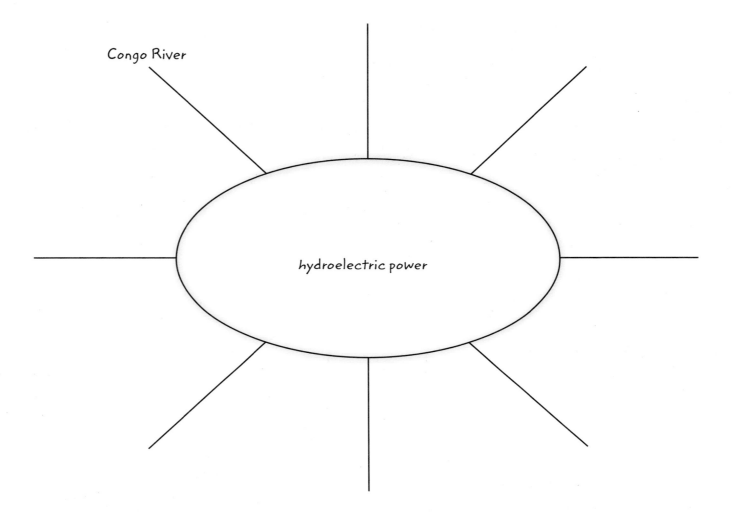

Congo River

hydroelectric power

© NGSP & HB

Name _____ Class _____ Date _____

SECTION **1** GEOGRAPHY

## GeoActivity

## Explore a Tropical Rain Forest

A tropical rain forest is divided into four layers:

- The **emergent layer** contains a few trees that tower above the rest of the forest. This layer receives direct sunlight. Birds, insects, and smaller mammals, such as bats, live here.

- The **canopy** is a layer of leaves and branches from trees that are over 100 feet tall. It forms a dense roof over the rain forest. About 90 percent of rain forest wildlife lives at this level, including reptiles, mammals, birds, and a large number of insects.

- The **understory** is dim and humid because it doesn't receive a lot of sunlight. Amphibians, reptiles, and mammals live among the tree trunks and branches at this level.

- The **forest floor** is dark and humid. Few plants can grow here. Animal life consists primarily of insects and worms that break down dead and decaying matter.

**Categorize** Study the diagram of a rain forest at right. Then read about wildlife that live in the Congo Basin. Draw a line from each animal to the rain forest layer where it lives. Share your diagram with a partner. Do you both agree?

*Use with Sub-Saharan Africa Geography & History, Section 1.4, in your textbook.*

Go to Interactive Whiteboard GeoActivities at **myNGconnect.com** to complete this activity online.

NATIONAL GEOGRAPHIC School Publishing

### LAYERS OF THE RAIN FOREST

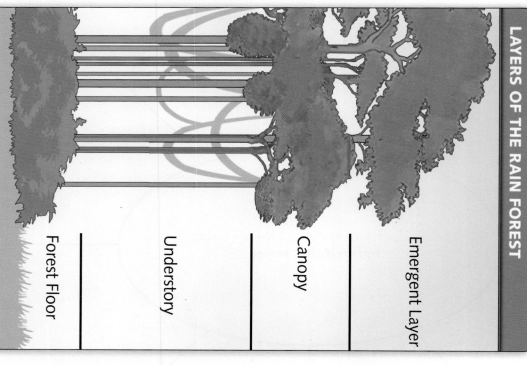

Emergent Layer

Canopy

Understory

Forest Floor

**1.**

**Colobus Monkey**
These long-tailed monkeys can leap great distances between trees and live in large groups high above the rain forest floor.

**2.**

**Driver Ant**
With millions of ants per colony, driver ants will swarm and overwhelm anything in their path, including larger mammals, reptiles, and birds.

**3.**

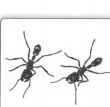

**Okapi**
These hoofed mammals, related to the giraffe, eat fruits and leaves and grow to about 5 feet tall.

**4.**

**African Grey Parrot**
These parrots can live to be 80 years old. They reach 13 inches in size and eat fruits and seeds. They can mimic human speech better than any other bird.

© NGSP & HB

**BLACK-AND-WHITE COPY READY**

SECTION **1** GEOGRAPHY

## 1.5 Southern Plateaus and Basins

*Use with* Sub-Saharan Africa Geography & History, Section 1.5, *in your textbook.*

## Reading and Note-Taking Describe Geographic Information

As you read Section 1.5, use an Information Map to describe the physical features and resources of Southern Africa.

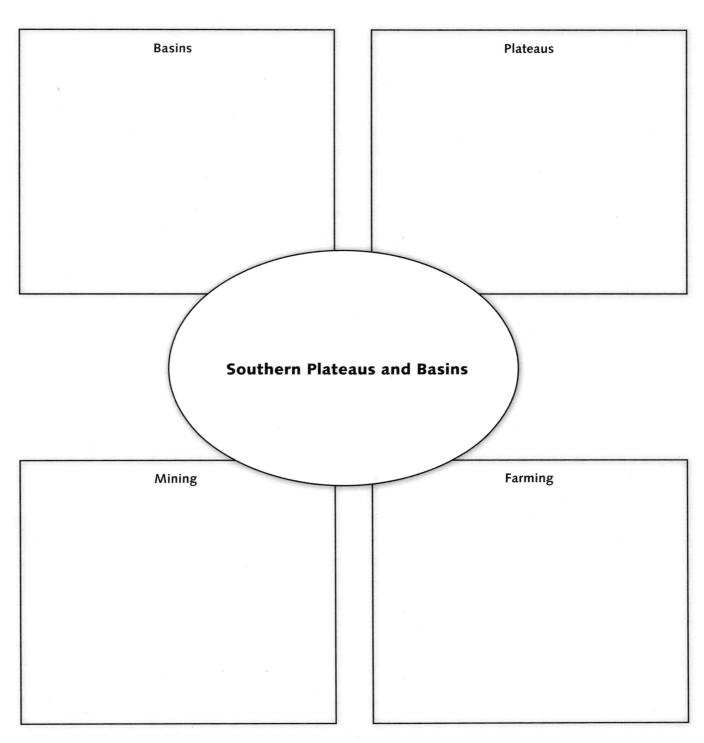

Basins

Plateaus

**Southern Plateaus and Basins**

Mining

Farming

SECTION **1** GEOGRAPHY

*Use with* Sub-Saharan Africa Geography & History, *Section 1.5, in your textbook.*

## 1.5 **Southern Plateaus and Basins**

## Vocabulary Practice

### KEY VOCABULARY
• **escarpment** (ehs-KARP-muhnt) n., a steep slope    • **landlocked** adj., having no direct access to a coast

**Vocabulary Pyramid** Complete a Vocabulary Pyramid for the word *escarpment*. Then create your own Vocabulary Pyramid for the word *landlocked*.

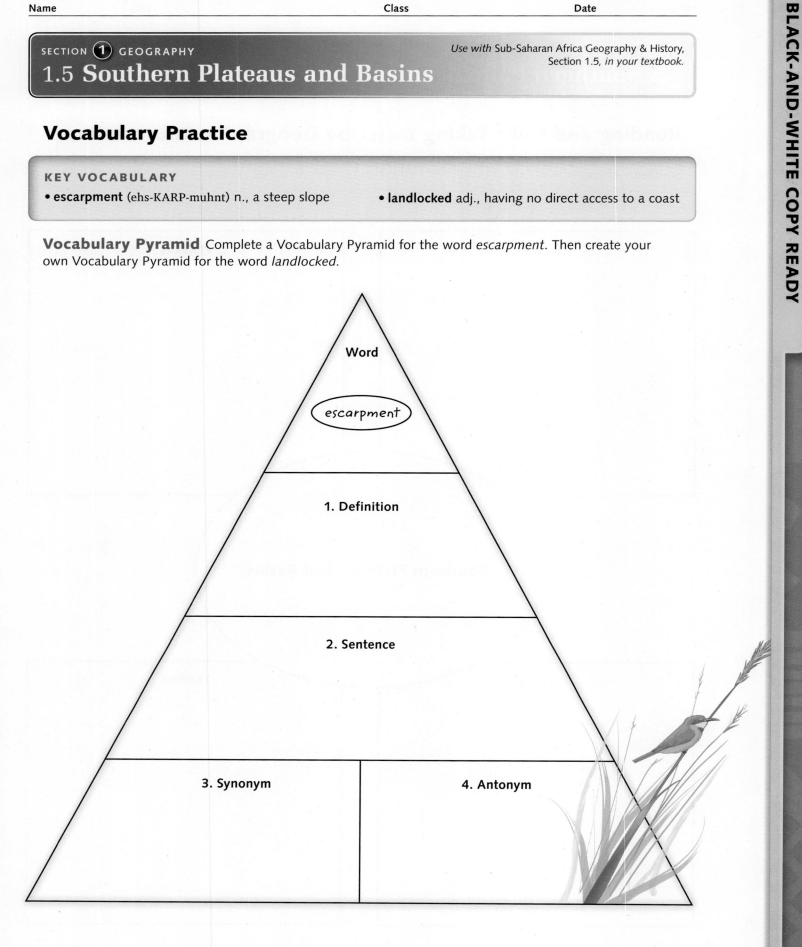

Word

escarpment

1. Definition

2. Sentence

3. Synonym

4. Antonym

Name _____  Class _____  Date _____

# GeoActivity

*Use with Sub-Saharan Africa Geography & History, Section 1.5, in your textbook.*

*Go to Interactive Whiteboard GeoActivities at*
**myNGconnect.com** *to complete this activity online.*

☐ NATIONAL
GEOGRAPHIC
School Publishing

## 1.5 SOUTHERN PLATEAUS AND BASINS

# Research Copper Exports

More than one-tenth of the world's copper deposits are contained in a single zone that extends across Zambia and the Democratic Republic of the Congo. Copper is the main export for each country. Where does the mined copper end up? Conduct research to find out which countries of the world import the most copper. Then find out how the copper is used.

**Step 1** Select Zambia or the Democratic Republic of the Congo to research.

Country: _____

**Step 2** Determine the top five countries that receive exports from the country you've selected. A useful resource for this research is

**http://cia.gov/library/publications/the-world-factbook**

| | |
|---|---|
| 1 | |
| 2 | |
| 3 | |
| 4 | |
| 5 | |

**Step 3** Investigate the different ways that copper is commonly used. List three major uses of copper. A useful resource is

**http://minerals.usgs.gov/minerals**

| | |
|---|---|
| 1 | |
| 2 | |
| 3 | |

**1. Interpret Maps** On the map, draw arrows from the copper-producing country you researched to the top five countries that import this country's copper. Vary the width of these arrows—the country that imports the most copper should have the thickest arrow, and the country that imports the least should have the thinnest arrow.

## COPPER EXPORTS

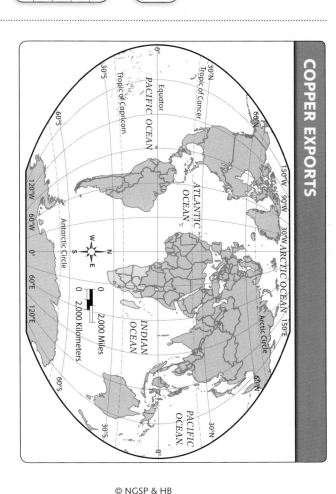

**2. Make Inferences** Copper is a valuable and scarce commodity that is unevenly distributed throughout the world. In what way does the uneven distribution affect local economies?

_____

_____

**3. Draw Conclusions** Based upon what you learned about the major uses of copper, what can you conclude about the economies of the top copper-importing countries?

_____

_____

© NGSP & HB

SECTION **1** GEOGRAPHY

# 1.6 Exploring Africa's Wildlife

*Use with* Sub-Saharan Africa Geography & History, Section 1.6, *in your textbook.*

## Reading and Note-Taking Identify Problems and Solutions

As you read Section 1.6, use the Problem-and-Solution-Diagram to identify problems that Africa's lions face and the solutions that might help them.

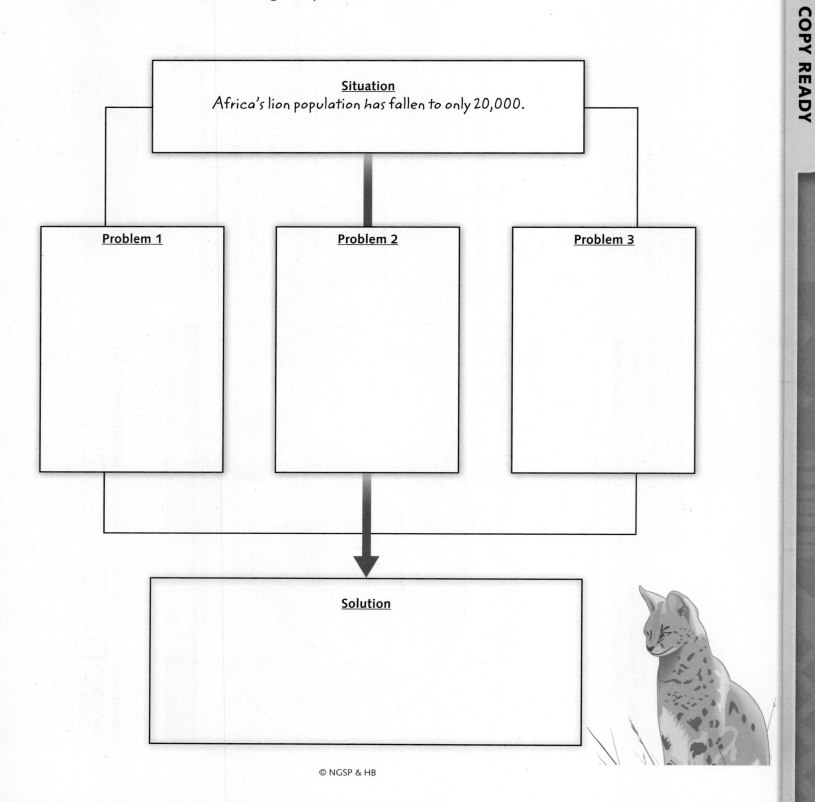

**Situation**
Africa's lion population has fallen to only 20,000.

**Problem 1**

**Problem 2**

**Problem 3**

**Solution**

SECTION **1** GEOGRAPHY

## 1.6 Exploring Africa's Wildlife

*Use with* Sub-Saharan Africa Geography & History, Section 1.6, *in your textbook.*

## Vocabulary Practice

**KEY VOCABULARY**
- **ecotourism** (ee-koh-TOOR-ihz-uhm) n., tourism that is focused on conservation and responsible use of land, wildlife, and resources
- **habitat** (HAB-ih-taht) n., a natural home
- **nocturnal** (nawk-TUHR-nal) adj., night-based
- **poaching** n., illegal hunting

**Definition and Details Tree** Complete the Definition and Details Tree below. Write down each Key Vocabulary word and its definition along with a detail about the word.

### Definition Tree

habitat —

Definition: *natural home*

Detail:

Definition:

Detail:

Definition:

Detail:

Definition:

Detail:

© NGSP & HB

Name _____ Class _____ Date _____

Use with Sub-Saharan Africa Geography & History, Section 1.6, in your textbook.

*Go to Interactive Whiteboard GeoActivities at*
**myNGconnect.com** *to complete this activity online.*

NATIONAL
GEOGRAPHIC
School Publishing

## SECTION 1 GEOGRAPHY
# GeoActivity

### 1.6 EXPLORING AFRICA'S WILDLIFE

## Locate a Wildlife Reserve

Conservationists Dereck and Beverly Joubert have been working for more than 25 years to protect the habitat of big cats in Botswana. They have helped set aside hundreds of thousands of acres of land where lions and other animals can thrive. Learn more about factors the Jouberts must consider when selecting land for a wildlife reserve. Then answer the questions that follow.

**1. Create Charts** For each factor in the chart, provide one reason why you think this would be important for a big cat habitat.

| FACTOR | REASON |
|---|---|
| a. A vast expanse of land with diverse wildlife and a stable water source | |
| b. Far from major population centers such as cities or towns | |
| c. Away from areas with high industrial activity | |
| d. Away from farms or large livestock pastures | |

**2. Evaluate** Study the map. Based on the factors above, which of the four shaded areas would you select for a wildlife reserve? Why?

**3. Make Inferences** Why might it be more difficult to set aside land as a wildlife reserve than to use the land for farming, ranching, or mining?

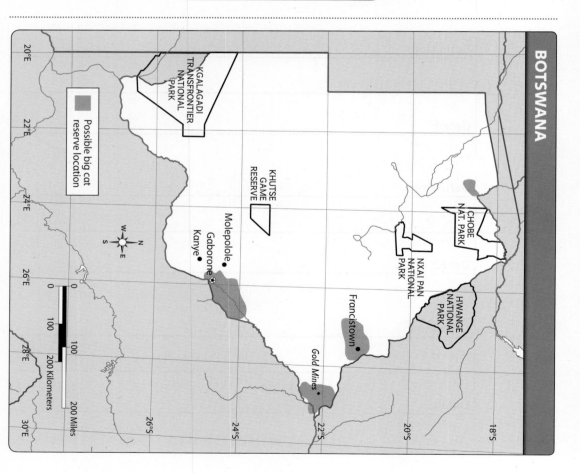

BOTSWANA

Possible big cat reserve location

KGALAGADI TRANSFRONTIER NATIONAL PARK

KHUTSE GAME RESERVE

CHOBE NAT. PARK

NXAI PAN NATIONAL PARK

HWANGE NATIONAL PARK

Molepolole
Kanye
Gaborone
Francistown
Gold Mines

0 100 200 Kilometers
0 100 200 Miles

© NGSP & HB

SECTION **1** GEOGRAPHY

## 1.1–1.6 Review and Assessment

*Use with* Sub-Saharan Africa Geography & History, Sections 1.1–1.6, *in your textbook.*

Follow the instructions below to review what you have learned in this section.

**Vocabulary** Next to each vocabulary word, write the letter of the correct definition.

1. _____ basin
2. _____ savanna
3. _____ desertification
4. _____ pride
5. _____ interior
6. _____ deforestation
7. _____ transition zone
8. _____ rain forest
9. _____ hydroelectric power
10. _____ landlocked
11. _____ escarpment
12. _____ nocturnal

A. a steep slope
B. the practice of cutting down forests to make way for crops
C. a region drained by a river system
D. electric power produced by a water source such as a river
E. tropical grasslands
F. the land area away from the coast
G. the process in which the soil becomes less fertile
H. night-based
I. a group of lions
J. an area between two geographic regions that has characteristics of both
K. having no direct access to a coast
L. a forest with warm temperatures, lots of rain, high humidity, and thick vegetation

**Main Ideas** Use what you've learned about the geography of Sub-Saharan Africa to answer these questions.

13. **Describe** Where is Sub-Saharan Africa located?

_____

14. **Summarize** Why are Sub-Saharan rivers not very useful for travel?

_____

15. **Explain** How was the Great Rift Valley in East Africa created?

_____

16. **Explain** How were the deep lakes in the Great Rift Valley created?

_____

17. **Identify** Name the types of landforms in West Africa.

_____

18. **Describe** List the features of the Congo Basin of Central Africa.

_____

19. **Analyze** Why does Southern Africa have the highest standard of living in Sub-Saharan Africa?

_____

20. **Define and Explain** What is ecotourism, and how can it help protect wildlife?

_____

© NGSP & HB

## Focus Skill: Draw Conclusions

Answer the questions below to draw conclusions about how the physical geography of Sub-Saharan Africa has affected people's lives.

**21.** How would lack of access to fresh water affect the lives of people in Sub-Saharan Africa?

_____

_____

**22.** Why is the Great Rift Valley such an important geographical feature of East Africa?

_____

_____

**23.** How might the higher elevations and cooler temperatures of East Africa affect the lives of its human population?

_____

_____

**24.** Why do countries on the coast of West Africa have more cities and higher populations that other parts of West Africa?

_____

_____

**25.** What positive effects might exporting oil have on the economy of Chad?

_____

_____

**26.** What does the Zambezi River contribute to the economy of Southern Africa?

_____

_____

**27.** What other factors, in addition to its physical geography, affect the economies of Southern Africa?

_____

_____

**28.** Explain why South Africa, Botswana, and Namibia have the highest gross domestic product in South Africa.

_____

_____

## Synthesize: Answer the Essential Question

How has the varied geography of Sub-Saharan Africa affected people's lives? Consider the information you have learned about Sub-Saharan Africa. Think about the region's physical geography, landforms and rivers, location and climate, access to fresh water, natural resources, and economy.

_____

_____

_____

_____

_____

© NGSP & HB

SECTION **1** GEOGRAPHY

## 1.1–1.6 Standardized Test Practice

*Use with* Sub-Saharan Africa Geography & History, Sections 1.1–1.6, *in your textbook.*

Follow the instructions below to practice test-taking on what you've learned from this section.

**Multiple Choice** Circle the best answer for each question from the options available.

1. What phrase best defines basin?
   A land area away from the coast
   B tropical grasslands
   C region drained by a river system
   D area of higher mountainous land

2. The steppes of Sub-Saharan Africa are becoming less fertile. Which reason does **not** explain why this is happening?
   A climate change
   B plate tectonics
   C human activity
   D overusing water resources

3. What is the most important feature of the Great Rift Valley in East Africa?
   A the region's deepwater lakes
   B the region's inactive volcanoes
   C the region's mineral resources
   D the region's rare animal species

4. Which of the following is **not** an effect of the growing population in West Africa?
   A shortened rainy season
   B increased demand for food crops
   C deforestation
   D desertification

5. Which phrase best describes the interior countries of West Africa?
   A abundant rainfall
   B desert and poor soil
   C rich farmland
   D proximity to the coast

6. What is a transition area?
   A area in which volcanoes are inactive
   B area where tourism is focused on conservation and the responsible use of land
   C area damaged by desertification and not suitable for farming
   D area between two geographic regions that has characteristics of both

7. Which statement does **not** describe the Congo River in Central Africa?
   A It is located in an equatorial region.
   B It is the longest river in the world.
   C It flows into the Atlantic Ocean.
   D It is a major waterway.

8. Which statement best explains why Southern Africa has the highest standard of living in Sub-Saharan Africa?
   A Southern Africa has abundant wildlife.
   B Southern Africa has many deep lakes.
   C Southern Africa can export its many natural resources.
   D Southern Africa has many plateaus.

9. Which word best describes the climate of Southern Africa?
   A temperate
   B hot
   C rainy
   D cool

10. What is the mission of Dereck and Beverly Joubert?
    A living a nocturnal life
    B conserving big cat habitats
    C making a film about big cats
    D exploring Southern Africa

## Document-Based Question

The following excerpt is taken from the article **When Green Earth Turns Into Sand** by Donald Smith, which appeared on *NationalGeographic.com* on December 19, 2000. Read the excerpt and answer the questions that follow.

> *Scientists define desertification as the conversion [change] of arid or semiarid regions to deserts due to climatic changes, human activities or both. Drought often sets the stage. Removal of trees and other vegetation deprives the land of its ability to retain water, leading to excessive erosion. . . . Poor cultivation [planting] techniques often exhaust the soil of newly cleared land within a few planting seasons, resulting in the need to clear more forest.*

**Constructed Response** Read each question carefully and write your answer in the space provided.

**11.** What is desertification?

_____

**12.** How does removal of trees and other vegetation contribute to the process of desertification?

_____

**Extended Response** Read the question carefully and write your responses in the space provided.

**13.** In the last sentence of the excerpt, the author describes a circular—or repeating—process. Summarize the process. What could be done to keep the process from repeating itself?

_____

_____

| Net Hydroelectric Power Generation, Selected Sub-Saharan African Countries, 2003–2005 (Billion Kilowatthours) | | | |
|---|---|---|---|
| COUNTRY | 2003 | 2004 | 2005 |
| Angola | 1.23 | 1.73 | 2.20 |
| Mali | 0.23 | 0.24 | 0.24 |
| Mozambique | 10.76 | 11.55 | 13.13 |
| Tanzania | 2.52 | 2.33 | 1.76 |

Source: U.S. Department of Energy, Energy Information Administration

**14.** According to the chart, what country generates the most hydroelectric power? What country generates the least?

_____

_____

**15.** From what you have learned about the varied geographic features of countries in Sub-Saharan Africa, what can you infer about the geography of Mozambique as compared with the geography of Mali?

_____

_____

© NGSP & HB

BLACK-AND-WHITE COPY READY

Name ______________________ Class ______________ Date ______________

SECTION 2 HISTORY

# 2.1 Bantu Migration

*Use with* Sub-Saharan Africa Geography & History, Section 2.1, *in your textbook.*

## Reading and Note-Taking Sentence Map

Use the chart below to help you create a sentence map about the Bantu migration across Africa as you read Section 2.1. Complete the first sentence and then add additional sentences.

### Bantu Migration

1. Bantu-speaking people ______________________

2. ______________________

3. ______________________

4. ______________________

5. Historians and anthropologists aren't sure why the Bantu migrated.

SECTION **2** HISTORY

## 2.1 Bantu Migration

*Use with* Sub-Saharan Africa Geography & History, *Section 2.1, in your textbook.*

## Vocabulary Practice

**KEY VOCABULARY**

- **agricultural revolution** (A-grih-KUL-chur-uhl REH-voh-LOO-shuhn) n., the development of agriculture by humans
- **caravan** (KAIR-uh-van) n., a group of merchants traveling together for safety
- **first language** n., mother tongue
- **lingua franca** (LEEN-gwa-FRAWN-kah) n., a language common to two groups with different languages

**WDS Chart** Complete a Word-Definition-Sentence (WDS) Chart for each Key Vocabulary word.

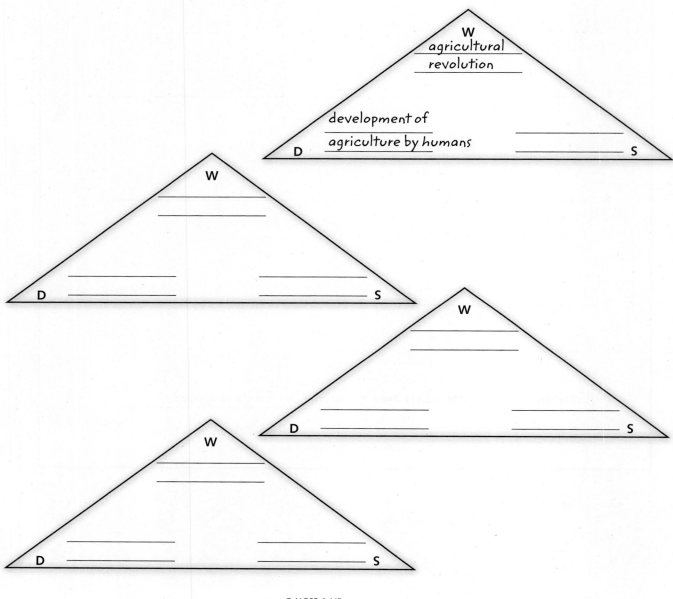

© NGSP & HB

Name _____ Class _____ Date _____

Use with Sub-Saharan Africa Geography & History, Section 2.1, in your textbook.

Go to Interactive Whiteboard GeoActivities at
**myNGconnect.com** to complete this activity online.

☐ **NATIONAL GEOGRAPHIC**
School Publishing

2.1 BANTU MIGRATIONS

## Map the Swahili Language

Read the passage about the Swahili language and answer the questions.

### A Language Develops

Over several centuries, Swahili emerged as the common language of Bantu tribes along East Africa's coast. As Arab traders made their way westward from the coast, they brought Swahili into areas that are now Uganda and the Democratic Republic of the Congo. When European colonial powers later gained control in the region, they worked to establish Swahili as an official language there.

Along with English, Swahili is today the official language in both Kenya and Tanzania. In Kenya, Swahili is widely used in schools, media, and small businesses, and English is used by the government. In Tanzania, government business is conducted in Swahili, and highly educated Tanzanians speak English. Swahili is also spoken by many people in Burundi, the Democratic Republic of the Congo, Rwanda, and Uganda. However, it is neither the official nor the most common language.

1. **Create Maps** Fill in the map at right, using two colors to distinguish between the countries where Swahili is the official language and the countries where it is commonly spoken but not the official language. Also label the countries.

2. **Interpret Maps** What patterns do you notice about where Swahili is spoken?

_____
_____
_____

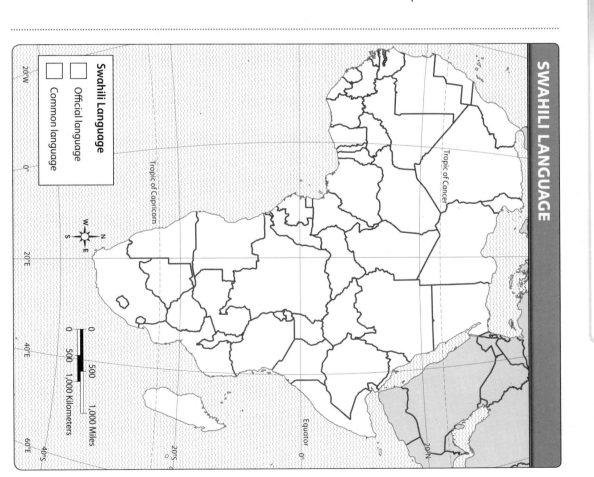

**SWAHILI LANGUAGE**

Swahili Language
☐ Official language
☐ Common language

Tropic of Cancer

20°N

0°

Equator 0°

Tropic of Capricorn

20°S

40°S

20°W    0°    20°E    40°E    60°E

0    500    1,000 Miles
0    500    1,000 Kilometers

© NGSP & HB

SECTION **2** HISTORY

## 2.2 Early States and Trade

*Use with* Sub-Saharan Africa Geography & History, Section 2.2, *in your textbook.*

## Reading and Note-Taking Sequence Events

As you read Section 2.2, complete the time line below to keep track of the sequence of events. Put events in the correct order.

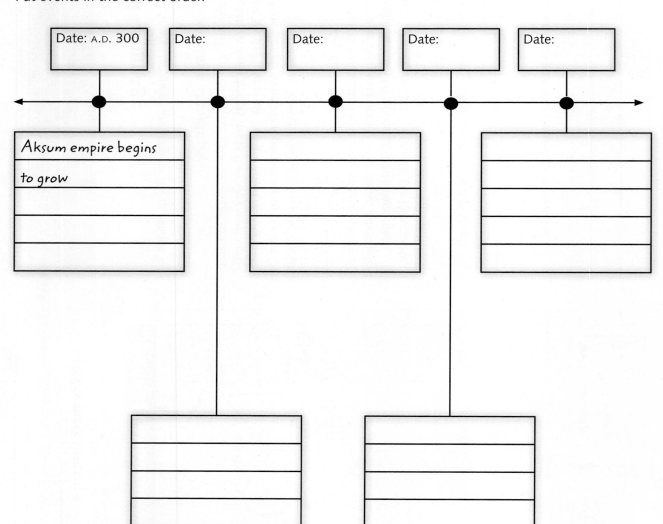

Date: A.D. 300    Date:    Date:    Date:    Date:

*Aksum empire begins to grow*

© NGSP & HB

SECTION **2** HISTORY

## 2.2 Early States and Trade

*Use with* Sub-Saharan Africa Geography & History,
Section 2.2, *in your textbook.*

## Vocabulary Practice

**KEY VOCABULARY**
- **alluvial** (a-LOO-vee-ahl) adj., deposited by a river
- **city-state** n., an independent state made up of a city and the territories depending on it
- **trans-Saharan** adj., across the Sahara

**Descriptive Paragraph** Use each of the Key Vocabulary words in a paragraph that describes trade between West and East African kingdoms. Start with a topic sentence, then write four to six sentences, and end with a summarizing sentence.

**Topic Sentence:** _____

_____

_____

_____

_____

_____

_____

_____

_____

_____

_____

_____

**Summary Sentence:** _____

_____

_____

_____

Name _____     Class _____     Date _____

Use with Sub-Saharan Africa Geography & History, Section 2.2, in your textbook.

Go to Interactive Whiteboard GeoActivities at
**myNGconnect.com** to complete this activity online.

**NATIONAL
GEOGRAPHIC**
School Publishing

## SECTION ②
### HISTORY
## GeoActivity

**2.2 EARLY STATES AND TRADE**

## Map Historic Trade Routes

Trans-Saharan trade routes connected the kingdoms of West Africa with the cities of North Africa. These routes developed because of an uneven distribution of resources. The following chart shows trans-Saharan trading cities and their trading partners at the beginning of the 15th century. Study the chart and then answer the questions that follow.

| TRADING CITIES | TRADING PARTNERS | MAIN EXPORTS |
|---|---|---|
| Algiers | Sijilmasa | African goods (from other cities) to Europe |
| Aoudaghost | Sijilmasa | Gold |
| Gao | Sijilmasa | Gold |
| | Tunis | Slaves |
| Djenne | Timbuktu | Gold |
| | | Slaves |
| Marrakech | Sijilmasa | Salt |
| Sijilmasa | Marrakech | Salt |
| | Timbuktu | |
| Timbuktu | Algiers | |
| | Gao | |
| | Djenne | Gold |
| | Sijilmasa | Ivory |
| Tunis | Gao | Slaves |
| | | African goods (from other cities) to Europe |

**1. Interpret Charts** What types of goods were exported by more than one city? What can we conclude about the availability of these goods in Africa?

_____

_____

## TRANS-SAHARAN TRADE ROUTES (c. 1400)

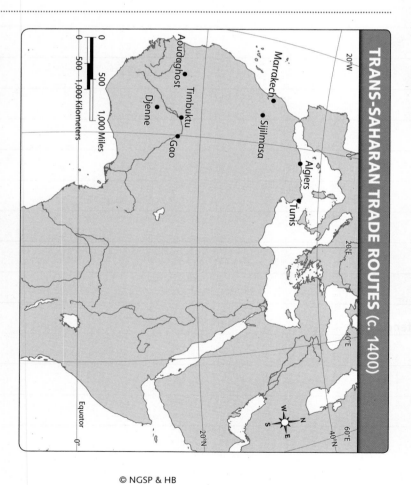

© NGSP & HB

**2. Create Maps** Using the information in the chart, draw lines between cities on the map to show major trade routes.

_____

**3. Interpret Maps** Which city is a major center of trade? Why might this be the case?

_____

_____

Name _____ Class _____ Date _____

## Reading and Note-Taking Find Main Ideas and Details

After you read Section 2.3, use the organizer below to record details that will help you identify the main idea.

| Subject |
|---|
| trans-Atlantic slave trade |

| Detail | Detail | Detail |
|---|---|---|
| The Portuguese, Spanish Dutch, French, and English all purchased slaves at African coastal ports. | | |

| Main Idea |
|---|
| |

SECTION **2** HISTORY

*Use with* Sub-Saharan Africa Geography & History, Section 2.3, *in your textbook.*

## 2.3 Impact of the Slave Trade

## Vocabulary Practice

**KEY VOCABULARY**

• **trans-Atlantic slave trade** n., the trading of slaves across the Atlantic Ocean

**ACADEMIC VOCABULARY**

• **incentive** (ihn-SEN-tihv) n., a motivating reason

• **malnutrition** (mal-noo-TRIH-shuhn) n., faulty or inadequate food or nourishment

Write a sentence using the Academic Vocabulary words *incentive* and *malnutrition*.

_____

_____

**Word Wheel** Follow the instructions below to analyze the vocabulary word *trans-Atlantic slave trade*.

1. Write the word in the center of the wheel.

2. Look in your textbook for examples of descriptions related to the word, or think of any related words you already know.

3. Write your descriptions and related words on the spokes of the wheel. Add more spokes if needed.

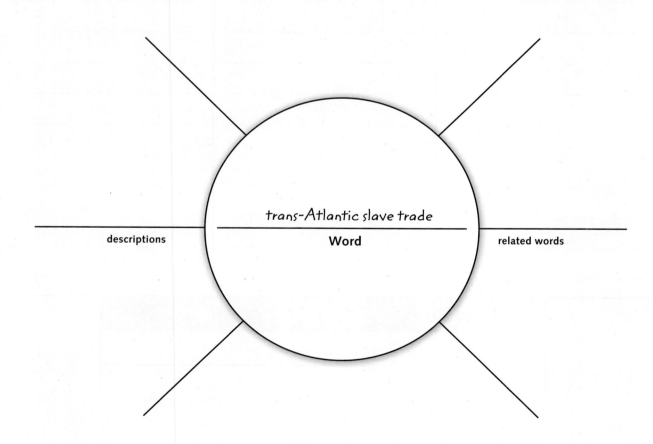

descriptions        *trans-Atlantic slave trade*        related words

**Word**

## SECTION 2 HISTORY
# GeoActivity

Use with Sub-Saharan Africa Geography & History, Section 2.3, in your textbook.

Go to Interactive Whiteboard GeoActivities at
**myNGconnect.com** to complete this activity online.

NATIONAL
GEOGRAPHIC
School Publishing

### 2.3 IMPACT OF THE SLAVE TRADE

# Analyze Primary Sources: The Slave Trade

The Middle Passage took an unspeakable toll on the millions of enslaved Africans who were held captive and taken to the Americas. Many narratives exist that tell about this experience. The following documents are from Olaudah Equiano, who was enslaved in the 1750s at the age of 11, and from an English slave ship captain, John Newton. Analyze these primary sources and answer the questions.

### Document 1: Equiano's Experience Aboard the Slave Ship

The closeness of the place, and the heat of the climate, added to the number in the ship, which was so crowded that each had scarcely room to turn himself, almost suffocated us. This produced copious perspirations [a lot of sweat], so that the air soon became unfit for respiration, from a variety of loathsome smells, and brought on a sickness among the slaves, of which many died.

—from The Interesting Narrative of the Life of Olaudah Equiano, or Gustavus Vassa, the African, 1789

Olaudah Equiano, c. 1789

### Document 2: Newton on the Middle Passage

Thursday 25th January. . . . 6 of our white people and about 5 slaves ill with the flux [dysentery], but none, I hope, without a prospect for recovery. For these 3 days have omitted giving the slaves pease [porridge] for breakfast and try them for a while with rice twice a day.

—from the journals of John Newton, 1750–1754

John Newton, c. 1775

1. **Make Inferences** Why would slave traders force enslaved Africans to endure the types of conditions that Equiano describes in the passage?

_____

_____

_____

2. **Analyze Primary Sources** What in Newton's passage suggests he was concerned with the health and survival of the slaves aboard his ship? How concerned do you think he was?

_____

_____

_____

3. **Make Generalizations** Based on these passages, how common do you think illness and disease were during the Middle Passage? Why?

_____

_____

_____

© NGSP & HB

SECTION **2** HISTORY

## 2.4 Colonization to Independence

*Use with* Sub-Saharan Africa Geography & History, Section 2.4, *in your textbook.*

# Reading and Note-Taking Track Important Information

As you read Section 2.4, use a Concept Cluster chart to help you track important information about colonization and independence in Africa.

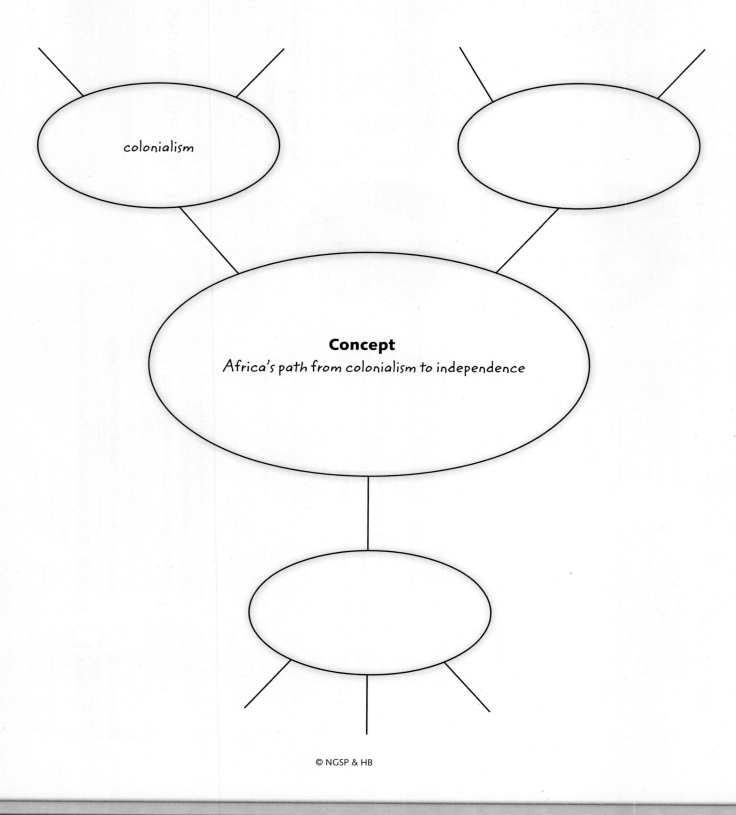

colonialism

**Concept**
Africa's path from colonialism to independence

© NGSP & HB

SECTION ② HISTORY

## 2.4 Colonization to Independence

*Use with* Sub-Saharan Africa Geography & History, Section 2.4, *in your textbook.*

## Vocabulary Practice

**KEY VOCABULARY**

- **colonialism** (kuh-LOH-nee-uh-lihz-uhm) n., one country exploring, conquering, settling—and sometimes exploiting—another area of the world
- **imperialism** (ihm-PEER-ee-uh-lihz-uhm) n., policy of extending foreign rule

- **missionary** (MIHSH-uh-NAIR-ee) n., person sent on religious missions to advance causes or ideas he or she believes in

**Word Squares** Complete Word Squares for the Key Vocabulary words.

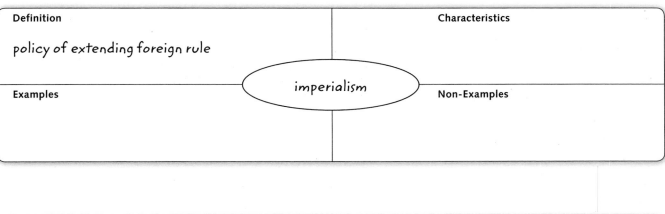

Definition: policy of extending foreign rule

Characteristics

Examples

*imperialism*

Non-Examples

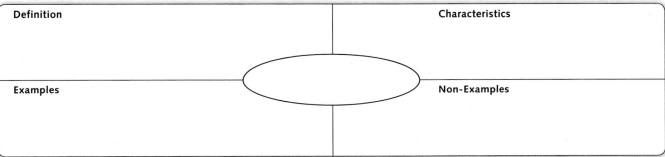

Definition

Characteristics

Examples

Non-Examples

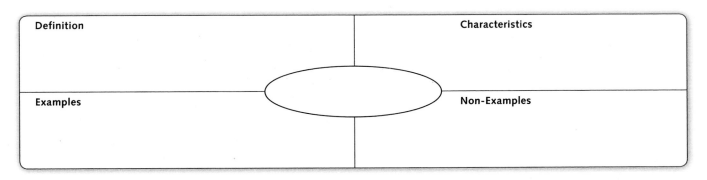

Definition

Characteristics

Examples

Non-Examples

© NGSP & HB

Name _____  Class _____  Date _____

*Go to Interactive Whiteboard GeoActivities at*
**myNGconnect.com** *to complete this activity online.*

☐ **NATIONAL GEOGRAPHIC** School Publishing

SECTION ② HISTORY

# GeoActivity

## 2.4 COLONIZATION TO INDEPENDENCE

# Build a Time Line of Ghana's Independence

Learn more about Ghana's history and the country's struggle for independence. Then build your own time line to organize events.

## The Long Struggle for Sovereignty

After Portuguese explorers first arrived in 1471, the European traders who came to the area that is now Ghana were primarily interested in its gold. This led to the name Gold Coast, by which the country was known for hundreds of years. By the 1600s, the slave trade became a major focus of European traders. The British, Dutch, and other Europeans leased land from native states and conducted trade from fortresses they had built along the coast.

Although the British abolished the slave trade in 1807, their control over the region grew. In 1821, the British government took control of the fortresses, and the colony of the Gold Coast was officially established. The Asante (or Ashanti) people, who lived inland, had grown powerful through trading with the Dutch, and they chose to resist British rule. The Asante and the British clashed throughout the 19th century, until the British ultimately gained control of Asante areas in 1902.

**continued ⟶**

When Ghana finally gained independence, it was through a peaceful political process. In the early 1950s, a new constitution granted local people much more control over their government. Pan-African leader Kwame Nkrumah became a major voice in this government, and he led the push for total independence with the slogan "self government now." Nkrumah would be the country's Prime Minister when Ghana became a fully independent nation in 1957.

1. **Create Time Lines** Underline key dates in the passage. Then mark these dates and their events on the time line below.

2. **Interpret Time Lines** For how many years did the British have official control of the Gold Coast colony?

3. **Make Inferences** If the British were no longer participating in the slave trade after 1807, why do you think they were still interested in control of Ghana?

4. **Draw Conclusions** Britain gave up control of Ghana in the 1950s. Think about major world events in the previous decade, the 1940s. Why might Britain have been willing to negotiate and accept Ghana's independence?

**Time Line Title:** _____

*1471 — Portuguese explorers arrive.*

| 1400 | 1500 | 1600 | 1700 | 1800 | 1900 | 2000 |

SECTION **2** HISTORY

*Use with* Sub-Saharan Africa Geography & History, Sections 2.1–2.4, *in your textbook.*

## 2.1–2.4 **Review and Assessment**

Follow the instructions below to review what you have learned in this section.

**Vocabulary** Next to each vocabulary word, write the letter of the correct definition.

1.____ agricultural revolution

2.____ first language

3.____ caravan

4.____ lingua franca

5.____ trans-Saharan

6.____ alluvial

7.____ city-state

8.____ trans-Atlantic slave trade

9.____ colonialism

10.____ imperialism

**A.** mother tongue

**B.** an independent state made up of a city and the territories depending on it

**C.** a language common to two groups with different languages

**D.** a group of merchants traveling together for safety

**E.** the trading of slaves across the Atlantic Ocean

**F.** policy of extending foreign rule

**G.** across the Sahara

**H.** one country exploring, conquering, settling—and sometimes exploiting—another area of the world

**I.** the development of agriculture by humans

**J.** deposited by a river

**Main Ideas** Use what you've learned about the history of Sub-Saharan Africa to answer these questions.

**11. Explain** What important change occurred during the agricultural revolution?

_____

_____

**12. Monitor Comprehension** Where is Swahili mainly spoken?

_____

_____

**13. Explain** What is the meaning of the term *lingua franca*?

_____

_____

**14. Analyze** What was the effect of trans-Saharan trade on Sub-Saharan Africa?

_____

_____

**15. Explain** From A.D. 700 to the 1200s Ghana gained wealth and power. How did this happen?

_____

_____

**16. Compare and Contrast** How did trans-Atlantic slave trade differ from Sub-Saharan trade?

_____

_____

## Focus Skill: Analyze Cause and Effect

Answer the questions below to analyze how trade networks and migration influenced the development of African civilization.

**17.** What were the effects of the Bantu migration south and east across East Africa?

_____

_____

**18.** How did Arab traders influence the development of the Swahili language?

_____

_____

**19.** Describe the effect of trade on the development of Sub-Saharan African kingdoms?

_____

_____

**20.** What effect did the presence of natural resources—gold and salt—have on the development of early African states?

_____

_____

**21.** Slavery existed in Africa for many years before European contact. What possible effect did this history of slave ownership have on the Portuguese and other Europeans' decision to purchase slaves at African ports?

_____

_____

**22.** What effect did increased European demand for sugar, cotton, tobacco, and cotton have on the growth of slave trade in the Americas?

_____

_____

**23.** What was the effect of increased slave trade on the African communities from which the slaves were taken?

_____

_____

**24.** What has been the impact of slave trade on the Americas?

_____

_____

**25.** For what reason did Europeans, beginning in the mid 1800s, go to war concerning their possessions in Africa?

_____

_____

**26.** What is Pan-Africanism, a movement that developed in the early 1900s?

_____

_____

## Synthesize: Answer the Essential Question

How did trade networks and migration influence the development of African civilization? Consider the information you have learned about the history of the region. Think about the Bantu migration, early African states and trade, the impact of slave trade, and the move of African countries toward independence.

_____

_____

_____

© NGSP & HB

SECTION **2** HISTORY

## 2.1–2.4 Standardized Test Practice

*Use with* Sub-Saharan Africa Geography & History, Sections 2.1–2.4, *in your textbook.*

Follow the instructions below to practice test-taking on what you've learned from this section.

**Multiple Choice** Circle the best answer for each question from the options available.

1. What sentence best describes the Swahili language?

   A It is the first language of many people in Sub-Saharan Africa.
   B It is one of the best-known of the surviving Bantu languages.
   C It is a language brought to Sub-Saharan Africa by Arab traders.
   D Swahili is the "mother tongue" for all of Africa.

2. Which phrase best describes the term *alluvial gold*?

   A gold deposited by a river
   B precious gold deposits
   C gold found in the northern deserts
   D gold found in the southern forests

3. Which sentence describes the powerful East African empire of Aksum?

   A It was located in present day Malawi.
   B It flourished at the same time as the kingdom of Benin.
   C Its main port on the Indian Ocean was a trading center.
   D Mogadishu was one of its many city-states.

4. What is the historic kingdom of Kongo best known for?

   A its highly organized government
   B its location on the Red Sea
   C the Spanish, who took over its politics and trade
   D its trade in gold and iron

5. Which African kingdom built a walled city out of stone?

   A Ghana
   B Shona
   C Kongo
   D Songhai

6. Who were the first Europeans to explore the African coast?

   A the Portuguese
   B the Spanish
   C the French
   D the English

7. What statement does **not** describe what happened to enslaved Africans?

   A Most worked on small farms.
   B They were crowded into large ships.
   C Many died of malnutrition.
   D They were sold at auctions.

8. Which phrase best describes the meaning of the word *incentive*?

   A bribes and other illegal acts
   B plantation crops
   C good trade relations
   D a motivating reason

9. Why would a young enslaved person be more valuable than an older enslaved person?

   A A younger person could survive on less water.
   B A younger person would be more likely to obey orders.
   C A younger person could be expected to work harder and longer.
   D A younger person would not care as much about leaving home.

10. What are Jomo Kenyatta and Kwame Nkrumah known for?

    A fighting to gain independence for their people
    B leading their countries to economic prosperity
    C bringing peace to their countries
    D sending the missionaries back to Europe

## Document-Based Question

The following excerpt is taken from the article **Africa's Imperiled Rock Art Documented Before It Disappears** by David Braun. It appeared in *National Geographic News* on October 2, 2001. Read the passage and answer the questions below.

*Panoramas of hunting and war, graceful images of animals loping across the savanna, ghostly handprints of people who lived long ago—artists daubed [painted] millions of images like these across Africa, recording the world as they saw it. . . . Whereas their bones and implements may tell us when and where they existed, how they lived and died, and even what they ate, it is only through their art that we can know a little about their thoughts.*

**Constructed Response** Read each question carefully and write your answer in the space provided.

**11.** What kinds of images does the rock art described by the author show?

_____

_____

**12.** What kinds of information do the bones and implements of early Africans tell scientists?

_____

_____

**Extended Response** Read the question carefully and write your responses in the space provided.

**13.** Why is it important to preserve African rock art?

_____

_____

### TRANS-ATLANTIC SLAVE TRADE

| CENTURY | LEFT FROM AFRICA | ARRIVED IN AMERICAS |
|---|---|---|
| 1500–1600 | 277,506 | 199,285 |
| 1601–1700 | 1,875,631 | 1,522,677 |
| 1701–1800 | 6,494,619 | 5,609,869 |
| 1801–1867 | 3,873,580 | 3,370,825 |
| TOTAL | 12,521,336 | 10,702,656 |

Source: http://slavevoyages.org/tast/assessment/estimates.faces

**14.** According to the chart, during what years was slave trade the highest?

_____

**15.** From what you have learned about the history and effects of slave trade in Sub-Saharan Africa, what can you infer from the figures given on this chart?

_____

_____

© NGSP & HB

# SUB-SAHARAN AFRICA

## TODAY • RESOURCE BANK

SECTION **1** CULTURE

*Use with* Sub-Saharan Africa Today, Section 1.1, *in your textbook.*

## 1.1 Africa's Borders and Cultures

## Reading and Note-Taking Analyze Cause and Effect

Fill in the chart below as you read Section 1.1, to help you analyze the effect of European colonialism on the borders and cultures of sub-Saharan Africa. Write details about situations before, during, and after colonization.

| Before Colonization | During Colonization | After Colonization |
|---|---|---|
| 1. Borders between African cultural groups developed through agreement or conflict. | 1. Europeans regularly ignored the borders of African cultural groups. | 1. |
| 2. | 2. | 2. |
| 3. | 3. | 3. |

© NGSP & HB

SECTION **1** CULTURE

## 1.1 Africa's Borders and Cultures

Use with Sub-Saharan Africa Today, Section 1.1, *in your textbook.*

## Vocabulary Practice

**KEY VOCABULARY**
- **ethnic group** n., a group of people who share a common culture, language, and sometimes racial heritage
- **transportation corridor** (KOHR-ih-dohr) n., a route to move people and goods easily between places

**Definition and Details** Complete a Definition and Details Chart for the Key Vocabulary words *ethnic group* and *transportation corridor.*

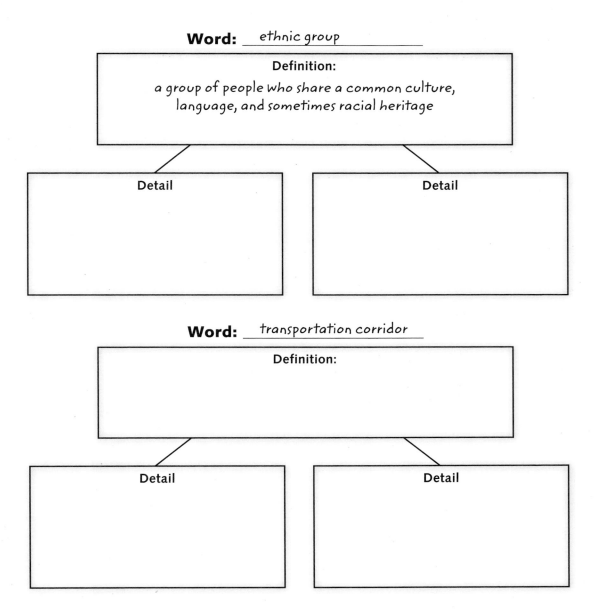

**Word:** _ethnic group_

Definition:
a group of people who share a common culture, language, and sometimes racial heritage

Detail

Detail

**Word:** _transportation corridor_

Definition:

Detail

Detail

Name _____     Class _____     Date _____

Use with Sub-Saharan Africa Today, Section 1.1, in your textbook.

Go to Interactive Whiteboard GeoActivities at
**myNGconnect.com** to complete this activity online.

**NATIONAL
GEOGRAPHIC**
School Publishing

## SECTION ① CULTURE
# GeoActivity

### 1.1 AFRICA'S BORDERS AND CULTURES

## Analyze Central Africa's Borders

When Europeans set colonial boundaries in Central Africa, they did so without considering the territories of the cultural groups living there. Although colonialism ended decades ago, many of those borders still exist today. As a result, many cultural groups are divided across national borders, and countries often include several different groups. Analyze the map and explore the effects that the European-created borders have had on the region.

**1. Interpret Maps** In which countries are the Borno people found? What challenges might this create? Could there be any advantages to these circumstances?

_____

**2. Make Inferences** European colonial powers were not concerned with keeping kingdoms or cultural groups intact. What factors might have contributed to the borders they created?

_____

**3. Turn and Talk** If colonial boundaries have produced a large number of problems for African countries, could the continent's people revert to the boundaries that existed before European colonialism? Discuss with a partner whether or not this would be possible. What other solutions might there be to the problems created by Africa's borders?

_____

### PRE- AND POST-COLONIAL BORDERS

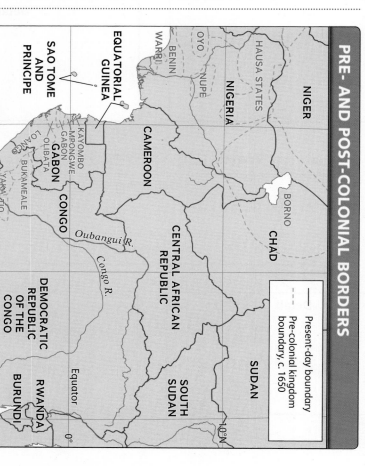

Legend:
— Present-day boundary
- - - Pre-colonial kingdom boundary, c. 1650

© NGSP & HB

SECTION **1** CULTURE

## 1.2 Africa's Music Goes Global

*Use with Sub-Saharan Africa Today, Section 1.2, in your textbook.*

## Reading and Note-Taking Summarize Information

Use a Topic Triangle to help you put the topics in Section 1.2 in order from broad to narrow. Then write a summary about African music.

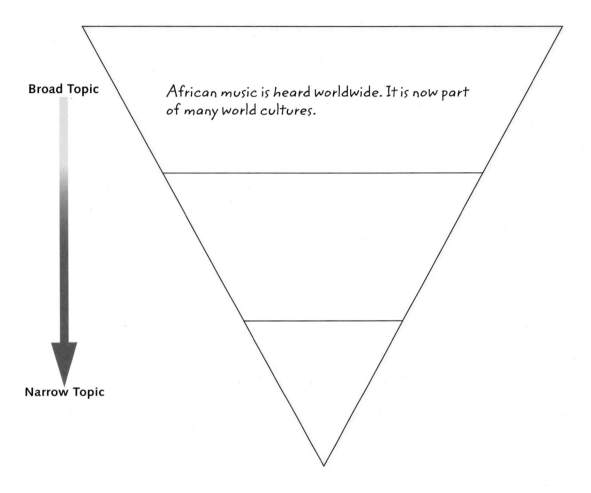

**Broad Topic**

African music is heard worldwide. It is now part of many world cultures.

**Narrow Topic**

Using your completed Topic Triangle as a guide, summarize what you have learned about African music.

_____

_____

_____

_____

_____

_____

© NGSP & HB

SECTION **1** CULTURE

## 1.2 Africa's Music Goes Global

*Use with* Sub-Saharan Africa Today, Section 1.2, *in your textbook.*

## Vocabulary Practice

**KEY VOCABULARY**

- **griot** (GREE-oh) n., a musician-storyteller of western Africa whose performances include tribal histories
- **oral tradition** n., stories shared verbally from one generation to the next

**ACADEMIC VOCABULARY**

- **evident** adj., clear to the sight or mind

What African influences are *evident* in the music you listen to?

_____

_____

**Venn Diagram** Use a Venn Diagram to compare the meaning of the Key Vocabulary words *griot* and *oral tradition*. Write the definitions. Where the circles overlap, write what associations the words have in common.

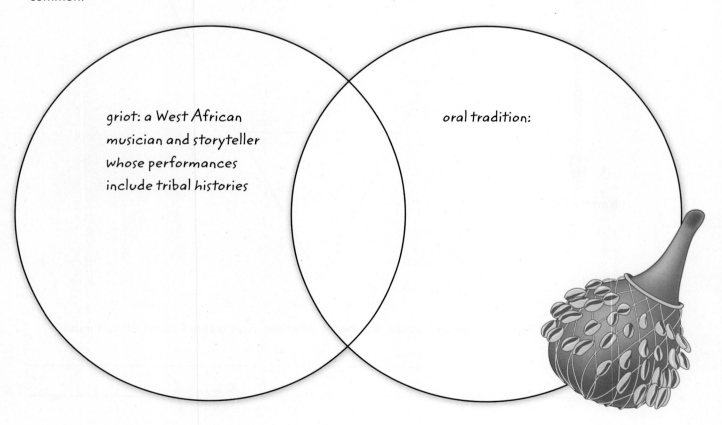

griot: a West African musician and storyteller whose performances include tribal histories

oral tradition:

Write a sentence using the Key Vocabulary words *griot* and *oral tradition*.

_____

_____

© NGSP & HB

Use with Sub-Saharan Africa Today, Section 1.2, in your textbook.

Go to Interactive Whiteboard GeoActivities at
**myNGconnect.com** to complete this activity online.

NATIONAL
GEOGRAPHIC
School Publishing

## SECTION 1 CULTURE
# GeoActivity

1.2 AFRICAN MUSIC GOES GLOBAL

## Solve a Puzzle About African Music

Use what you learned about African music in Section 1.2 of your
textbook to complete the crossword puzzle.

**Crossword Puzzle Tips**

1. Go through the clues and fill in the answers that you know.
2. Read the clues again, and see if the letters you filled in help you with
   the clues you did not know.
3. If an answer has two words, do not put a space between the words.
   If an answer has a punctuation mark, do not include the mark.
4. Look at Section 1.2 in your textbook only if you cannot think of all
   the answers.

**Across**

1  Type of music that is focused on politics
4  Traditional storyteller
6  Type of American music inspired by African music
8  Practice of sharing stories verbally
9  Clearly present
10 Type of music that blends griot music with
   Afro-Cuban influences

**Down**

2  Musician who protested South Africa's
   government policies
3  Internationally known griot
5  Blend
7  Type of instrument played by griots

© NGSP & HB

SECTION **1** CULTURE

## 1.3 Kenya Modernizes

*Use with* Sub-Saharan Africa Today, Section 1.3, *in your textbook.*

## Reading and Note-Taking Identify Goals and Outcomes

As you read about Kenya's modernization in Section 1.3, use a Goal and Outcome Chart to help you identify Kenya's goal, as well as challenges, strategies, and outcomes.

---

**Goal**

to modernize Kenya's economy and improve its standard of living

↓

**Challenges**

1. Kenya has 40 ethnic groups, and sometimes cultural diversity has led to rivalry and conflict there.
2. Education is a key factor in modernization for any country, including Kenya.
3.

↓

**Strategies**

1.

2. Most children in Kenya attend free elementary schools.

3.

↓

**Outcomes**

1.

2.

3.

---

© NGSP & HB

SECTION **1** CULTURE

## 1.3 Kenya Modernizes

*Use with* Sub-Saharan Africa Today, Section 1.3, *in your textbook.*

# Vocabulary Practice

**KEY VOCABULARY**

- **domestic policy** n., a government plan that relates to or originates within a country, especially one's own country
- **literacy** (LIH-tur-ah-see) **rate** n., the percentage of people who can read
- **modernization** (mah-dur-nih-ZAY-shun) n., the development of policies and actions designed to bring a country up to current world standards
- **reserve** n., an area of land set apart for a certain purpose, such as the protection of animals

**Definition Clues** Follow the instructions for the Key Vocabulary word indicated.

**1.** Write the sentence in which the Key Vocabulary word *modernization* appears in the lesson.

_____

_____

**2.** Write the actual definition of *modernization* here using your own words.

_____

_____

**3.** Use the Key Vocabulary word *domestic policy* in a sentence.

_____

_____

**4.** What does Kenya's high *literacy rate* show about its *modernization*?

_____

_____

_____

**5.** What aspect of Kenya's *modernization* has to do with its *reserves*?

_____

_____

_____

© NGSP & HB

Name _____  Class _____  Date _____

NATIONAL
GEOGRAPHIC
School Publishing

Go to Interactive Whiteboard GeoActivities at
**myNGconnect.com** to complete this activity online.

*Use with Sub-Saharan Africa Today, Section 1.3, in your textbook.*

## SECTION ① CULTURE
# GeoActivity

### 1.3 KENYA MODERNIZES

# Graph Kenya's Economic Indicators

Standards of living have improved dramatically as Kenya has modernized over the past several decades. Use the data in the tables below to create a line graph showing how Kenya has improved over time in literacy and GDP per capita. Remember that GDP per capita is the value of products a country produces per person.

### Literacy Rate in Kenya

| YEAR | ADULT LITERACY RATE |
|------|---------------------|
| 1960 | 20% |
| 1976 | 46% |
| 1988 | 54% |
| 2000 | 74% |
| 2008 | 86% |

Source: UNESCO

### GDP Per Capita in Kenya

| YEAR | GDP PER CAPITA (Current U.S. Dollars) |
|------|----------------------------------------|
| 1960 | $98 |
| 1976 | $248 |
| 1988 | $381 |
| 2000 | $414 |
| 2008 | $788 |

Sources: CIA World Factbook; the World Bank

---

**1. Create Graphs** Plot the data from the tables on the line graph. Use the left y-axis for literacy rates and the right y-axis for GDP per capita. Use a different color for each line on the graph.

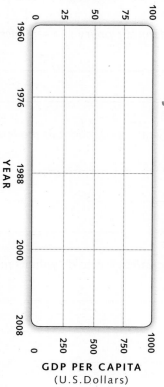

**Kenya's Economic Indicators**

**2. Interpret Graphs** According to the graph, around what year did Kenya's adult literacy rate exceed 50 percent for the first time?

_____

**3. Draw Conclusions** Based on the information you have, could you say that improved literacy rates caused the increased GDP per capita, or that the increased GDP per capita caused the improved literacy rates? Why or why not?

_____
_____
_____
_____

© NGSP & HB

SECTION **1** CULTURE

## 1.4 Exploring Traditional Cultures

*Use with* Sub-Saharan Africa Today, Section 1.4, *in your textbook.*

## Reading and Note-Taking Make Generalizations

As you read about explorers Grace Gobbo and Wade Davis in Section 1.4, use an Explorer Description Chart to help you make generalizations about the benefits of their work as ethnobotanists.

| Explorer | What the Explorer Does | Explorer's Goals | Benefits of the Work |
|---|---|---|---|
| Grace Gobbo | researches ways in which plants might help cure diseases | | |
| Wade Davis | | | |

© NGSP & HB

SECTION **1** CULTURE

## 1.4 **Exploring Traditional Cultures**

*Use with* Sub-Saharan Africa Today, Section 1.4, *in your textbook.*

## Vocabulary Practice

**KEY VOCABULARY**

- **ethnobotanist** (ehth-noh-BAH-tih-nihzt) n., someone who studies the relationship between cultures and plants

- **medicinal** (muh-DIS-ih-nuhl) **plant** n., a plant used to treat illness

**Vocabulary T-Chart** Use the T-Chart to compare the meanings of the Key Vocabulary words *ethnobotanist* and *medicinal plant*. Write the definition of each word and fill in details about each word from what you know and what you have read. Then answer the question.

| **Word:** *ethnobotanist* | **Word:** *medicinal plants* |
|---|---|
| **Definition:** *someone who studies the relationship between cultures and plants*<br><br>*ethno = people or cultural group*<br><br>*botanist = a scientist who studies plant life*<br><br>*could study native plants or medicinal plants* | **Definition:** |

**Compare** What is one way the meanings of the two Key Vocabulary words are related?

_____

_____

_____

## SECTION ① GEOGRAPHY

# GeoActivity

### 1.4 EXPLORING TRADITIONAL CULTURES

# Research Vanishing Cultures

Many indigenous groups around the world are at risk of disappearing because of a number of environmental and political threats. As these cultures are lost, so are their knowledge and cultural traditions. Work with a team to research one of the groups listed below. Consider ways the indigenous culture could be protected, and create a presentation to share with your class.

**Penan (Borneo and Malaysia)**   **Kogi (Colombia)**
**Tuareg (Northern Africa)**   **Inuit (Canada)**

**Step 1 Develop Your Research Topic** Answer the questions below to help you develop a topic. Write your topic in the Project Organizer.

- Where does the group live?
- What distinguishes this culture from others in the region?
- Are there major political or environmental threats in the region that may affect this group?

**Step 2 Identify Your Sources** Work with your teacher or librarian to find sources to help you explore your topic. You can also use the research links at **Connect to NG.**

**Step 3 Research and Take Notes** Take notes from your sources. Write down the most important facts from each source.

**Step 4 Identify Your Main Idea** Write your main idea in a complete sentence. The main idea should be about your topic.

**Step 5 Present Your Findings** Create a presentation of the research that supports your main idea. Use the ideas on the right to help you choose a format.

Use with Sub-Saharan Africa Today, Section 1.4, in your textbook.

*Go to Interactive Whiteboard Activities at*
**myNGconnect.com** *to complete this activity online.*

NATIONAL GEOGRAPHIC
School Publishing

## Project Organizer

**Step 1 Develop Your Research Topic**

Your Research Topic: _____

**Step 2 Identify Your Sources**

Source 1: _____
Source 2: _____

**Step 3 Research and Take Notes**

Source 1 Fact: _____
Source 2 Fact: _____

**Step 4 Identify Your Main Idea**

_____

**Step 5 Present Your Findings**

**Essay**
- Create an outline.
- Use a formal tone.
- Read your essay to the class.

**Blog**
- Use a less formal tone.
- Post your blog entries.
- Respond to questions in comments section.

**Slide Show**
- Write clear, simple bullet points.
- Use appropriate visuals.
- Project your presentation in class.

**Video/Photo Essay**
- Stay under 5 minutes.
- Include charts or graphs.
- Play your visual essay for the class.

Presentation Format: _____

SECTION **1** CULTURE

## 1.1–1.4 Review and Assessment

*Use with* Sub-Saharan Africa Today, Sections 1.1–1.4, *in your textbook.*

Follow the instructions below to review what you have learned in this section.

**Vocabulary** Next to each vocabulary word, write the letter of the correct definition.

1. _____ ethnic group
2. _____ transportation corridor
3. _____ oral tradition
4. _____ literacy rate
5. _____ reserve
6. _____ ethnobotanist
7. _____ medicinal plant

A. the percentage of people who can read

B. a plant used to treat illness

C. a group of people who share a common culture, language, and sometimes racial heritage

D. a route to move people and goods easily between places

E. someone who studies the relationship between cultures and plants

F. stories shared verbally from one generation to another

G. an area of land set apart for a certain purpose

**Main Ideas** Use what you've learned about sub-Saharan culture to answer these questions.

8. **Monitor Comprehension** Before the Europeans arrived, how did the borders between African cultural groups develop?

_____

_____

9. **Explain** What has been the function of military dictatorships in countries in which ethnic groups have failed to unite to form a single nation?

_____

_____

10. **Describe** What is the function of the African Union?

_____

_____

11. **Analyze** How have griots influenced African music?

_____

_____

12. **Identify** What is protest music?

_____

_____

13. **Make Inferences** What is the East African Community and how does this group plan to expand the economy in the region?

_____

_____

14. **Analyze** What are possible results of the work of ethnobotanists like Grace Gobbo and Wade Davis?

_____

_____

15. **Draw Conclusions** Why is it important to preserve indigenous cultures and traditional ways of life in Africa?

_____

_____

© NGSP & HB

## Focus Skill: Draw Conclusions

Answer the questions below to draw conclusions about the factors that helped influence the cultures of sub-Saharan Africa.

**16.** Why do many Africans identify themselves first as members of their tribe rather than their country?

_____

_____

**17.** Why did European colonizers ignore the existing borders of African cultural groups?

_____

_____

**18.** What has been the long-term effect of changing Africa's original borders?

_____

_____

**19.** What contribution have griots made to African culture?

_____

_____

**20.** How has African music influenced the development of American and European musical forms such as jazz and rock-and-roll?

_____

_____

**21.** What factors help make Kenya a multicultural society?

_____

_____

**22.** After independence in 1963, how did Jomo Kenyatta help all Kenyans pull together?

_____

_____

**23.** How has modernization helped improve life in Kenya?

_____

_____

**24.** Why did ethnobotanist Grace Gobbo interview more than 80 traditional healers?

_____

_____

**25.** Why does Wade Davis believe it is important to preserve cultural diversity?

_____

_____

## Synthesize: Answer the Essential Question

What historical and geographic factors have influenced the cultures of sub-Saharan Africa? Consider the information you have learned about the culture of sub-Saharan Africa. Think about Africa's borders and cultures, African music, Kenyan modernization, and recent efforts to explore the connections between African medicine and culture.

_____

_____

_____

_____

SECTION **1** CULTURE

*Use with* Sub-Saharan Africa Today, Sections 1.1–1.4, *in your textbook.*

# 1.1–1.4 Standardized Test Practice

Follow the instructions below to practice test-taking on what you've learned from this section.

**Multiple Choice** Circle the best answer for each question from the options available.

**1.** About how many languages are spoken in Africa?

  A 50
  B 75
  C 500
  D 1000

**2.** What are transportation corridors?

  A paved roads through mountain ranges
  B borders with natural barriers, such as mountain ranges
  C routes for large ships
  D routes to move people and goods easily between places

**3.** What does the word *evident* mean in the sentence below?
The griot influence is evident in today's West African music.

  A clearly present
  B hidden
  C weak
  D clearly absent

**4.** Who is Youssou N'Dour?

  A a musician who sang protests songs
  B a musician who performs jazz music
  C an internationally known griot
  D a South African pop star

**5.** Who is Miriam Makeba?

  A a musician who sang protest songs
  B a musician who performs jazz music
  C an internationally known griot
  D a West African pop star

**6.** Which of the following are all examples of African culture?

  A music, domestic policy, and modernization
  B language, oral traditions, and domestic policy
  C modernization, language, and music
  D language, music, and oral traditions

**7.** About how many ethnic groups live in Kenya?

  A 10
  B 40
  C 60
  D 80

**8.** When did Kenya gain its independence?

  A 1951
  B 1959
  C 1963
  D 1967

**9.** What is an ethnobotanist?

  A someone who interviews traditional healers
  B someone who encourages the use of medicinal plants
  C someone who studies the relationship between cultures and plants
  D someone who teaches traditional healing methods

**10.** What does "cultural web of life" refer to?

  A It refers to the belief that every culture is connected.
  B It refers to the belief that no culture should be modernized.
  C It refers to the belief that modern cultures have stronger connections.
  D It refers to the belief that indigenous cultures should be modernized.

## Document-Based Question

The following excerpt is taken from an article on world music at *NationalGeographic.com*. Read the excerpt and answer the questions that follow.

> *Mbalax was born in the 1970s when two cultural worlds collided. One was the domain of popular musicians in the capital, Dakar, a port city known . . . for its . . . Afro-Cuban music, jazz, funk, rock, and French pop. The other force was a welling resurgence [renewal] of African traditional culture that included Wolof sabar drummers and hurricane-throated praise singers whose songs carried the wisdom and heroic deeds of bygone ages.*

**Constructed Response** Read each question carefully and write your answer in the space provided.

**11.** What did the city of Dakar contribute to mbalax?

_____

_____

**12.** How was mbalax created?

_____

_____

**Extended Response** Read the question carefully and write your responses in the space provided.

**13.** What elements need to be present to create fusion—or a blend of different musical traditions?

_____

_____

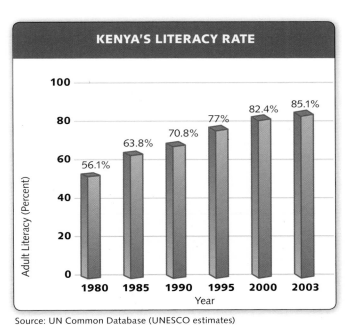

**KENYA'S LITERACY RATE**

Adult Literacy (Percent)

56.1% (1980)
63.8% (1985)
70.8% (1990)
77% (1995)
82.4% (2000)
85.1% (2003)

Year

Source: UN Common Database (UNESCO estimates)

**14.** What does the graph tell you about Kenyan literacy rates since 1980?

_____

_____

**15.** From what you know about Kenyan history, what does the graph tell you about Kenyan modernization?

_____

_____

© NGSP & HB

SECTION **2** GOVERNMENT & ECONOMICS

## 2.1 Prized Mineral Resources

*Use with* Sub-Saharan Africa Today, Section 2.1, *in your textbook.*

## Reading and Note-Taking Outline and Take Notes

As you read about sub-Saharan Africa's mineral resources in Section 2.1, use an outline to help you take notes.

I. Sub-Saharan Africa's mineral riches _____

   A. The region has large deposits of gold, diamonds, and other minerals. _____

   B. _____

II. _____

   A. _____

   B. _____

III. _____

   A. _____

   B. _____

© NGSP & HB

SECTION **2** GOVERNMENT & ECONOMICS

## 2.1 Prized Mineral Resources

*Use with* Sub-Saharan Africa Today, Section 2.1, *in your textbook.*

# Vocabulary Practice

**KEY VOCABULARY**
- **commodity** (kuh-MAH-dih-tee) n., something that is bought, sold, or traded
- **mineral** n., a naturally occurring inorganic substance that is usually found underground

**Word Map** Complete a Word Map for the Key Vocabulary words *commodity* and *mineral*. Write the definition in your own words. Then give examples of the words from what you read in Section 2.1. Finally, explain how it helps you in your life.

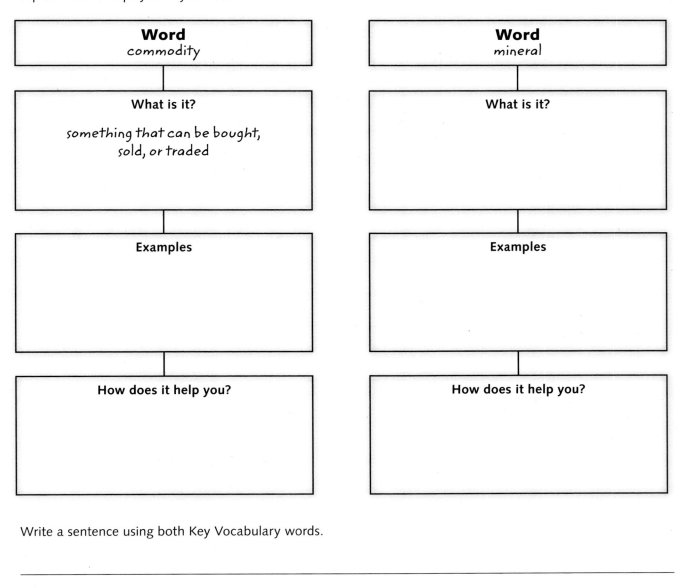

| **Word** *commodity* | **Word** *mineral* |
| --- | --- |
| **What is it?** something that can be bought, sold, or traded | **What is it?** |
| **Examples** | **Examples** |
| **How does it help you?** | **How does it help you?** |

Write a sentence using both Key Vocabulary words.

_____

_____

© NGSP & HB

Name _____    Class _____    Date _____

SECTION **2** GOVERNMENT & ECONOMICS

**GeoActivity**

2.1 PRIZED MINERAL RESOURCES

# Evaluate Diamond Practices

Africa's mineral resources are valuable, but the mining industry can sometimes have a negative impact on miners, their communities, and the environment. In some instances, diamond miners face dangerous working conditions and receive very little of the money that is paid for these valuable gems. Instead, the money goes towards corrupt governments that violate the human rights of their citizens.

Today, many people want to know the details of how diamonds were mined before buying them. They want to be sure that the miners have been treated fairly. However, while many companies in the diamond industry claim to have "fair" practices, there is no official definition of what is fair. Read the following case studies of different mining and jewelry-making practices. Then answer the questions.

**Case Study 1:** A mining company guarantees the health and safety of its miners, and it advertises this fact to attract consumers. However, the miners receive only a tiny fraction of the profits from their diamonds, and are not paid well enough to increase their standard of living.

**Case Study 2:** A diamond cutter receives uncut diamonds from hundreds of different mines. The cutter guarantees that only 1 percent of the diamonds come from mining organizations with unfair and unsafe working conditions. All of the cutter's diamonds are mixed together, so consumers have no way of knowing the source of any one diamond.

Use with Sub-Saharan Africa Today Section 2.1, in your textbook.

*Go to Interactive Whiteboard GeoActivities at*
**myNGconnect.com** *to complete this activity online.*

NATIONAL
GEOGRAPHIC
School Publishing

**Case Study 3:** An international nonprofit organization raises awareness about 1) abusive practices at some diamond mines and 2) the flow of money from mining organizations to corrupt governments. The organization promotes diamonds from countries with democratically elected governments, in which the money from mining helps support local communities.

1. **Evaluate** Which case study group has the "fairest" diamond practices? Explain your reasoning.

_____
_____
_____

2. **Form and Support Opinions** Which group has the least "fair" diamond practices? Explain your reasoning.

_____
_____
_____

3. **Identify Problems and Solutions** What can consumers do to help improve conditions at companies with unfair practices?

_____
_____
_____

© NGSP & HB

SECTION **2** GOVERNMENT & ECONOMICS

## 2.2 Nigeria and Oil

*Use with* Sub-Saharan Africa Today, Section 2.2, *in your textbook.*

## Reading and Note-Taking Analyze Cause and Effect

As you read about Nigeria's oil in Section 2.2, use a Cause and Effect Web to understand why Nigeria's people have experienced little benefit from its oil wealth.

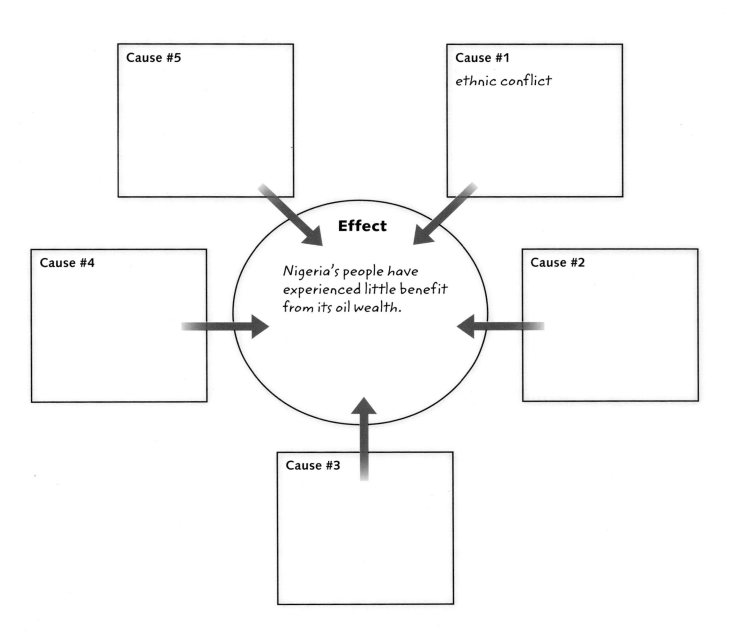

**Cause #5**

**Cause #1**
ethnic conflict

**Effect**

Nigeria's people have experienced little benefit from its oil wealth.

**Cause #4**

**Cause #2**

**Cause #3**

© NGSP & HB

SECTION **2** GOVERNMENT & ECONOMICS
# 2.2 Nigeria and Oil

*Use with* Sub-Saharan Africa Today,
Section 2.2, *in your textbook.*

## Vocabulary Practice

**KEY VOCABULARY**
- **coup** (KOO) n., an illegal takeover of
  a government by force

**ACADEMIC VOCABULARY**
- **concentrate** v., to center, focus, or gather

Write a sentence describing a place where creative
activities are *concentrated* at your school.

_____

_____

**Vocabulary Cluster** Complete a Vocabulary Cluster for the Vocabulary words *coup* and *concentrate*.
Write down the definition for each word. Then add information, ideas, examples, and related words to help
show what the word means.

**Word:** _____coup_____

**Word:** _____concentrate_____

Nigeria had many
coups after gaining
independence.

**Definition**

an illegal takeover of
a government by force

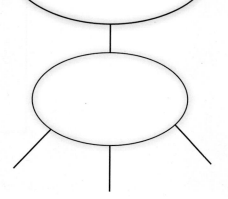

**Definition**

Use with Sub-Saharan Africa Today, Section 2.2, in your textbook.

Go to Interactive Whiteboard GeoActivities at
**myNGconnect.com** to complete this activity online.

☐ NATIONAL
GEOGRAPHIC
School Publishing

# GeoActivity

SECTION ② GOVERNMENT & ECONOMICS

2.2 NIGERIA AND OIL

## Compare Nigeria's Oil Revenue and Incomes

Nigeria is one of the top oil-producing nations in the world. Oil and other petroleum products make up 95 percent of Nigeria's exports each year. However, the Nigerian people have not always benefited from the money made through the oil trade. Use the data in the tables to create a graph showing the relationship between the country's oil exports and GDP per capita, an indicator of the people's standard of living.

| YEAR | GDP PER CAPITA (Current U.S. Dollars) |
|------|----------------------------------------|
| 1960 | 103 |
| 1970 | 233 |
| 1980 | 903 |
| 1990 | 301 |
| 2000 | 368 |

Sources: World Development Indicators Database; CIA World Factbook

| YEAR | CRUDE OIL EXPORTS (Barrels) |
|------|------------------------------|
| 1960 | 17 million |
| 1970 | 383 million |
| 1980 | 700 million |
| 1990 | 565 million |
| 2000 | 790 million |

Sources: 1997 and 2008 Annual Statistical Bulletins, Nigerian National Petroleum Corporation

1. **Create Graphs** Plot the data from the tables on the line graph. Use the left y-axis for GDP per capita and the right y-axis for oil exports.

## Oil Exports and GDP Per Capita

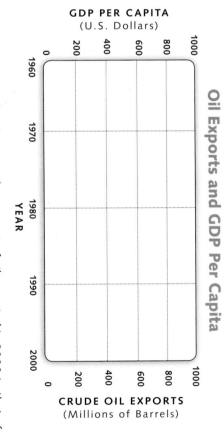

**GDP PER CAPITA**
(U.S. Dollars)

**YEAR**

**CRUDE OIL EXPORTS**
(Millions of Barrels)

2. **Interpret Graphs** Compare the amount of oil exported in 2000 to that of 1980. How did the GDP per capita compare to the amount of oil exported during this time? What does this suggest about the relationship between Nigeria's oil exports and the standard of living of its people?

3. **Make Inferences** In the 1970s, the world experienced an energy crisis, in which there was not enough oil. As a result, the price of oil rose greatly. What happened to Nigeria's GDP per capita at the time? Why?

4. **Draw Conclusions** The price of oil varies depending on its supply and demand. Is it good policy for Nigeria's economy to focus so heavily on oil? Why or why not?

© NGSP & HB

SECTION **2** GOVERNMENT & ECONOMICS

## 2.3 Agriculture and Food Supply

*Use with* Sub-Saharan Africa Today,
Section 2.3, *in your textbook.*

## Reading and Note-Taking Find Main Idea and Details

As you read about Africa's agriculture and food supply in Section 2.3, use a Main Idea Diagram to keep track of the supporting details for the main idea.

| Subject | | | |
|---|---|---|---|
| Agriculture and Food Supply | | | |

| Detail | Detail | Detail | Detail |
|---|---|---|---|
| | | | |
| | | | |
| | | | |
| | | | |
| | | | |
| | | | |
| | | | |
| | | | |
| | | | |
| | | | |

| Main Idea |
|---|
| *Africa is improving its ability to feed its growing population.* |
| |

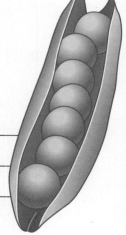

**Identify** What are some of the threats to Africa's food supply?

_____

_____

_____

SECTION ② GOVERNMENT & ECONOMICS

## 2.3 Agriculture and Food Supply

*Use with* Sub-Saharan Africa Today, Section 2.3, *in your textbook.*

## Vocabulary Practice

**KEY VOCABULARY**

- **erosion** (ee-ROH-shun) n., the wearing away of Earth's surface by natural forces
- **famine** (FA-mihn) n., a widespread and sustained shortage of food
- **legume** (leh-GYOOM) n., a type of plant, such as a pea or bean, with seeds that grow in long cases called pods
- **microcredit** n., loans of small sums of money, often made from one person to another

**Descriptive Paragraph** Write a paragraph describing agriculture and the food supply in Africa. Use each of the Key Vocabulary words. Start with a topic sentence. Support your topic sentence with details and examples from Section 2.3. End with a summarizing sentence.

**Topic Sentence:** _____

_____

_____

_____

_____

_____

_____

_____

_____

**Summarizing Sentence:** _____

_____

_____

_____

© NGSP & HB

Name _____ Class _____ Date _____

2.3 AGRICULTURE AND FOOD SUPPLY

## Compare Zimbabwe's Crop Production

Agricultural production across Africa has not kept up with population growth. In Zimbabwe, although production of cash crops such as sugarcane continues to increase, the country today produces less maize, millet, and other food crops than it did decades ago. Analyze the table showing how Zimbabwe's agricultural production and population have changed over the decades, and plot this information on the graph. Then answer the questions about the effect that a diminishing food supply has on a growing population.

| YEAR | MAIZE PRODUCTION (Millions of Metric tons) | SUGARCANE PRODUCTION (Millions of Metric tons) | POPULATION (in Millions) |
|------|------|------|------|
| 1960 | 1.0 millions | 0.3 millions | 4.1 |
| 1975 | 1.8 millions | 2.6 millions | 6.3 |
| 1990 | 2.0 millions | 3.1 millions | 10.1 |
| 2005 | 0.9 millions | 3.3 millions | 11.6 |

Source: UNESCO

**1. Create Graphs** Use the information from the table to create a combined bar graph and line graph. Use the right y-axis for population growth, and plot this information as a line graph. Use the left y-axis for agricultural production, and plot this information as a bar graph. There should be two bars for each year: one for maize production and one for sugarcane production. Draw a legend in the space below to show what each line and bar represent on your graph.

Use with Sub-Saharan Africa Today, Section 2.3, in your textbook.

Go to Interactive Whiteboard GeoActivities at **myNGconnect.com** to complete this activity online.

NATIONAL GEOGRAPHIC
School Publishing

## Population and Agricultural Production

AMOUNT PRODUCED (Millions of Metric Tons)

POPULATION (in Millions)

YEAR

**2. Make Calculations** How many metric tons of maize did Zimbabwe produce per person in 1961? How did this number change by 2005? (To calculate the amount produced per person, divide the total amount produced by the total population.)

_____

**3. Make Inferences** By about how much did sugarcane production increase between 1961 and 2005? Who did this benefit and why?

_____

**4. Draw Conclusions** What happened to maize production over time? Why might this have occurred?

_____

© NGSP & HB

SECTION **2** GOVERNMENT & ECONOMICS

## 2.4 Improving Public Health

*Use with* Sub-Saharan Africa Today, Section 2.4, *in your textbook.*

## Reading and Note-Taking Identify Problems and Solutions

As you read Section 2.4, identify some of the obstacles to fighting malaria and some of the strategies used to fight the disease. Then write what you think is a solution to the problem.

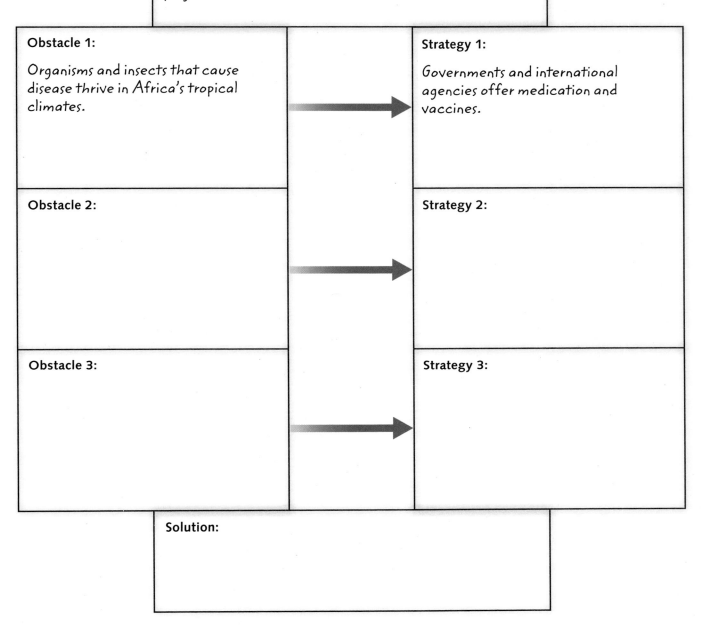

**Problem:**

Malaria is one of many chronic diseases that plague Africa.

**Obstacle 1:**

Organisms and insects that cause disease thrive in Africa's tropical climates.

**Strategy 1:**

Governments and international agencies offer medication and vaccines.

**Obstacle 2:**

**Strategy 2:**

**Obstacle 3:**

**Strategy 3:**

**Solution:**

SECTION 2 GOVERNMENT & ECONOMICS
## 2.4 Improving Public Health

*Use with* Sub-Saharan Africa Today, Section 2.4, *in your textbook.*

## Vocabulary Practice

### KEY VOCABULARY

- **epidemic** (eh-pih-DEH-mik) n., a rapid outbreak of disease that affects a high percentage of a particular population
- **pandemic** n., an outbreak of disease that spreads very quickly and affects a large number of people over a wide area or throughout the world
- **vaccine** (vak-SEEN) n., a treatment designed to increase a person's immunity, or resistance, to a particular disease

### ACADEMIC VOCABULARY

- **infectious** (ihn-FEHK-shuhsh) adj., capable of being passed to someone else by germs that enter the body

Write a sentence using the Academic Vocabulary word *infectious*.

_____

_____

**Definition Tree** For each Key Vocabulary word in the Tree Diagram below, write the definition in your own words on the branch to the right. Then use each word in a sentence.

**epidemic**

Definition: *when a large number of people in a place get a disease that spreads fast*

Sentence:

**pandemic**

Definition:

Sentence:

**vaccine**

Definition:

Sentence:

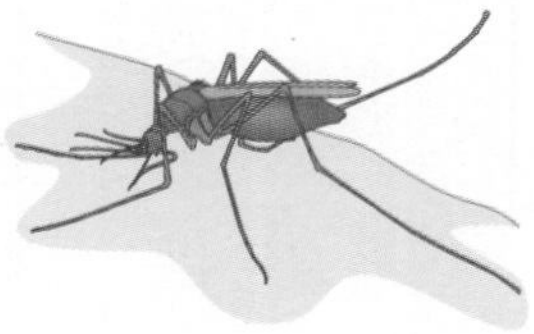

© NGSP & HB

Name _____ Class _____ Date _____

# GeoActivity

Use with Sub-Saharan Africa Today, Section 2.4, in your textbook.

Go to Interactive Whiteboard GeoActivities at
**myNGconnect.com** to complete this activity online.

☐ NATIONAL
GEOGRAPHIC
School Publishing

2.4 GLOBAL ISSUES: IMPROVING PUBLIC HEALTH

## Interpret a Map of Malaria Outbreaks

How can public health experts and government officials fight deadly diseases such as malaria? Knowing how diseases spread and who is vulnerable is important. Epidemiology (eh-puh-DEE-mee-AH-luh-jee) is the study of how diseases are spread and how to control them. Epidemiology maps show where diseases are and how widespread they are. These maps allow scientists to determine the best way to use resources in fighting the spread of the disease. Study the epidemiology map of malaria in Ethiopia. Then answer the questions.

**1. Interpret Maps** How does the map show areas with the most severe malaria crisis? Which parts of Ethiopia face the most severe conditions?

_____

**2. Interpret Maps** Is the malaria outbreak more or less severe in the area around Addis Ababa than it is in the northern part of the country? Why do you think this is the case?

_____

**3. Draw Conclusions** Why is it important for public health experts to determine where a disease outbreak is most severe?

_____

**4. Make Inferences** How would you expect public health efforts to differ between the northern and southern parts of the country?

_____

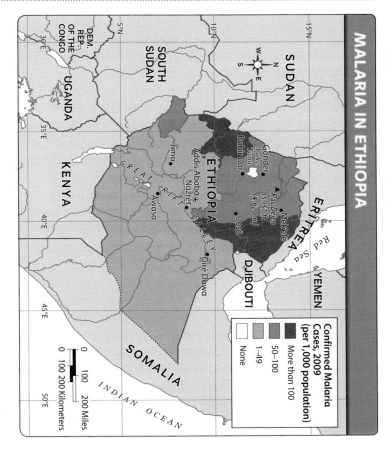

### MALARIA IN ETHIOPIA

Confirmed Malaria Cases, 2009 (per 1,000 population)
- More than 100
- 50–100
- 1–49
- None

© NGSP & HB

SECTION **2** GOVERNMENT & ECONOMICS

## 2.5 Sudan and Somalia

*Use with* Sub-Saharan Africa Today,
Section 2.5, *in your textbook.*

## Reading and Note-Taking Compare and Contrast

Use a Venn Diagram to compare and contrast Sudan and Somalia as you read Section 2.5. Write
down details that are unique to each country. Then write details common to both countries in the
middle section.

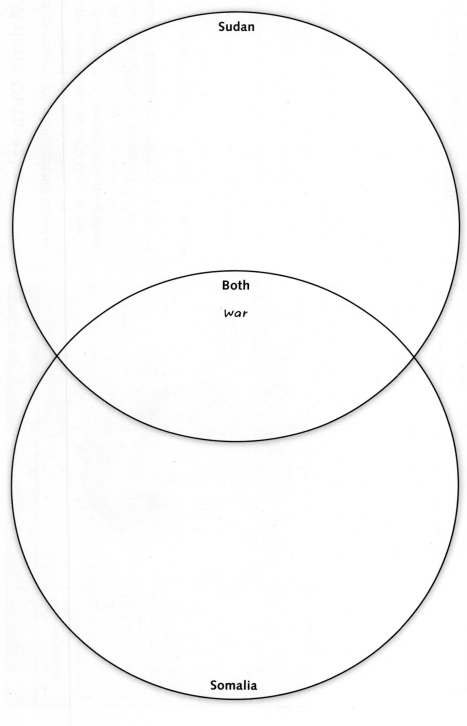

**Sudan**

**Both**

*war*

**Somalia**

SECTION ② GOVERNMENT & ECONOMICS

## 2.5 Sudan and Somalia

Use with Sub-Saharan Africa Today, Section 2.5, *in your textbook.*

## Vocabulary Practice

**KEY VOCABULARY**

- **clan** n., a large group of people who are related and are loyal to their group
- **failed state** n., a country in which government, economic institutions, and order have broken down
- **refugee** (REHF-yoo-JEE) n., someone who has been forced to leave a country because of war or for religious or political reasons

**Four-Column Chart** Complete the Four-Column Chart for the Key Vocabulary words *clan*, *failed state*, and *refugee*. Write each definition. Then note characteristics related to the word. Finally, write a sentence using the word.

| Word | Definition | Characteristic | Sentence |
|---|---|---|---|
| 1. clan | a large group of people who are related and are loyal to their group | | |
| 2. failed state | | | |
| 3. refugee | | | |

© NGSP & HB

Name _____  Class _____  Date _____

# GeoActivity

## 2.5 SUDAN AND SOMALIA

*Use with Sub-Saharan Africa Today, Section 2.5, in your textbook.*

Go to Interactive Whiteboard GeoActivities at
**myNGconnect.com** *to complete this activity online.*

NATIONAL
GEOGRAPHIC
School Publishing

## Build a Time Line of Events

Read about recent conflicts and crises in Sudan and Somalia, and underline key dates in both passages. Then put them in order on the time line. For each key date, write a short phrase that summarizes the event. Then answer the questions.

### Crisis in Sudan

For decades, Sudan has experienced conflict between the government in the north and people in the south. The first of two long civil wars between these groups began in 1955. Peace was established in 1972, but another civil war began in 1983. The civil war continued until 2002. It led to famine, forced millions of people from their homes, and caused an untold number of deaths. Between 2002 and 2005, the Sudanese government and southern rebel groups signed several peace agreements. Former southern rebels gained a voice in the national government, and a vote on southern independence occurred in January 2011. Nearly 99 percent of the southern population voted for independence. The Republic of South Sudan came into existence in July 2011.

A separate conflict has also erupted in Sudan's western province of Darfur. Since 2003, pro-government militia groups have been accused of killing hundreds of thousands of people and forcing millions of others to flee. The United Nations took control of a peacekeeping mission there in 2008, yet the violence continued.

### Chaos in Somalia

Somalia has also suffered from decades of conflict. In 1969, the country's military staged a coup, overthrowing the democratic government and establishing a dictatorship. This government collapsed in 1991, and widespread violence between rival clans sent the country into chaos. The conflict devastated farming regions, which led to widespread famine. In 1992, the United States led an international force in an attempt to restore order. However, these troops could not end the violence, and the peacekeeping forces withdrew in 1994. Peace talks were held in 2000 and throughout the following decade, but Somalia was unable to put an end to the violence.

1. **Make Calculations** Sudan became an independent country in 1956. How many total years of civil war has it experienced since then?

_____

2. **Make Inferences** Somalia is divided among five major clans. Why would this make establishing peace difficult?

_____

3. **Interpret Time Lines** What pattern do you notice in the events occurring in both Sudan and Somalia? Why might this pattern be significant?

_____

**Time Line Title:** _____

```
        |-----|-----|-----|-----|-----|-----|-----|
      1960   1970  1980  1990  2000  2010  2020
```

1955 – Civil war begins in Sudan.

© NGSP & HB

SECTION **2** GOVERNMENT & ECONOMICS

## 2.6 Ending Apartheid

*Use with* Sub-Saharan Africa Today, Section 2.6, *in your textbook.*

## Reading and Note-Taking **Sequence Events**

As you read about the end of apartheid in South Africa in Section 2.6, use a Sequence Chart to keep track of events. Write down specific dates, people, and places related to the foundations, beginning, or ending of apartheid.

**Foundations of Apartheid**

*1800s: Dutch and British lay claim to lands in South Africa.*

↓

**Beginning of Apartheid**

↓

**End of Apartheid**

End Apartheid

South Africa Must Be Free Divest Now

SECTION ② GOVERNMENT & ECONOMICS

## 2.6 Ending Apartheid

*Use with* Sub-Saharan Africa Today, Section 2.6, *in your textbook.*

## Vocabulary Practice

**KEY VOCABULARY**

• **apartheid** (uh-PART-hite) n., a former social system in South Africa in which black people and people from other racial groups did not have the same political and economic rights as white people and were forced to live separately from them

• **homeland** n., a native land or an area set aside where a particular group of people can live

• **segregation** n., the practice of keeping people of different races or religions separate from each other

**Definition Chart** Complete a Definition Chart for the Key Vocabulary words *apartheid*, *homeland*, and *segregation*.

| Word | apartheid | homeland | segregation |
|---|---|---|---|
| Definition | | a native land or an area set aside where a particular group of people can live | |
| In Your Own Words | | | |
| Sentence Using the Word | | | |

© NGSP & HB

# GeoActivity

2.6 ENDING APARTHEID

## Analyze Primary Sources: Apartheid and Segregation

Both South Africa's system of apartheid and racial segregation in the United States divided people by race and subjected racial groups to unjust and inhumane treatment. What was it like for people to live under these conditions? Read the passage from Nelson Mandela, the anti-apartheid activist who would later become South Africa's president in 1994. Compare Mandela's description of life under apartheid with the description of segregation in the United States by Will W. Alexander, who led a group dedicated to ending racial violence.

### Document 1: Mandela on Apartheid in South Africa

Year after year [the African people] have raised their voices to condemn the grinding poverty of the people, the low wages, the acute shortage of land, the inhuman exploitation, and the whole policy of White domination. But instead of more freedom, repression began to grow in volume and intensity and it seemed that all their sacrifices would end in smoke and dust.

—from *No Easy Walk to Freedom*, 1965

A men's bathroom in Cape Town in 1989 illustrates the system of apartheid in South Africa.

### Document 2: Alexander on Segregation in the United States

In cities North and South, housing is far poorer for Negroes than for whites. Colored people are largely forced to live in slum areas which have been abandoned by other groups. . . . The segregation of Negroes in jobs, their exclusion from free access to the ways in which other citizens earn a living, has meant permanent poverty, degradation [loss of power], and defeat—not only for the majority of Negroes, but for other large sections of the American people.

—from "Our Conflicting Racial Policies," 1945

This sign at a bus station in Georgia in 1943 illustrates segregation in the United States.

Use with Sub-Saharan Africa Today, Section 2.6, in your textbook.

Go to Interactive Whiteboard GeoActivities at
**myNGconnect.com** to complete this activity online.

1. **Analyze Primary Sources** What does Nelson Mandela mean when he writes that all of the African people's sacrifices seemed as if they would "end in smoke and dust"? How do you think he wants readers to react?

_____
_____
_____

2. **Compare and Contrast** Under apartheid, Black Africans were forced out of cities and onto nonproductive areas of land. How does this compare with the living situation of African Americans under segregation, as described by Will W. Alexander?

_____
_____
_____

3. **Make Predictions** Neither passage directly addresses the lack of political rights held by racial groups. In what way would a guarantee of political rights affect the types of problems that Mandela and Alexander describe?

_____
_____
_____

SECTION **2** GOVERNMENT & ECONOMICS

## 2.1–2.6 **Review and Assessment**

*Use with* Sub-Saharan Africa Today, Sections 2.1–2.6, *in your textbook.*

Follow the instructions below to review what you have learned in this section.

**Vocabulary** Next to each vocabulary word, write the letter of the correct definition.

1. _____ mineral
2. _____ commodity
3. _____ famine
4. _____ epidemic
5. _____ vaccine
6. _____ segregation

**A.** a rapid outbreak of disease that affects a high percentage of a particular population

**B.** the practice of keeping people of different races or religions separate from each other

**C.** a widespread shortage of food

**D.** something that is bought, sold, or traded

**E.** a naturally occurring inorganic substance that is usually found underground

**F.** a treatment designed to increase a person's immunity, or resistance, to a disease

**Main Ideas** Use what you've learned about sub-Saharan African government and economics to answer these questions.

7. **Monitor Comprehension** What important resource holds hope for a brighter economic future for the people of sub-Saharan Africa?

_____

_____

8. **Analyze** What factors have limited the economic progress of the Central African Republic, a country rich in diamond resources?

_____

_____

9. **Compare and Contrast** What is the difference between famine and constant, long-term hunger?

_____

_____

10. **Explain** How can malaria be prevented?

_____

_____

11. **Monitor Comprehension** What is a major source of funding in the battle against malaria?

_____

_____

12. **Describe** Who are the Lost Boys of the Sudan?

_____

_____

13. **Describe** Who are the Boers and how did they affect the history of South Africa?

_____

_____

© NGSP & HB

## Focus Skill: Analyze Cause and Effect

Answer the questions below to analyze the causes and effects of conflict and government instability on the economic development of sub-Saharan Africa.

14. How and why do unstable governments challenge the economic growth of many sub-Saharan governments?

_____

_____

15. How has ethnic conflict limited Nigeria's ability to use its oil resources to improve economic conditions?

_____

_____

16. What has been the effect of rapid population growth and a less rapid rate of food production in sub-Saharan Africa?

_____

_____

17. What are legumes and how can they help improve the food supply?

_____

_____

18. How has microcredit helped poor farmers?

_____

_____

19. How can vaccines help prevent the spread of malaria?

_____

_____

20. What has been the effect of the government-created Arab militia on the people of Darfur?

_____

_____

21. What causes a person to become a refugee?

_____

_____

22. What has been the effect of clan rivalry in Somalia?

_____

_____

23. What were South African homelands?

_____

_____

## Synthesize: Answer the Essential Question

How have conflict and government instability slowed economic development in sub-Saharan Africa? Consider the information you have learned about the government and economics of sub-Saharan Africa. Think about Africa's prized mineral resources, Nigeria and oil, food supply, efforts to improve health care, the effect of civil wars and ethnic conflict, and apartheid in South Africa.

_____

_____

_____

© NGSP & HB

SECTION ② GOVERNMENT & ECONOMICS
## 2.1–2.6 Standardized Test Practice

*Use with* Sub-Saharan Africa Today, Sections 2.1–2.6, *in your textbook.*

Follow the instructions below to practice test-taking on what you've learned from this section.

**Multiple Choice** Circle the best answer for each question from the options available.

1. Which list represents African countries that have successfully used their minerals to build their economies?
   A South Africa, Namibia, Tanzania, and Botswana
   B South Africa, Nigeria, Sudan, and Zambia
   C Tanzania, Nigeria, Somalia, and Sudan
   D Botswana, Sudan, Chad, and Somalia

2. What sub-Saharan country produces more oil than any other African country?
   A Zambia
   B Tanzania
   C South Africa
   D Nigeria

3. What is a coup?
   A the legal takeover of a government
   B an illegal takeover of a government by force
   C a democratic takeover of a government
   D the takeover of a government by a religious group

4. How much less percentage of calories does the average African eat today as compared with 20 years ago?
   A 5 percent
   B 10 percent
   C 20 percent
   D 25 percent

5. What has been the result of farmers growing cash crops rather than food crops?
   A Less food is grown to feed Africans.
   B More farmers are growing legumes.
   C Many farmers are going out of business.
   D Farmland is more susceptible to drought.

6. What is a pandemic?
   A an outbreak of disease that spreads only within a particular community
   B a disease that is spread by mosquitoes
   C a disease that is spread by poor sanitation
   D an outbreak of disease that spreads over a large area, even over much of the world

7. Worldwide, about how many cases of malaria are there each year?
   A 10 million
   B 100 million
   C 250 million
   D 500 million

8. What happened to the Lost Boys of the Sudan who were taken in by the United States?
   A Most were homesick and returned home.
   B Many attended high school and college.
   C Many moved to other countries.
   D Many contracted diseases.

9. What did the Boers do to the South Africans under their control?
   A They gave them the best land to farm.
   B They converted them to Christianity.
   C They educated them.
   D They enslaved them.

10. What government official began in 1989 to change apartheid laws?
    A Nelson Mandela
    B F.W. de Klerk
    C Bill Gates
    D Stephen Biko

© NGSP & HB

## Document-Based Question

The following excerpt is from the article **Botswana: Adopted Land** by Arthur Zich, which appeared in *National Geographic* in December 1990. Read the excerpt and answer the questions that follow.

> *Men from the village of Mochudi take part in the kgotla, a forum for discussion of community affairs. Their tribal chief will not make decisions until he has considered the opinions of all who wish to speak. . . . [This forum] helped ease Botswana into parliamentary government at independence. . . . Since then, free elections have fostered a stability uncommon in Africa. Skillfully managing a diamond boom, the government has promoted modest, practical development to benefit all levels of society.*

**Constructed Response** Read each question carefully and write your answer in the space provided.

**11.** What is the kgotla?

_____

**12.** What does the tribal chief do before he makes a decision?

_____

**Extended Response** Read the question carefully and write your answer in the space provided.

**13.** How do you think the kgotla helped ease Botswana into parliamentary government?

_____

_____

### DATA FOR SELECTED AFRICAN NATIONS

| COUNTRY | LIFE EXPECTANCY (years) | GDP (billions of U.S. dollars) | GDP PER CAPITA (U.S. dollars) |
|---------|---------|---------|---------|
| Botswana | 61 | 25.4 | 12,700 |
| DRC | 54 | 21.7 | 300 |
| Kenya | 58 | 62.4 | 1,600 |
| Nigeria | 47 | 341.1 | 2,300 |
| Sudan | 54 | 92.5 | 2,200 |
| Tanzania | 52 | 57.6 | 1,400 |

Source: CIA World Factbook (estimates from 2007–2010)

**14.** What does the chart tell you about the economy of Nigeria?

_____

_____

**15.** From what you know about the history and geography of sub-Saharan Africa, what does the data confirm about the governments of the various countries and the wealth and health of their people?

_____

_____

_____

© NGSP & HB

# Sub-Saharan Africa

**Sub-Saharan Africa Geography & History**

# QUIZ: SECTION ❶ GEOGRAPHY

**Multiple Choice** Circle the best answer for each question from the choices available.

**1** Which physical feature was formed by the movement of tectonic plates?
   A Congo River
   B Great Rift Valley
   C Great Escarpment
   D Kalahari Desert

**2** Which of the following is a cause of desertification?
   A rivers flowing outward to the oceans
   B basins being drained by river systems
   C the soil becoming less fertile for farming
   D too many people using the water supply

**3** Why does much of East Africa have cooler temperatures than other regions?
   A The region sits at a higher elevation.
   B The region has enormous grasslands.
   C The region benefits from deepwater lakes.
   D The region is divided by a series of rift valleys.

**4** Why does West Africa support a wide variety of ways of life?
   A The coastal area has one of the largest cities in the world.
   B The varied geography causes very different climates.
   C The countries of the interior are mostly covered by desert.
   D Human activity has altered the environment in some places.

**5** What is the principal difference between the geography of Central Africa and that of the other regions?
   A several natural resources
   B much more rain
   C important coastal cities
   D a major river

**6** Which of the following has blocked economic success in some Southern African nations?
   A overuse of natural resources
   B poor soil
   C conflict within countries
   D lack of rainfall

**Constructed Response** Write the answer to each question in the space provided.

**7** How can deforestation reduce the amount of land that can be farmed?

_____

_____

**8** Why are rivers important natural resources in Southern Africa?

_____

_____

_____

**Sub-Saharan Africa Geography & History**

# QUIZ: SECTION ❷ HISTORY

**Multiple Choice** Circle the best answer for each question from the choices available.

1   What asset helped the Bantu
    dominate other cultures?
    A  the ability to make weapons of iron
    B  a language that others wanted to use
    C  knowledge of agricultural techniques
    D  cultural diversity among Bantu migrants

2   Which group helped spread Swahili
    into the interior of Africa?
    A  Arab traders
    B  Bantu migrants
    C  European traders
    D  Songhai warriors

3   What was the basis of Ghana's wealth?
    A  its sources of alluvial gold
    B  its trade with countries outside of Africa
    C  its salt mines in the deserts
    D  its position between two important
        resources

4   What strong kingdom arose in Central Africa?
    A  Kongo
    B  Mali
    C  Songhai
    D  Zimbabwe

5   What was the Middle Passage?
    A  a voyage carrying enslaved Africans from
        island to island in the Caribbean
    B  a voyage carrying enslaved Africans across
        the Atlantic
    C  a caravan taking enslaved Africans from
        Central Africa to the coast
    D  a caravan taking enslaved Africans across
        the Sahara

6   What was the Organization of African
    Unity founded to promote?
    A  Christianity
    B  industrialism
    C  imperialism
    D  Pan-Africanism

**Constructed Response** Write the answer to each question in the space provided.

7   How are colonialism and imperialism related?

    _____

    _____

8   How did losing young men to slavery affect the communities from which they were taken?

    _____

    _____

© NGSP & HB

## Sub-Saharan Africa Geography & History
# CHAPTER TEST A

**Part 1: Multiple Choice** Circle the best answer for each question from the choices available.

1. What was responsible for the formation of Africa's major valleys, lakes, and volcanoes?
   A climate change
   B desertification
   C erosion
   D plate tectonics

2. What is the greatest challenge to farmers in Sub-Saharan Africa?
   A too much rainfall
   B lack of technology
   C scarcity of fresh water
   D land at high elevations

3. Which of the following helps coastal cities support their populations?
   A greater access to trade
   B more land for farming
   C nearness to rain forests
   D benefit of a warmer climate

4. Which countries in the region have the greatest economic wealth?
   A those in the north
   B those with natural resources
   C those in the interior
   D those with deepwater lakes

5. How has human activity affected the Sahel?
   A New land management techniques have opened new fields.
   B Forests are gradually replacing the grasslands.
   C Farming has allowed people to grow new crops on the land.
   D Poor use of resources has made the soil less fertile.

6. Why is Swahili so widely spoken as a second language?
   A It is an easy language to learn.
   B It was the official language used to govern colonies in Africa.
   C It is descended from Bantu languages.
   D It developed as a trade language so people from different cultures found it useful to know.

7. What aspects of Sub-Saharan African culture were influenced by Arab traders?
   A agriculture and technology
   B language and religion
   C cities and transportation
   D sculpture and dance

8. What was the reason behind the African slave trade?
   A Plantation owners thought slaves were harder workers.
   B Slaves were better at growing tobacco, sugar, and cotton.
   C Plantation owners could make more money using slave labor.
   D It was easy to bring large numbers of slaves safely across the ocean.

9. What did the Bantu and the Europeans have in common?
   A better weapons than the people they conquered
   B a government that other people copied
   C deep interest in helping African nations work together
   D a desire to spread their religion

10. What was the goal of Pan-Africanism?
    A to support colonial powers in Africa
    B to support the economies of African countries
    C to promote unity among all Africans
    D to help African leaders living in cities around the world

© NGSP & HB

## Sub-Saharan Africa Geography & History
# CHAPTER TEST A

**Part 2: Interpret Maps** Use the map and your knowledge of Sub-Saharan Africa to answer the questions below.

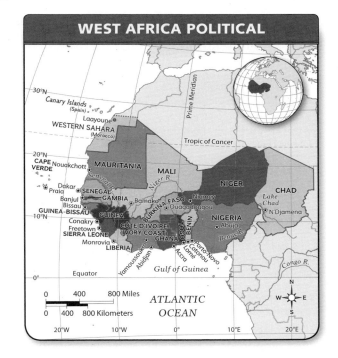

**11** Which river forms a border in Nigeria?
   **A** Benue
   **B** Congo
   **C** Niger
   **D** Senegal

**12** Which capital is not located on a river or on the coast?
   **A** Abidjan
   **B** Dakar
   **C** N'Djamena
   **D** Ouagadougou

**13** The Niger River passes through what countries?
   **A** Togo, Ghana, and Côte d'Ivoire
   **B** Niger, Mali, and Mauritania
   **C** Nigeria, Niger, and Mali
   **D** Nigeria, Benin, and Burkina Faso

**14** What country on the map shows two capital cities?
   **A** Benin
   **B** Cote D'Ivoire
   **C** Mali
   **D** Sierra Leone

Sub-Saharan Africa Geography & History

# CHAPTER TEST A

**Part 3: Interpret Charts** Use the chart and your knowledge of Sub-Saharan Africa to answer the questions below.

| GEOGRAPHIC DATA FOR SELECTED SUB-SAHARAN COUNTRIES | | | |
|---|---|---|---|
| Country | Land Area (sq. mi.) | Arable Land (%) | Irrigated Land (sq. mi.) (2003) |
| Angola | 481,354 | 2.65 | 309 |
| Burkina Faso | 105,714 | 17.66 | 97 |
| Madagascar | 224,534 | 5.03 | 4,193 |
| Malawi | 36,324 | 20.68 | 21 |
| South Africa | 468,909 | 12.10 | 5,784 |
| Sudan | 917,378 | 6.78 | 7,193 |
| Togo | 20,998 | 44.20 | 27 |

**Source:** CIA World Factbook

**15** Which country uses the greatest proportion of its land for farming?
A Angola
B Madagascar
C South Africa
D Togo

**16** Why does Sudan have a low percentage of arable land?
A Sudan does not have volcanic soil.
B Most of the country is arid and requires irrigation.
C East Africa has cooler temperatures.
D Only a small percentage of the land has been irrigated.

**17** Why would Burkina Faso have more square miles of arable land than Angola?
A Angola has a much larger land area.
B Angola invests more in irrigating its land.
C Burkina Faso has built a larger irrigation system.
D Burkina Faso has a higher percentage of arable land.

**18** Which country has the largest amount of land under irrigation?
A Angola
B Burkina Faso
C Sudan
D Togo

© NGSP & HB

Sub-Saharan Africa Geography & History

# CHAPTER TEST A

**Part 4: Document-Based Question** Use the documents and your knowledge of Sub-Saharan Africa to answer the questions below.

## Introduction

Jomo Kenyatta was a leader of the Pan-African movement. When his book *Facing Mount Kenya* was published in 1938, colonial powers still controlled nearly all of Sub-Saharan Africa. Kenyatta encouraged Africans to unite for independence. He became Kenya's first president when the country achieved independence from Great Britain in 1960. Kwame Nkruma, another Pan-African leader, helped Ghana achieve independence in 1960. He was in office as the country's first president when he spoke about Africa's situation in 1964.

**Objective:** Analyze effects of colonialism on African countries.

> **DOCUMENT 1** Quotation from a book by Jomo Kenyatta, *Facing Mount Kenya*, 1938
>
> Europeans assume that, given the right knowledge and ideas, personal relations can be left largely to take care of themselves, and this is perhaps the most fundamental [basic] difference in outlook between Africans and Europeans.
>
> Source: Jomo Kenyatta, Facing Mount Kenya, 1938

**Constructed Response** Write the answer to each question in the space provided.

19 According to Kenyatta, do Europeans put much effort into relationships between individuals? Why or why not?

_____

_____

20 What does Kenyatta imply about the African attitude toward relations among people?

_____

_____

© NGSP & HB

**DOCUMENT 2**  Quotation from a speech by Kwame Nkrumah, July 19, 1964

> By far the greatest wrong which the departing colonialists inflicted on us, and which we now continue to inflict on ourselves in our present state of disunity [opposition], was to leave us divided into economically unviable [unable to function] States which bear no possibility of real development.

**Source:** Kwame Nkrumah, Speech to the Organization of African Unity Summit Conference, Cairo, July 19, 1964

**Constructed Response**  Write the answer to each question in the space provided.

**21** According to Nkrumah, why is the way countries are divided in Africa harmful?

_____

**22** How might Nkrumah propose that Africans solve the problems left by the colonial powers?

_____

**DOCUMENT 3**  Cartoon of European colonialist Cecil Rhodes standing astride the African continent, published in *Punch*, December 10, 1892

THE RHODES COLOSSUS
STRIDING FROM CAPE TOWN TO CAIRO.

**Constructed Response**  Write the answer to each question in the space provided.

**23** What does the image in this cartoon symbolize?

_____

**24** How would members of the Pan-African movement react to this image?

_____

**Extended Response**  Write a paragraph to answer the question. Use information from all three documents and your knowledge of Sub-Saharan Africa in writing your paragraph. Use the back of this page or a separate piece of paper to write your answer.

**25** How has contact among cultures within Africa and with other countries shaped the African countries of today?

**Sub-Saharan Africa Geography & History**

# CHAPTER TEST B

**Part 1: Multiple Choice** Circle the best answer for each question from the choices available.

1 What is a savanna?
A desert
B grassland
C lake
D river

2 What did plate tectonics create in East Africa in addition to the Great Rift Valley?
A beaches
B rivers
C savannas
D volcanos

3 Which process alters the land through the action of humans?
A deforestation
B erosion
C eruption
D transition

4 How does the Congo Basin differ from most other parts of Sub-Saharan Africa?
A warmer temperatures
B more humidity
C higher elevations
D less wildlife

5 Why does Southern Africa have the highest standard of living in Sub-Saharan Africa?
A The countries have abundant mineral resources.
B The countries have rich and varied wildlife.
C The countries have fertile volcanic soil.
D The countries have large navigable rivers.

6 Which of the following would help protect big cats in Africa?
A Move the animals to a new location.
B Stop illegal hunting.
C Reduce the size of the grasslands.
D Adopt a nocturnal lifestyle.

7 What was the original homeland of the Bantu peoples?
A central East Africa
B eastern Southern Africa
C northern West Africa
D western Central Africa

8 What did the early empires of Sub-Saharan Africa have in common?
A They found gold in their deserts.
B They grew wealthy from taxes and trade.
C They were ruled by Arab traders.
D They were located in Eastern Africa.

9 Where were most of the enslaved Africans sent?
A United States
B countries in Europe
C other parts of Africa
D Brazil and the Caribbean

10 What policy led European countries to try to gain power by controlling Africa and its resources?
A colonialism
B conversion
C industrialism
D imperialism

© NGSP & HB

**Sub-Saharan Africa Geography & History**

# CHAPTER TEST B

**Part 2: Interpret Maps** Use the map and your knowledge of Sub-Saharan Africa to answer the questions below.

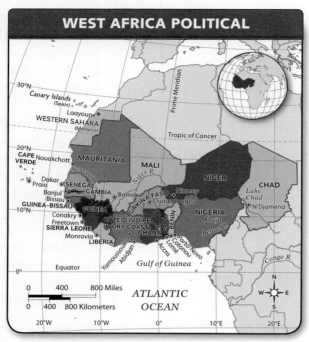

**WEST AFRICA POLITICAL**

⊛ **MAP TIP:** A circle with a star is the symbol for a country's capital.

11 Which city is the capital of Mauritania?
   A Abuja
   B Niamey
   C Nouakchott
   D N'Djamena

12 Which country has a capital that is inland?
   A Ghana
   B Nigeria
   C Senegal
   D Sierra Leone

13 Which country relies on the Niger River for fresh water?
   A Mali
   B Chad
   C Liberia
   D Mauritania

14 What river connects Niamey and Bamako?
   A Benue
   B Congo
   C Niger
   D Senegal

**Sub-Saharan Africa Geography & History**

# CHAPTER TEST B

**Part 3: Interpret Charts** Use the chart and your knowledge of Sub-Saharan Africa to answer the questions below.

### GEOGRAPHIC DATA FOR SELECTED SUB-SAHARAN COUNTRIES

| Country | Land Area (sq. mi.) | Arable Land (%) | Irrigated Land (sq. mi.) (2003) |
|---|---|---|---|
| Angola | 481,354 | 2.65 | 309 |
| Burkina Faso | 105,714 | 17.66 | 97 |
| Madagascar | 224,534 | 5.03 | 4,193 |
| Malawi | 36,324 | 20.68 | 21 |
| South Africa | 468,909 | 12.10 | 5,784 |
| Sudan | 917,378 | 6.78 | 7,193 |
| Togo | 20,998 | 44.20 | 27 |

**Source:** CIA World Factbook

**CHART TIP:** In this chart, arable land is land that is planted with crops.

**15** Which country has the smallest percentage of arable land?
A Angola
B Madagascar
C Malawi
D Sudan

**16** Which country is able to use nearly half its land for farming?
A Burkina Faso
B Malawi
C South Africa
D Togo

**17** Which country has a smaller land area than Malawi?
A Angola
B Madagascar
C South Africa
D Togo

**18** Which country has the smallest amount of land under irrigation?
A Angola
B Madagascar
C Malawi
D Togo

© NGSP & HB

**Sub-Saharan Africa Geography & History**

# CHAPTER TEST B

**Part 4: Document-Based Question** Use the documents and your knowledge of Sub-Saharan Africa to answer the questions below.

## Introduction

Jomo Kenyatta was a leader of the Pan-African movement. When his book *Facing Mount Kenya* was published in 1938, Europe still controlled nearly all of Sub-Saharan Africa. Kenyatta encouraged Africans to work together for independence. When Kenya gained its independence in 1960, Kenyatta became the country's first president. Kwame Nkruma was another Pan-African leader. He helped Ghana achieve independence in 1960 and became the country's first president. In 1964, he shared his thoughts about Africa's situation.

**Objective:** Analyze effects of colonialism on African countries.

> **DOCUMENT 1** Quotation from a book by Jomo Kenyatta, *Facing Mount Kenya*, 1938
>
> Europeans assume that, given the right knowledge and ideas, personal relations can be left largely to take care of themselves, and this is perhaps the most fundamental [basic] difference in outlook between Africans and Europeans.
>
> **Source:** Jomo Kenyatta, Facing Mount Kenya, 1938

**Constructed Response** Write the answer to each question in the space provided.

**19** According to Kenyatta, how do Europeans think of relations between people?

_____

**20** Does Kenyatta believe Europeans and Africans think the same way? Explain.

_____

_____

**DOCUMENT 2** Quotation from a speech by Kwame Nkrumah, July 19, 1964

By far the greatest wrong which the departing colonialists inflicted on us, and which we now continue to inflict on ourselves in our present state of disunity [opposition], was to leave us divided into economically unviable [unable to function] States which bear no possibility of real development.

Source: Kwame Nkrumah, Speech to the Organization of African Unity Summit Conference, Cairo, July 19, 1964

**Constructed Response** Write the answer to each question in the space provided.

21 According to Nkrumah, who is responsible for the economic problems of African countries?

_____

22 Why does Nkrumah believe the countries of Africa cannot develop?

_____

**DOCUMENT 3** Cartoon of European colonialist Cecil Rhodes standing astride the African continent, published in *Punch*, December 10, 1892

**Constructed Response** Write the answer to each question in the space provided.

23 What does the man in this cartoon symbolize?

_____

24 Why is the man shown carrying a gun?

_____

**Extended Response** Write a paragraph to answer the question. Use information from all three documents and your knowledge of Sub-Saharan Africa in writing your paragraph. Use the back of this page or a separate piece of paper to write your answer.

25 How has Sub-Saharan Africa been affected by contact with people from other places?

**Sub-Saharan Africa Today**

# QUIZ: SECTION ❶ CULTURE

**Multiple Choice** Circle the best answer for each question from the choices available.

1  About how many different languages are spoken in sub-Saharan Africa today?
   A  500
   B  750
   C  1,000
   D  1,500

2  How did Europeans decide where to put the borders of their colonies?
   A  They used Africa's natural features such as rivers.
   B  They divided Africa to meet their own resource needs.
   C  They asked Africans to identify their cultural borders.
   D  They researched the borders of ancient African empires.

3  Which of the following types of music was influenced by the music of Africa?
   A  classical
   B  country
   C  jazz
   D  opera

4  What was an important result of public education in Kenya?
   A  cultural diversity in government
   B  an increase in conservation efforts
   C  rivalry between ethnic groups
   D  a literacy rate that more than doubled

5  What two countries are in the East Africa Community with Kenya?
   A  Botswana and Namibia
   B  Ethiopia and Malawi
   C  Nigeria and Chad
   D  Uganda and Tanzania

6  Why are drug companies interested in traditional healers?
   A  their knowledge of medicinal plants
   B  their skill at low-cost treatment
   C  their influence over village doctors
   D  their lists of patient names

**Constructed Response** Write the answer to each question in the space provided.

7  What long-term problem was created by the borders that European colonists imposed on Africa?

   _____

   _____

8  Why do so many tourists visit Kenya?

   _____

   _____

   _____

© NGSP & HB

**BLACK-AND-WHITE COPY READY**

Sub-Saharan Africa Today

# QUIZ: SECTION ② GOVERNMENT & ECONOMICS

**Multiple Choice** Circle the best answer for each question from the choices available.

1   What type of resource is found in abundance throughout sub-Saharan Africa?
   A   fish
   B   grains
   C   minerals
   D   trees

2   Who has benefited from oil wealth in Nigeria?
   A   all the citizens of the country
   B   only the people who live in the delta
   C   mainly the people in power
   D   just the workers in oil refineries

3   Which term is used for a widespread shortage of food?
   A   drought
   B   famine
   C   malnutrition
   D   poverty

4   Which of the following helps to stop the spread of malaria?
   A   sleeping under nets
   B   drinking bottled water
   C   eating citrus fruit
   D   washing hands often

5   Why has Somalia had difficulty achieving unity?
   A   conflict between Muslim north and Christian south
   B   conflict among five rival clans
   C   conflict between military forces and democratic rebels
   D   conflict among pirate groups

6   What was apartheid?
   A   a Boer territory
   B   policies to redistribute land
   C   a protest group
   D   laws separating the races

**Constructed Response** Write the answer to each question in the space provided.

7   How did farming in sub-Saharan Africa change after colonization?

_____

_____

8   How did the government of South Africa change after 1994?

_____

_____

**Sub-Saharan Africa Today**

# CHAPTER TEST A

**Part 1: Multiple Choice** Circle the best answer for each question from the choices available.

**1** What was one of the main problems with the borders that Europeans established in Africa?
  A They crossed too many rivers and lakes.
  B They divided some cultural groups and grouped some rivals together.
  C They blocked British colonies from the ocean.
  D They made it very difficult for French colonists to transport resources.

**2** How has the history of West Africa been preserved?
  A Griots passed it down through generations.
  B Ancient books recorded it.
  C Wall paintings in tombs portrayed it.
  D Colonists wrote it down.

**3** Why did the government of Kenya establish national parks and reserves?
  A The army uses them for training grounds.
  B Industry needs to mine the mineral resources there.
  C Officials rent the lands to poor farmers.
  D The scenic beauty and wildlife attract tourists.

**4** What does an ethnobotanist study?
  A the languages of indigenous cultures
  B the class systems of various cultures
  C the methods of transportation cultures use
  D the relationship between cultures and plants

**5** Why haven't African nations benefited more from their mineral wealth?
  A They did not discover the minerals until very recently.
  B Corrupt governments took much of the profits from mining.
  C People with traditional beliefs oppose digging the land.
  D A lack of universities led to a shortage of engineers.

**6** Why has Nigeria had a history of conflict since it gained independence?
  A It has oil resources that neighboring countries want.
  B It is located between two nations that are at war.
  C It is divided among three major ethnic groups.
  D It has had to fight to gain access to the ocean.

**7** How did farming in Africa change after colonization?
  A Villages farmed as a community to feed everyone.
  B People switched from growing grain to raising livestock.
  C Colonial rulers distributed the land more fairly.
  D People began to grow cash crops rather than food crops.

**8** What are vaccines?
  A medicines to ease the symptoms of disease
  B cures for deadly infectious disease
  C treatments to increase resistance to disease
  D cleaners to kill disease-causing germs

**9** What did South Africa experience for the first time in 1994?
  A a system that separated people by race
  B protests against racism by a black political group
  C an election in which all races could vote
  D the elimination of the economic gap between races

**10** What term is used for a country in which government, economic institutions, and civil order have broken down?
  A clan system
  B failed state
  C federal system
  D military state

Name          Class          Date

Sub-Saharan Africa Today

# CHAPTER TEST A

**Part 2: Interpret Maps** Use the map and your knowledge of sub-Saharan Africa to answer the questions below.

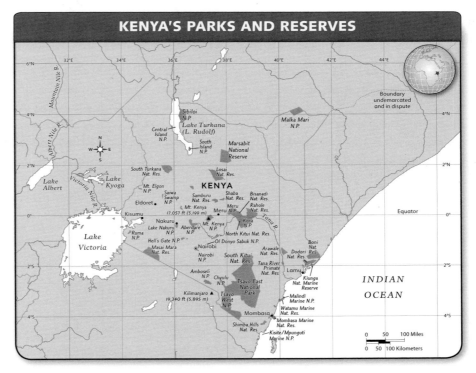

KENYA'S PARKS AND RESERVES

**11** What national park is four degrees north of the equator?
  A Malka Mari
  B Tsavo West
  C Aberdare
  D South Island

**12** Which lake contains Central Island National Park?
  A Albert
  B Kyoga
  C Turkana
  D Victoria

**13** Which national reserve focuses on marine life?
  A Bisandi
  B Marsabit
  C Malindi
  D Shaba

**Constructed Response** Use a complete sentence to write the answer in the space provided.

**14** What relationship exists between the location of national parks and Kenya's landforms? What reason might explain this?

_____

_____

Sub-Saharan Africa Today

# CHAPTER TEST A

**Part 3: Interpret Charts** Use the chart and your knowledge of sub-Saharan Africa to answer the questions below.

**15** Which country depends on oil for the highest percentage of its exports?

- **A** Angola
- **B** Chad
- **C** Nigeria
- **D** Sudan

**16** Which country depends on diamonds for the highest percentage of its exports?

- **A** Angola
- **B** Botswana
- **C** Central African Republic
- **D** Democratic Republic of Congo

**17** Which country is a leader in exporting both oil and diamonds?

- **A** Angola
- **B** Botswana
- **C** Chad
- **D** Namibia

### SELECTED OIL AND DIAMOND EXPORTS SUB-SAHARAN AFRICA, 2005–2006

| Oil | | |
|---|---|---|
| Country | World Rank | Percentage of Country's Total Exports |
| Nigeria | 6 | 91.9 |
| Angola | 12 | 96.6 |
| Equatorial Guinea | 21 | 92.7 |
| Democratic Republic of the Congo | 22 | 89.6 |
| Sudan | 29 | 88.0 |
| Chad | 37 | 94.6 |
| **Diamonds** | | |
| Country | World Rank | Percentage of Country's Total Exports |
| South Africa | 5 | 6.9 |
| Botswana | 9 | 83.5 |
| Namibia | 14 | 43.5 |
| Angola | 16 | 2.4 |
| Democratic Republic of the Congo | 17 | 41.5 |
| Central African Republic | 32 | 36.8 |

**Source:** The World Bank

**Constructed Response** Use a complete sentence to write the answer in the space provided.

**18** Would South Africa or Botswana be hurt more by a drop in diamond prices? Explain.

_____

_____

© NGSP & HB

Sub-Saharan Africa Today

# CHAPTER TEST A

**Part 4: Document-Based Question** Use the documents and your knowledge
of sub-Saharan Africa to answer the questions below.

## Introduction

Europeans established colonies in Africa mostly to gain resources to use in European industry.
Little effort was made to develop the African economy or preserve Africa's wealth for its own
people. Damage to the environment and loss of habitat caused animal populations to decline.
These problems have continued after African nations gained independence.

**Objective:** Analyze current environmental problems in Africa.

**DOCUMENT 1** Quotation by Nelson Mandela, 2001

> I dream of an Africa which is in peace with itself. I dream of the realization of the unity
> of Africa, whereby its leaders combine in their efforts to solve the problems of this
> continent. I dream of our vast deserts, of our forests, of all our great wildernesses.
> We must never forget that it is our duty to protect this environment.

**Source:** Nelson Mandela, in "Without Borders: Uniting Africa's Wildlife Reserves," by Peter Godwin, National Geographic Online Extra, September 2001

**Constructed Response** Write the answer to each question in the space provided.

**19** What does Mandela mean by "the unity of Africa"?

_____

_____

**20** According to Mandela how are Africa's political and environmental situations related?

_____

_____

© NGSP & HB

**DOCUMENT 2** Quotation by Dereck Joubert, 2010

As . . . wild resources on the planet shrink, we will all be looking at them as a shared and precious commodity [product] and with a universal responsibility to protect the last of them. In the next 50 years or so, we can expect wars to be fought over game reserves and natural resources other than gold or silver, or even water, because each lion will be a gem, each acre of untouched land will be worth more than the gold underneath it. Imagine the value of the last pride of lions!

**Source:** Dereck Joubert, interviewed by David Braun, November 23, 2010 (http://blogs.nationalgeographic.com/blogs/news/chiefeditor /2010/11/uganda-ends-sport-hunting.html

**Constructed Response** Write the answer to each question in the space provided.

**21** According to Joubert, what will happen to the value of wild animals as they become more and more endangered?

_____

**22** Why does Joubert think wars might be fought over game reserves?

_____

**DOCUMENT 3** Graph of lion populations

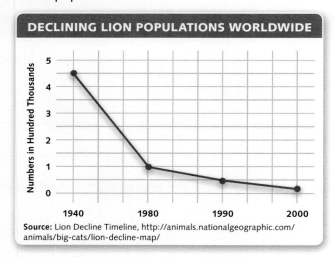

**Source:** Lion Decline Timeline, http://animals.nationalgeographic.com/ animals/big-cats/lion-decline-map/

**Constructed Response** Write the answer to each question in the space provided.

**23** How much did the worldwide lion population decline from the 1940s to the 2000s?

_____

**24** Does this graph support or contradict the views expressed in Document 2? Explain.

_____

**Extended Response** Write a paragraph to answer the question. Use information from all three documents and your knowledge of sub-Saharan Africa in writing your paragraph. Use the back of this page or a separate piece of paper to write your answer.

**25** What environmental actions would Nelson Mandela ask other African leaders to take, and what evidence might he use to persuade them?

© NGSP & HB

Sub-Saharan Africa Today

# CHAPTER TEST B

**Part 1: Multiple Choice** Circle the best answer for each question from the choices available.

1   Before Europeans colonized Africa, how did
    African cultural groups define their borders?
    **A** climate patterns
    **B** map lines
    **C** natural features
    **D** wooden fences

2   What are griots?
    **A** government policies
    **B** percussion instruments
    **C** protest musicians
    **D** traditional storytellers

3   What office was Jomo Kenyatta
    the first Kenyan to fill?
    **A** nationally elected leader
    **B** superintendent of national parks
    **C** minister of education
    **D** delegate to the East Africa Community

4   What do many traditional healers
    use to treat people?
    **A** imported drugs
    **B** hypnotic suggestion
    **C** medicinal plants
    **D** dietary change

5   When African minerals are exported to other
    regions, what are they used to make?
    **A** automotive and electronic products
    **B** houses and public buildings
    **C** steel and copper alloys
    **D** ships and electrical lighting

6   What is the main product of
    the Nigerian economy?
    **A** bananas
    **B** casava
    **C** gold
    **D** oil

7   What is malnutrition?
    **A** a lack of the food and other substances
        needed for health
    **B** a prolonged period without rain
    **C** a shortened lifespan caused by contagious
        diseases
    **D** a widespread shortage of food

8   What is one reason the average life expectancy
    for women is lower in sub-Saharan Africa than
    in North America?
    **A** cancer
    **B** heart attacks
    **C** pneumonia
    **D** tropical diseases

9   Who was the first black African elected
    president of South Africa?
    **A** Stephen Biko
    **B** F.W. de Klerk
    **C** Nelson Mandela
    **D** Desmond Tutu

10  Who were the Afrikaners in
    South African history?
    **A** African natives
    **B** British colonists
    **C** Dutch settlers
    **D** Indian immigrants

© NGSP & HB

## Sub-Saharan Africa Today
# CHAPTER TEST B

**Part 2: Interpret Maps** Use the map and your knowledge of sub-Saharan Africa to answer the questions below.

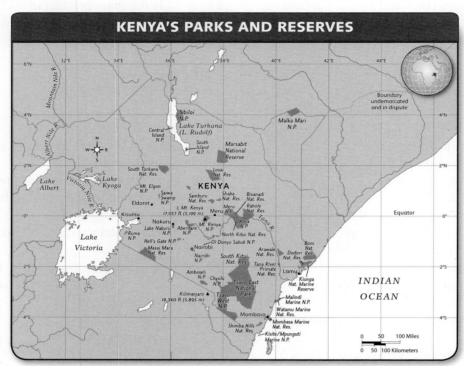

**KENYA'S PARKS AND RESERVES**

**MAP TIP:** The abbreviation N.P. stands for National Park.

**11** Which national park is largest?
- **A** Amboseli
- **B** Mt. Elgon
- **C** Ruma
- **D** Tsavo East

**12** Which river has several of Kenya's national parks and reserves on its banks?
- **A** Albert Nile
- **B** Congo
- **C** Tana
- **D** Victoria Nile

**13** What city is closest to the equator?
- **A** Eldoret
- **B** Meru
- **C** Mombasa
- **D** Nairobi

**14** What is the capital of Kenya?
- **A** Kisumu
- **B** Lamu
- **C** Mombasa
- **D** Nairobi

© NGSP & HB

Sub-Saharan Africa Today

# CHAPTER TEST B

**Part 3: Interpret Charts** Use the chart and your knowledge of sub-Saharan Africa to answer the questions below.

| SELECTED OIL AND DIAMOND EXPORTS SUB-SAHARAN AFRICA, 2005–2006 | | |
|---|---|---|
| **Oil** | | |
| Country | World Rank | Percentage of Country's Total Exports |
| Nigeria | 6 | 91.9 |
| Angola | 12 | 96.6 |
| Equatorial Guinea | 21 | 92.7 |
| Democratic Republic of the Congo | 22 | 89.6 |
| Sudan | 29 | 88.0 |
| Chad | 37 | 94.6 |
| **Diamonds** | | |
| Country | World Rank | Percentage of Country's Total Exports |
| South Africa | 5 | 6.9 |
| Botswana | 9 | 83.5 |
| Namibia | 14 | 43.5 |
| Angola | 16 | 2.4 |
| Democratic Republic of the Congo | 17 | 41.5 |
| Central African Republic | 32 | 36.8 |

Source: The World Bank

**CHART TIP:** World rank compares the total amount selected countries export of the same commodity.

15 Which African country exports the most oil?
  A Democratic Republic of Congo
  B Equatorial Guinea
  C Nigeria
  D Sudan

16 Which African country exports the most diamonds?
  A Angola
  B Botswana
  C Namibia
  D South Africa

17 Which country exports both oil and diamonds?
  A Botswana
  B Democratic Republic of Congo
  C Equatorial Guinea
  D Nigeria

18 For which country does oil make up the smallest percentage of exports?
  A Democratic Republic of Congo
  B Equatorial Guinea
  C Nigeria
  D Sudan

Sub-Saharan Africa Today

# CHAPTER TEST B

**Part 4: Document-Based Question** Use the documents and your knowledge of sub-Saharan Africa to answer the questions below.

## Introduction

Europeans wanted colonies in Africa mostly to gain resources. They exported those resources to use in industry. Little effort was made to help the African economy grow or preserve African resources. Damage to the environment and loss of habitat caused animal populations to decline. These problems have continued after African nations gained independence.

**Objective:** Analyze current environmental problems in Africa.

**DOCUMENT 1** Quotation by Nelson Mandela, 2001

> I dream of an Africa which is in peace with itself. I dream of the realization of the unity of Africa, whereby its leaders combine in their efforts to solve the problems of this continent. I dream of our vast deserts, of our forests, of all our great wildernesses. We must never forget that it is our duty to protect this environment.

**Source:** Nelson Mandela, in "Without Borders: Uniting Africa's Wildlife Reserves," by Peter Godwin, National Geographic Online Extra, September 2001

**Constructed Response** Write the answer to each question in the space provided. You do not need to write complete sentences.

**19** What does Nelson Mandela dream of?

_____

_____

**20** What does Mandela believe it is the duty of African leaders to protect?

_____

_____

© NGSP & HB

**DOCUMENT 2** Quotation by Dereck Joubert, 2010

As . . . wild resources on the planet shrink, we will all be looking at them as a shared and precious commodity [product] and with a universal responsibility to protect the last of them. In the next 50 years or so, we can expect wars to be fought over game reserves and natural resources other than gold or silver, or even water, because each lion will be a gem, each acre of untouched land will be worth more than the gold underneath it. Imagine the value of the last pride of lions!

**Source:** Dereck Joubert, interviewed by David Braun, November 23, 2010 (http://blogs.nationalgeographic.com/blogs/news/chiefeditor /2010/11/uganda-ends-sport-hunting.html

**Constructed Response** Write the answer to each question in the space provided.

**21** What does Joubert believe will become a "shared and precious commodity"?

_____

**22** Why might land become more valuable than gold?

_____

**DOCUMENT 3** Graph of lion populations

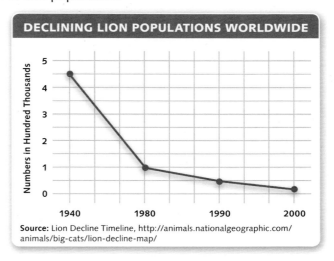

**Source:** Lion Decline Timeline, http://animals.nationalgeographic.com/ animals/big-cats/lion-decline-map/

**Constructed Response** Write the answer to each question in the space provided.

**23** What was the worldwide lion population in the 1940s?

_____

**24** What was the worldwide lion population in the 2000s?

_____

**Extended Response** Write a paragraph to answer the question. Use information from all three documents and your knowledge of sub-Saharan Africa in writing your paragraph. Use the back of this page or a separate piece of paper to write your answer.

**25** What problem do all three documents address, and what are specific examples of that problem?

© NGSP & HB

# GEOGRAPHY & HISTORY

## SECTION 1.1  PHYSICAL GEOGRAPHY

### Reading and Note-Taking

Western Africa has steppes and savannahs.; Central Africa has large areas of rain forest.; East Africa's rift valleys stretch from the Red Sea south to Mozambique.; Southern Africa has the Kalahari Desert and great plateaus.

### Vocabulary Practice

**basin:**  region drained by a water system
**desertification:**  soil gets drier so plants can't grow
**rift valley:**  place where the earth's crust has broken apart
**savanna:**  grassy area in tropic environment.
Students' illustrations will vary.

### GeoActivity  Compare Precipitation Across Regions

1. Countries with little precipitation have smaller populations; countries with more precipitation have higher populations.
2. Responses will vary based upon the areas chosen. Students should consider the effects that latitude and elevation have on climate.

## SECTION 1.2 EAST AFRICA AND THE RIFT VALLEY

### Reading and Note-Taking

**Great Rift Valley:**  chain of valleys, SW Asia to southern Africa; 6,000-foot valley walls
**Deep water lakes:**  Lake Turkana, Lake Tanganika (4,700 feet deep)
**Horn of Africa:**  shaped like rhinoceros horn, includes four countries;
**plateaus:**  higher elevation, cooler temperature
**volcanoes:**  Mt. Kilimanjaro in Tanzania is over 19,000 feet
**savannas:**  grasses in Tanzania and Kenya where wildlife can live

### Vocabulary Practice

ACADEMIC VOCABULARY
Possible response: Both Kilimanjaro and Mt. Kenya are dormant, or inactive, volcanoes.

### Compare Vocabulary

Student responses for Y-chart should include definition for each and might also include: dormant: an adjective; describes a condition of a volcano or a plant's growth

**pride:**  a noun; a collective noun—a word that identifies a group, like "flock," "herd," or "hive"

**Similarities:**  Both are words used when writing about physical geography.

### GeoActivity  Relate Topography and Plate Tectonics

1. Mount Kilimanjaro is approximately 19,000 feet above sea level and Lake Turkana, the lowest point in the Great Rift Valley, is approximately 400 feet above sea level, which means that Kilimanjaro is approximately 18,600 feet higher than the lowest point.
2. No—tectonic plate movement will continue to occur, so the topography of East Africa might look very different millions of years from now.
3. If these plates have been separating, they have probably been pushing together with other plates, resulting in the creation of other types of landforms.

## SECTION 1.3  WEST AFRICA'S STEPPES

### Reading and Note-Taking

West Africa's physical geography ranges from steppes and highlands to tropical coast and dry, or arid, desert.; The interior areas are dry, have a short growing season, and there has been deforestation. The coastal areas are tropical and receive much more rain.; The coastal areas have several advantages including greater rainfall, fishing, and trade, which make it easier to support large cities.

### Vocabulary Practice

**Word:** interior
**Definition:** land area away from a coast
**In Your Own Words:** inland area

**Word:** deforestation
**Definition:** the practice of cutting down trees to make way for crops
**In Your Own Words:** the clearing of forests so farmers can plant crops

**Word:** transition zone
**Definition:** area between two geographic regions that has characteristics of both
**In Your Own Words:** between two regions, an area that's similar to both

**Word:** highland
**Definitions:** area of higher mountainous land
**In Your Own Words:** land at a higher altitude that is usually mountainous

## GeoActivity  Graph Water Levels in Lake Chad

1. approximately 94 percent
2. If there were periods of drought, people would depend more heavily on the water in the lake, which would further reduce the water level.
3. Students' graphs should resemble the following:

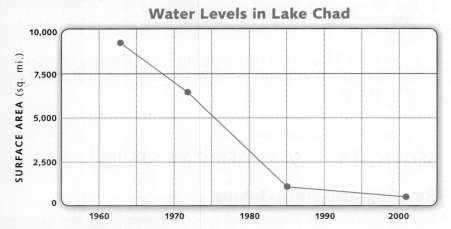

Water Levels in Lake Chad

4. between 1972 and 1985
5. The Aral Sea has lost approximately 50 percent of its surface area, which is less than the percentage lost by Lake Chad.

## SECTION 1.4  RAIN FORESTS AND RESOURCES

### Reading and Note-Taking

**Rain Forests and Resources: Introduction:** Central Africa is defined by the geographical landforms around it: highlands, the rift valley, and plateaus.
**Rain Forest in the Congo Basin:** on equator; has a rain forest; thick vegetation; most people live on edge of forest; wildlife such as gorillas, leopards, rhino; many large rivers
**Resources of Central Africa:** DRC is the largest country of several countries; copper, forests, and diamonds are resources; Congo River provides hydroelectric power.
**Generalization:** A huge rain forest and the Congo River are major geographical features of Central Africa.

### Vocabulary Practice

**hydroelectric power:** Congo River, Inga dams, water source, land use, turbines, electricity
**rain forest:** Congo Basin, sunlight can't reach the ground, lots of rain, okapi, dense plant growth, diverse wildlife and plant life

### GeoActivity  Explore a Tropical Rain Forest

1. Colobus monkey—canopy
2. Driver ant—forest floor
3. Okapi—understory, forest floor
4. African grey parrot—emergent layer, canopy

## SECTION 1.5  SOUTHERN PLATEAUS AND BASINS

### Reading and Note-Taking

**Basins:** Congo Basin; Kalahari Basin
**Plateaus:** Zambezi River
**Mining:** copper, gold, diamonds
**Farming:** grapes, tea, coffee, bananas, pineapples, apples, corn, wheat

### Vocabulary Practice

**escarpment:**
1. steep slope
2. Southern Africa's plateau is defined by the Great Escarpment.
3. high slanting hills
4. flat land
**landlocked:**
1. having no direct access to a coast
2. Six countries in Southern Africa are landlocked.
3. blocked on all sides by land
4. coastal

### GeoActivity  Research Copper Exports

Students' research results will vary based on the sources they used and the country they chose.

1. Students' map arrows should accurately show the top copper importers for either Zambia or the Democratic Republic of the Congo.
2. The economies of places with large copper deposits probably depend highly on international copper trading.
3. Given the common uses for copper, these countries likely have many people working in either electronics production or building construction.

## SECTION 1.6  EXPLORING AFRICA'S WILDLIFE

### Reading and Note-Taking

**Situation:** Africa's lion population has fallen to only 20,000.
**Problem 1.** people hunting big cats
**Problem 2.** people moving into big cat habitats
**Problem 3.** people poaching big cats
**Solution:** conserving big cat habitats; ecotourism

### Vocabulary Practice

**habitat:** natural home; habitat is both where you live and what you live on
**ecotourism:** tourism that is focused on conservation and responsible use of land, wildlife, and resources; eco- is short for ecological
**poaching:** illegal hunting; animals need to be protected from poaching
**nocturnal:** night-based; nocturnal is the opposite of diurnal

## GeoActivity  Locate a Wildlife Reserve

**1.** a. Big cats require large amounts of space and depend on other species for food; b. Populated areas would not have enough space for a big cat habitat. Interactions between people and big cats are a risk for both; c. Industries might desire valuable resources in a reserve area, threatening the long-term survival of big cats. Pollution is a risk to wildlife; d. Big cats could be a threat to livestock, or they could become targeted by ranchers.

**2.** Students should select the location in the north part of the country, which in fact is the location of the Jouberts' Selinda Reserve. It is far from highly populated areas or areas of major industrial activity.

**3.** Possible response: Creating a wildlife reserve might be more difficult because it would require a lot of money to purchase the land and would not help support many people.

## SECTION 1  REVIEW AND ASSESSMENT

### Vocabulary

**1.** C   **4.** I   **7.** J   **10.** K
**2.** E   **5.** F   **8.** L   **11.** A
**3.** G   **6.** B   **9.** D   **12.** H

### Main Idea

**13.** Sub-Saharan Africa is located south of the Sahara desert.

**14.** The Sub-Saharan rivers are not very useful for travel because many of them do not flow all the way to the ocean. Rivers that do flow into the ocean, like the Congo River and the Zambezi River, are impossible to travel at certain points because of waterfalls and rapids.

**15.** The Great Rift Valley was created by two tectonic plates separating from each other and breaking Earth's crust.

**16.** The lakes were also created by plate movements. As the rifts formed, they filled with rainwater and became lakes.

**17.** The types of landforms in West Africa are steppes, highlands, tropical coast, and dry desert.

**18.** The Congo Basin is located on the equator and surrounded by higher elevations. It also contains the second largest rain forest in the world.

**19.** Southern Africa has the highest standard of living because it has good farmland and many natural resources.

**20.** Ecotourism is tourism that focuses on wildlife or habitat protection. It teaches visitors about conservation issues.

### Focus Skill: Draw Conclusions

**21.** Lack of access to fresh water would have a devastating effect on people, crops, and animals, all of which need water to survive.

**22.** The Great Rift Valley's lakes provide fresh water to East African countries. Because rainfall is not plentiful, access to fresh water is critical.

**23.** Cooler temperatures would make farming more possible. Also, cooler temperatures would make it easier for people and animals to live.

**24.** The countries on the coast of West Africa have more cities and higher populations because they are on the coast and because they have adequate rainfall, fishing, and trade. These factors make it easier for people to live and support themselves.

**25.** Exporting oil would help improve Chad's economy and make money available for improved farming technology.

**26.** The Zambezi River provides hydroelectric power. The countries of Zambia and Zimbabwe get most of their electricity from the Kariba Dam on the Zambezi River.

**27.** Other factors that affect the economies of Southern Africa are civil war and disease.

**28.** South Africa, Botswana, and Namibia each have a high gross domestic product because of their natural resources (mining) and crop production.

### Synthesize: Answer the Essential Question

The varied geography of Sub-Saharan Africa has had both a positive and negative effect on people's lives. Semiarid grasslands and deserts do not support farming. Some Sub-Saharan rivers are not useful for travel or trade, either because they do not flow into the ocean or because rapids and waterfalls make them too dangerous to travel. Access to fresh water is also a challenge for much of Sub-Saharan Africa. On the other hand, cities in Sub-Saharan Africa on or near the Atlantic coast have adequate rainfall and fishing and trade. Rivers supply hydroelectricity to parts of Sub-Saharan Africa, and the many natural resources of the region provide many trade and work opportunities.

## SECTION 1  STANDARDIZED TEST PRACTICE

**1.** C   **3.** A   **5.** B   **7.** B   **9.** A
**2.** B   **4.** A   **6.** D   **8.** C   **10.** B

### Constructed Response

**11.** Desertification is the conversion of arid or semiarid regions to deserts.

**12.** The removal of trees and other vegetation deprives the land of its ability to retain water.

### Extended Response

**13.** First, poor planting techniques often exhaust the soil within a few seasons. Because the land will no longer support crops, more forest needs to be cleared. Because poor planting techniques soon exhaust this soil as well, even more forest is cleared. Better planting techniques might help to keep the process from repeating itself.

**14.** Mozambique generates the most hydroelectric power. Mali generates the least.

**15.** Possible response: Mozambique has greater access to water sources than Mali has. Mozambique is located on the coast of Southern Africa and has access to the Zambezi River, a source of hydroelectric power. Mali, on the other hand is an interior desert country located in West Africa. It has few sources of hydroelectric power.

# SECTION 2.1 BANTU MIGRATIONS

## Reading and Note-Taking

Possible responses:

1. Bantu-speaking people migrated from West Africa.
2. They carried their cultural traits, skills, and language with them.
3. The migration lasted from 2000 B.C. to A.D. 1000.
4. The Bantu spread from West Africa south and east across sub-Saharan Africa.
5. Historians and anthropologists aren't sure why the Bantu migrated.

## Vocabulary Practice

**agricultural revolution:** development of agriculture by humans; The agricultural revolution took place 10,000 years ago.
**caravans:** groups of merchants traveling together for safety; Traders in caravans spread Swahili.
**first language:** mother tongue; Swahili is the first language for millions in East Africa.
**lingua franca:** a language common to two groups with different languages; A lingua franca helps people communicate.

## GeoActivity Map the Swahili Language

1. Students' maps should resemble the following:

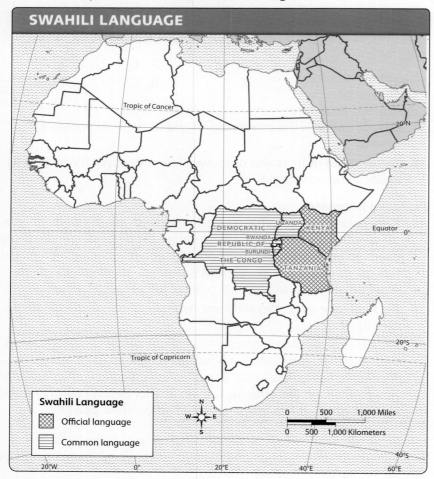

SWAHILI LANGUAGE

Swahili Language
- Official language
- Common language

2. Possible response: The countries in which Swahili is spoken as an official language or a common language are all in East Africa.

# SECTION 2.2 EARLY STATES AND TRADE

## Reading and Note-Taking

**Date:** A.D. 300; Aksum empire begins to grow.
**Date:** 700; Ghana begins control of West Africa.
**Date:** 900; Songhai empire begins to prosper.
**Date:** 1200; Benin kingdom, which traded with Europe, begins its six hundreds years; Shona people
**Date:** 1390; Kongo was founded.
**Date:** 1235; Empire of Mali overtakes Ghana's control.

## Vocabulary Practice

**Topic Sentence:** Trade between kingdoms in West African and East Africa was important to the development of powerful empires over hundreds of years.

The trade was trans-Saharan, which means it crossed the Sahara. From North Africa, traders came to West Africa, where there were kingdoms that traded in salt and alluvial gold. This is gold that flows and settles in a river. In East Africa, there were city-states that had ports on the Red Sea or the Indian Ocean. These were large cities, like Adulis and Mogandishu.

**Summary Sentence:** Many powerful kingdoms in all parts of Africa came and went over the centuries, and it was through trading among themselves and with European countries that they could grow so powerful.

## GeoActivity Map Historic Trade Routes

1. gold, slaves, and salt; these goods were abundant in Africa
2. Students' maps should resemble the following:

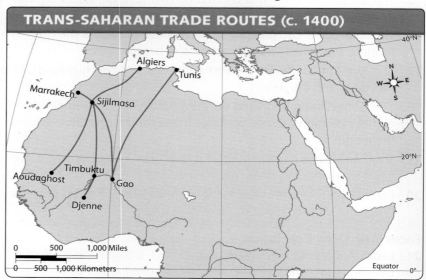

TRANS-SAHARAN TRADE ROUTES (c. 1400)

3. Sijilmasa; it is midway between cities on the Mediterranean and the cities of West Africa

## SECTION 2.3 IMPACT OF THE SLAVE TRADE

### Reading and Note-Taking

**Subject:** trans-Atlantic slave trade
**Details:**
- The Portuguese, Spanish, Dutch, French, and English all purchased slaves at African coastal ports.
- started around 1500
- African slaves were crowded onto large ships headed for the colonies.
- The trip took several months, and many became sick and died.
- 2 million people died in the Middle Passage.
- Malnutrition and disease were common.

**Main Idea:** The European slave trade involved millions of people and had lasting effects on Africa and the Americas.

### Vocabulary Practice

ACADEMIC VOCABULARY
Possible response: Avoiding malnutrition is an incentive to eat a balanced diet.

#### Word Wheel

**trans-Atlantic slave trade:**
**Related Words:** Middle Passage; captive; sold at ports, chains, death from malnutrition, crowded ships, free labor, plantations
**Descriptions:** 12 million enslaved Africans sold between Europeans and the Americas; 2 million died in the journey

### GeoActivity  Analyze Primary Sources: The Slave Trade

1. Slave traders were willing to force enslaved Africans to endure these conditions so they could transport as many slaves as possible on each voyage for as inexpensively as possible.
2. Newton says that he hopes the sick slaves will recover and he has changed their food because of their illness. However, he could not have been too concerned because he was not giving them enough food for a healthy diet.
3. Illness and disease must have been quite common. Both documents discuss slaves becoming sick, and other slave ships probably had the same conditions.

## SECTION 2.4 COLONIZATION TO INDEPENDENCE

### Reading and Note-Taking

**Concept:** African's path from colonization to independence

colonialism; imperialism; missionaries; scramble for Africa; independence; African unity and cooperation; Pan-Africanism

### Vocabulary Practice

**Word:** imperialism
**Definition:** policy of extending foreign rule
**Characteristics:** economic incentives; sense of superiority; more powerful weapons; declare rule with no regard for those who are ruled
**Examples:** France, Portugal, Great Britain, Belgium in Africa
**Non-Examples:** countries that are colonies

**Word:** missionary
**Definition:** person on religious missions to advance what he or she believes in
**Characteristics:** going where one's religion is not present; believing one can convert others
**Examples:** Christian missionaries in Africa
**Non-Examples:** Red Cross worker; Peace Corps worker

**Word:** colonialism
**Definition:** one country exploring, conquering, settling—and sometimes exploiting—another area of the world
**Characteristics:** moving into other's land; putting one's own culture first
**Examples:** slave merchants from European countries set up trading centers
**Non-Examples:** self-rule, Pan-Africanism

### GeoActivity  Build a Time Line of Ghana's Independence

1. 1471—Portuguese explorers arrive; 1600s—Many European nations are involved in the slave trade; 1800s—The British clash with the Asante; 1807—The British abolish the slave trade; 1821—The Gold Coast becomes an official colony; 1902—The British gain control of Asante areas; 1950s—Ghana's new constitution gives the people more control; 1957—Ghana becomes fully independent.
2. 136 years
3. They may have wanted access to Ghana's other resources, such as gold. They also may have wanted to prevent other European countries from gaining control of Ghana.
4. World War II had recently occurred. Britain and other European powers were devastated by the war and needed to focus their resources on rebuilding their own countries.

## SECTION 2  REVIEW AND ASSESSMENT

### Vocabulary

| | | | | |
|---|---|---|---|---|
| **1.** I | **3.** D | **5.** G | **7.** B | **9.** H |
| **2.** A | **4.** C | **6.** J | **8.** E | **10.** F |

### Main Ideas
11. During the agricultural revolution humans began growing food instead of gathering food.
12. Swahili is spoken mainly in East Africa.
13. Lingua franca is a common language shared among multiple groups of people.
14. Trans-Saharan trade brought Arab traders from North Africa and introduced Africans to the Islamic religion.
15. Ghana gained wealth and power by taxing the gold and salt trade.
16. Trans-Saharan trade was trade across the Sahara and confined to trade within Africa. Trans-Atlantic slave trade was trading of slaves across the Atlantic Ocean.

**Focus Skill: Analyze Cause and Effect**

17. As the Bantu moved, they forced other groups to move or become absorbed into Bantu culture.

18. Arab traders and Bantu-speaking people met and exchanged goods over many centuries. Over time, Swahili (a surviving Bantu language) became the language they used to communicate.

19. Trade brought Arab traders from North Africa to West Africa. This trade introduced Africans to the Islamic religions and encouraged trade and the rise of city-states.

20. The presence of natural resources resulted in thriving and prosperous kingdoms in all parts of Sub-Saharan Africa.

21. Because the practice of buying and selling slaves already existed, it may have made it easier for European traders to justify buying and selling slaves.

22. Because of increased European demand for sugar, cotton, tobacco, and cotton, plantations got bigger and so did the demand for slave labor.

23. Many of the Africans taken were young, male, and potential leaders in their community. The loss of so many people weakened some African communities and completely destroyed others.

24. Possible response: The impact of slave trade on the Americas is that much of its population is made up of the descendents of enslaved Africans. This has brought African languages, customs, and communities to the regions in which they now live.

25. Europeans were willing to go to war because they wanted control of Africa's natural resources to fuel industrialization and large-scale industries.

26. Pan-Africanism sought to unify the peoples of Africa and support them in their fight for independence.

**Synthesize: Answer the Essential Question**

The Bantu migration—south and east across Sub-Saharan Africa—was one of the greatest migrations in human history. When the Bantu migrated they brought their cultural traits, language, and skills along with them and had a great influence on the people they came into contact with. Trade brought Arab traders from North Africa to West Africa, introduced Africans to Islamic religion, and gave rise to a number of kingdoms that thrived because of the gold and salt trade. The European slave trade, which started in 1500, involved millions of people and had lasting effects on Africa, most notably the loss of over 12 million Africans. Pan-Africanism, a movement that began in the early 1900s, supported Africans in their efforts to gain independence from European colonial powers.

---

## SECTION 2  STANDARDIZED TEST PRACTICE

**Multiple Choice**

| | | | | |
|---|---|---|---|---|
| 1. B | 3. D | 5. B | 7. A | 9. C |
| 2. A | 4. A | 6. A | 8. D | 10. A |

**Constructed Response**

11. The rock art described by the author shows scenes of hunting and war, graceful images of animals, and handprints of people.

12. Bones and implements can tell scientists when and where people lived, how they lived and died, and what they ate.

**Extended Response**

13. Possible response: It is important to preserve African rock art because ancient African drawings can tell scientists what these people were thinking and feeling.

14. Slave trade was the highest between 1701–1800.

15. Possible responses: Over 2 million enslaved persons did not survive the trip across the Atlantic Ocean. The years during which the most enslaved persons were traded (1701–1800) were also the years during which the highest rates of deaths were recorded.

# FORMAL ASSESSMENT

## SECTION 1  QUIZ

| | | |
|---|---|---|
| 1. B | 3. A | 5. B |
| 2. D | 4. B | 6. C |

7. Deforestation exposes the land to erosion and to poor use by people. This leads to desertification, leaving the soil less fertile for farming.

8. Rivers provide fresh water for farming, transportation over short distances, and electricity through hydroelectric dams.

---

## SECTION 2  QUIZ

| | | |
|---|---|---|
| 1. A | 3. D | 5. B |
| 2. A | 4. A | 6. D |

7. Colonialism is the process of directly ruling and settling foreign territories. It is an important part of imperialism, which is the practice of extending a nation's influence by controlling foreign territories.

8. The communities suffered economically because they lost the labor of young, strong workers. Because some of the people taken might have become leaders, some communities had a lack of leadership.

---

## GEOGRAPHY & HISTORY  TEST A

**Part 1: Multiple Choice**

| | | | | |
|---|---|---|---|---|
| 1. D | 3. A | 5. D | 7. B | 9. A |
| 2. C | 4. B | 6. D | 8. C | 10. C |

**Part 2: Interpret Maps**

| | | | |
|---|---|---|---|
| 11. A | 12. D | 13. C | 14. B |

**Part 3: Interpret Charts**

| | | | |
|---|---|---|---|
| 15. D | 16. B | 17. D | 18. C |

**Part 4: Document-Based Question**

19. According to Kenyatta, they do not, because they Europeans don't believe people need to make an effort to relate to each other as long they share certain ideas.

20. He implies that Africans believe people do need to pay attention to and work at relations with other individuals.

21. The countries are divided in such a way that they cannot improve their economies.

22. Possible answer: He would propose that Africans from all countries unite to work together and overcome the problems left by the colonialists.

23. It symbolizes the way Europe dominated the entire African continent.

24. Possible answer: They would feel anger or sadness at this illustration of European power over Africa.

**Extended Response** Possible response:

25. Contact among cultures and with outside traders helped create unity through shared languages. The Bantu migration led different peoples to share parts of the same culture. On the other hand, contact with outside countries caused many problems. The taking of slaves damaged or destroyed communities. For decades, European colonial powers dominated Africa, as shown by the cartoon, and used Africa's resources. They did not share African views about relationships, thinking the only thing that mattered was shared beliefs. In keeping with this, they tried to convert Africans to Christianity. After independence, Europeans left Africa with divisions that caused economic difficulties.

········································································································

# GEOGRAPHY & HISTORY  TEST B

## Part 1: Multiple Choice

| | | | | |
|---|---|---|---|---|
| **1.** B | **3.** A | **5.** A | **7.** D | **9.** D |
| **2.** D | **4.** B | **6.** B | **8.** B | **10.** D |

## Part 2: Interpret Maps

| | | | |
|---|---|---|---|
| **11.** C | **12.** B | **13.** A | **14.** C |

## Part 3: Interpret Charts

| | | | |
|---|---|---|---|
| **15.** A | **16.** D | **17.** D | **18.** C |

## Part 4: Document-Based Question

19. Europeans think people don't necessarily need to work at relations with others.

20. No. Kenyatta believes Africans do not see personal relations in the same way as Europeans do.

21. Both European colonialists and Africans are responsible.

22. The countries are divided in a way that makes them unable to function economically.

23. Possible answer: The man symbolizes the colonizing countries of Europe.

24. Possible answer: The gun symbolizes the fact that the colonizers had better weapons than the Africans and used those weapons to take control of Africa.

**Extended Response** Possible response:

25. Early contact with Arab traders helped spread the Swahili language. The early empires also benefited from trade with outside countries. Later, contact with Europeans did much damage to the people of sub-Saharan Africa. The African slave trade harmed or destroyed many communities. European countries took over African territory, as shown by the cartoon, and ruled it for their benefit. They did not share the African view of relationships, and so did not govern the way Africans would rule themselves. When the colonialists left, Africa was divided in ways that made it difficult for countries to function economically.

# TODAY

## SECTION 1.1 AFRICA'S BORDERS AND CULTURES

### Reading and Note-Taking

**Before Colonization:**
1. Borders between African cultural groups developed through agreement or conflict.
2. Natural features often defined the borders, which were easy to identify and control.
3. Natural borders along bodies of water provided transportation corridors.

**During Colonization:**
1. Europeans regularly ignored the borders of African cultural groups.
2. Borders met European needs for resources and for compromise with other colonial powers.
3. Cultural groups were divided, forced to share territory with rivals, or both.

**After Colonization:**
1. There are few sub-Saharan African countries in which people share one common culture.
2. Cultural differences have often led to civil wars over power, territory, and resources.
3. Military dictatorships often formed to impose order.

### Vocabulary Practice

**Word:** ethnic group
**Detail:** Many Africans identify themselves first as members of their tribe rather than their country.
**Detail:** Most sub-Saharan African countries have many ethnic groups.

**Word:** transportation corridor
**Definition:** a route to move people and goods easily between places
**Detail:** Borders along bodies of water were often transportation corridors in sub-Saharan Africa before colonization.
**Detail:** Landscape features such as oceans and lakes were natural transportation corridors, and were relatively easy to identify and control.

### GeoActivity Analyze Central Africa's Borders

1. The Borno people live in Niger, Chad, Cameroon, and Nigeria. They probably have less political power because they are now only a minority group in several different countries. Learning to live with different cultures in one country could be an advantage.
2. Factors may have included access to and distribution of natural resources and natural boundaries such as rivers.
3. Student discussions will vary, but students should note that colonialism occurred over the course of hundreds of years, affecting different parts of the continent at different times. Practicality aside, there is no single historical point to which Africa's borders could revert. Students should also note that several territories in the region, such as South Sudan and Western Sahara, have declared independence from post-colonial countries.

## SECTION 1.2 AFRICAN MUSIC GOES GLOBAL

### Reading and Note-Taking

**Broad Topic:** African music is heard worldwide. It is now part of many world cultures.
**Narrower Topic:** African music connects the people to their past and communicates their cultures to the world. It is evident in many kinds of music, such as jazz, blues, rock, and gospel.
**Narrowest Topic:** West African music is often a fusion of griot music with other African and global music.
Possible summary: African music is heard all over the globe. Sometimes the music is from individual countries, and sometimes it is a blend of African musical influences, such as the storytelling tradition of griots. Influences from the music of sub-Saharan Africa can be in jazz, blues, rock-and-roll, and gospel music in the U.S. African musicians have become international performers, communicating their cultural traditions to the world.

### Vocabulary Practice

ACADEMIC VOCABULARY
Possible sentence response: Musical influences from Africa are heard in a lot of dance music, such as rock, hip-hop, and Afro-Cuban music. (Students may cite specific musicians or groups.)

**Venn Diagram**

**overlap:** stories
**oral tradition:** verbally shared stories; stories about cultures

Possible sentence: For centuries, griots passed on the histories and oral traditions of West African cultures.

### GeoActivity Solve a Puzzle About African Music

**Across**
1 PROTESTMUSIC
4 GRIOT
6 BLUES
8 ORAL TRADITION (no space)
9 EVIDENT
10 MBALAX
**Down**
2 MIRIAM MAKEBA (no space)
3 YOUSSOU N'DOUR (no space or apostrophe)
5 FUSION
7 LUTE

## SECTION 1.3 KENYA MODERNIZES

### Reading and Note-Taking

**Goal:** to modernize Kenya's economy and improve its standard of living
**Challenges**
1. Kenya has 40 ethnic groups, and sometimes such cultural diversity leads to rivalry and conflict there.

2. Education is a key factor in modernization for any country, including Kenya.

3. Kenya's diverse geography and wildlife draw many tourists.

**Strategies**

1. Jomo Kenyatta, Kenya's first elected leader, appointed members from different ethnic groups as his advisors. He and other leaders encouraged domestic policies that led to economic growth and modernization.

2. Most children in Kenya attend free elementary schools.

3. The Kenyan government wants to protect the national parks and nature reserves.

**Outcomes**

1. Kenyatta helped all Kenyans pull together and work toward the common goal of modernization and economic growth.

2. Between 1970 and 2003, the adult literacy rate increased from 32 percent to 85 percent.

3. Kenya's national parks and nature reserves attract tourists and bring jobs and wealth into the country.

## Vocabulary Practice

1. Modernization is the development of policies and actions designed to bring a country up to current world standards in technology and other areas.

2. Modernization is the act of making a country up-to-date in technology.

3. Jomo Kenyatta's domestic policy helped spur Kenya's modernization.

4. Kenya's high literacy rate shows that most Kenyans have an education, which is a key factor in its modernization.

5. The government wants to protect the nation's parks and reserves because they bring jobs and money into Kenya.

## GeoActivity  Graph Kenya's Economic Indicators

1. Students' graphs should resemble the following:

### Kenya's Economic Indicators

2. around 1982

3. It is not possible to draw either conclusion with the data provided. Both GDP per capita and literacy rates have improved, but it is not clear whether the improvements in one category caused the improvements in the other.

# SECTION 1.4  TRADITIONAL CULTURES

## Reading and Note-Taking

**Explorer:** Grace Gobbo
**What the Explorer Does:** researches ways in which plants might help cure diseases; interviews traditional healers in Tanzania to find out how they use medicinal plants; teaches the value of medicinal plants; studies the relationship between cultures and plants
**Explorer's Goals:** Gobbo hopes to inspire people to preserve their forests along with traditional healing methods.
**Benefits of the Work:** Gobbo's work may lead to finding cures for illnesses and diseases, as well as help preserve forests from logging and agriculture. Not only will her work help conserve the plants and forests, but she will create a written record of traditional knowledge and cultures.

**Explorer:** Wade Davis
**What the Explorer Does:** studies the experiences and practices of indigenous cultures; studies how people of different cultures live; has lived among 15 groups in the Americas, Asia, Africa, and the Arctic; proposes that there is a "cultural web of life" and that every culture is connected
**Goals:** By showing that every culture is connected and that all indigenous cultures have contributed to the cultural web, Davis hopes to preserve cultural diversity.
**Benefits of the Work:** Indigenous cultures and their traditions will be more highly valued, and if they are protected, then the world will benefit by their contribution to humanity.

## Vocabulary Practice

**Word:** ethnobotanist
**Definition:** someone who studies the relationship between cultures and plants
  ethno = people or cultural group
  botanist = a scientist who studies plant life
  could study native plants or medicinal plants
  Ethnobotanists like Grace Gobbo work in the rain forests; they hope to show the value of medicinal plants.

**Word:** medicinal plants
**Definition:** plants used to treat illnesses
  Medicinal comes from the word medicine.
  Medicinal plants found in Africa are used to treat low blood pressure, rheumatism, stomach problems, swelling, cancer, heart disease, and chest pain.

**Compare:** The words are related in that ethnobotanists study the way that cultures view and use medicinal plants.

## GeoActivity  Research Vanishing Cultures

Students' Project Organizers will vary based on their specific topic. Be sure students have gone through all the steps to complete the Project Organizer.

# SECTION 1  REVIEW AND ASSESSMENT

## Vocabulary

| | | | |
|---|---|---|---|
| **1.** C | **3.** F | **5.** G | **7.** B |
| **2.** D | **4.** A | **6.** E | |

## Main Ideas

**8.** Before the Europeans arrived, borders between African cultural groups were determined by agreement or conflict.

**9.** In countries in which ethnic groups failed to unite to form a single nation, military dictatorships have often imposed order.

**10.** The African Union promotes peace, unity, and economic development and opposes colonization.

**11.** Possible response: The stories, music, and instruments of the griots have been incorporated into many aspects of African music.

**12.** Protest music is music that is focused on politics and on improving people's lives.

**13.** The East African Community is composed of Uganda, Tanzania, and Kenya. The group plans to expand the economy by improving trade, industry, and transportation in the region.

**14.** Some possible results of the work of scientists like Gobbo and Wade are that people recognize the value of medicinal plants and want to preserve forests and traditional healing methods.

**15.** Possible response: It is important to preserve indigenous cultures and traditional ways of life in Africa because they benefit all cultures, particularly in the area of medicine.

## Focus Skill: Draw Conclusions

**16.** Many Africans identify themselves first as members of their tribe because their tribe, rather than their country, more often shares their culture, language, and racial heritage.

**17.** European colonizers ignored the existing borders of African cultural groups because they wanted to create borders that would meet their desire to extract resources and to compromise with other colonial powers.

**18.** The long-term effect of changing Africa's original borders has been that there are few sub-Saharan African countries that share one common culture.

**19.** Possible response: Through their oral traditions, griots have helped preserve African history and culture.

**20.** Possible response: Many Africans were forced from their homes and sold into slavery, especially in the United States. Quite possibly they brought their African music and traditions with them and passed them on to their own children. In this way, African music influenced the development of American musical forms.

**21.** The factor that makes Kenya a multicultural society is the more than 40 ethnic groups that live there.

**22.** After he was elected Kenya's leader, Kenyatta appointed members from different ethnic groups to be his advisors.

**23.** Modernization improved Kenyan life by focusing on education, raising the literacy rate, and establishing national parks and reserves.

**24.** Ethnobotanist Grace Gobbo interviewed more than 80 traditional healers because she wanted to find out how they used plants to treat illnesses and possibly identify those plants for broader use.

**25.** Possible response: Wade Davis believes it is important to preserve cultural diversity because he believes in a cultural web of life and that different cultures contribute to humanity.

### Synthesize: Answer the Essential Question

The practice on the part of European colonizers of ignoring traditional African borders, permanently altered African culture by making tribes, rather than unified countries. African music has connected Africans with their past and helped to communicate African culture to the world. The modernization of Kenya has helped Kenya's diverse ethnic groups and cultures to thrive. Finally, Africa's indigenous cultures and traditional ways, once in danger of being lost forever, now have advocates working to preserve both cultures and traditional ways because of all they contribute to humanity.

# SECTION 1  STANDARDIZED TEST PRACTICE

## Multiple Choice

| | | | | |
|---|---|---|---|---|
| **1.** D | **3.** A | **5.** A | **7.** B | **9.** C |
| **2.** D | **4.** C | **6.** D | **8.** C | **10.** A |

## Constructed Response

**11.** The city of Dakar contributed its Afro-Cuban music, jazz, funk, rock, and French pop.

**12.** Mbalax was created by the fusion of musical styles from Dakar with a renewal of African traditional culture that included Wolof sabar drummers and hurricane-throated praise singers.

## Extended Response

**13.** Fusion requires the meeting of at least two different musical traditions and the willingness of musicians to experiment with and put together these musical traditions.

**14.** The graph shows that Kenyan literacy rates have been steadily rising since 1980.

**15.** The graph shows that Kenyan modernization, especially in the area of education, has produced dramatically positive results.

# SECTION 2.1  PRIZED MINERAL RESOURCES

## Reading and Note-Taking

**I.  Sub-Saharan Africa's mineral riches**

**A.** The region has large deposits of gold, diamonds, and other minerals.

**B.** Many of these minerals are exported to Europe, North America, and Asia.

**II.  Mineral resources as commodities**

**A.** Many sub-Saharan countries use mineral resources as valuable commodities.

**B.** Economic development has been slow, however, and colonial governments and corrupt local government officials took much of the profits.

**III. Economic improvement**

**A.** Unstable governments still challenge many sub-Saharan countries, and some are among the poorest in the world, despite their rich resources.

B. Some countries have successfully used their mineral wealth to build their economies and have invested profits in education, infrastructure, and health care to improve the lives of their people.

## Vocabulary Practice

**Word:** commodity
**What is it?** something that can be bought, sold, or traded
**Examples:** minerals, grains, vegetables, timber
**How does it help you?** People can earn money by buying, selling, or trading commodities. Commodities are often materials that industries use to make products.

**Word:** mineral
**What is it?** It's an inorganic substance that occurs naturally and can be found underground.
**Examples:** gold, diamonds, coal, petroleum, salt
**How does it help you?** Minerals are valuable commodities and are used to make many products.

**Possible sentence:** In many sub-Saharan African countries, large mineral deposits provide valuable commodities that bring in enormous wealth.

### GeoActivity  Evaluate Diamond Practices

1. Possible response: The group in Case Study 3 has the fairest practices. It tries to raise awareness about unsafe conditions and promote companies that have fair practices.

2. Possible response: The group in Case Study 1 has the least fair practices. It misleads people in its advertising because it doesn't tell the whole story about the workers' conditions.

3. Possible response: Consumers can put pressure on organizations to improve conditions by refusing to buy diamonds from them.

## SECTION 2.2 NIGERIA AND OIL

### Reading and Note-Taking

**Cause:**
1. ethnic conflict
2. coups
3. Agricultural production declined.
4. corruption
5. pollution from oil spills

**Effect:** Nigeria's people have experienced little benefit from its oil wealth.

### Vocabulary Practice

ACADEMIC VOCABULARY
Possible response: Most Nigerian oil production is concentrated in the Niger River delta.

**Key Vocabulary**

**Word:** coup
**Definition:** an illegal takeover of the government by force
**Oval:** Nigeria had many coups after gaining independence.
**Spoke:** Rival ethnic groups replaced existing governments, often with military leaders.
**Oval:** Nigeria's coups were caused by ethnic conflicts.
**Spoke:** Three major ethnic groups: Hausa-Fulani, Igbo, Yoruba and 250 smaller groups
**Spoke:** at least two major religions
**Oval:** Future coups could disrupt Nigeria's economic progress.
**Spoke:** loans to repay its debts
**Spoke:** economic reforms to improve infrastructure

**Word:** concentrate
**Definition:** to center, focus, or gather
**Oval:** Nigeria's economy is concentrated on oil.
**Spoke:** Nigeria produces more oil than any other African country.
**Spoke:** Nigeria also has the largest population in Africa.
**Oval:** Nigeria's oil production is concentrated.
**Spoke:** in the Niger River delta
**Spoke:** where most people live in poverty
**Oval:** Nigeria's oil profits are concentrated.
**Spoke:** Most Nigerians do not benefit from the oil wealth.
**Spoke:** Profits have not been used to improve the production area and working conditions.

### GeoActivity  Compare Nigeria's Oil Revenue and Incomes

1. Students' graphs should resemble the following:

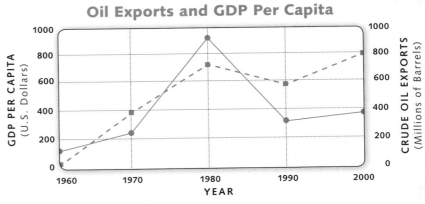

Oil Exports and GDP Per Capita

2. The amount of oil exported in 2000 was more than the amount exported in 1980, but GDP per capita was lower than it was in 1980. This shows that the country's standard of living is not directly related to oil exports.

3. The GDP per capita increased considerably. The country had increased the amount of oil it exported and prices were higher, so the country benefited greatly from the circumstances.

4. Possible response: No, it is not good policy because if the price of oil falls, then the economy will be greatly affected.

# SECTION 2.3 AGRICULTURE AND FOOD SUPPLY

## Reading and Note-Taking

**Detail:** Farmers are moving animals from place to place to avoid overgrazing.
**Detail:** Growing different crops on the same plot helps farmers avoid exhausting the soil.
**Detail:** More legumes are being planted, which add to the food supply and release helpful nutrients into the soil.
**Detail:** Farmers are using more fertilizer with animal and plant waste instead of chemicals.
**Main Idea:** Africa is improving its ability to feed its growing population.
**Identify:** Natural disasters, droughts, floods, armed conflicts, and Africa's population growth are all threaten Africa's food supply.

## Vocabulary Practice

Students' descriptive paragraphs will vary but should accurately describe Africa's agriculture and food supply and use each of the Key Vocabulary words correctly. Paragraphs should also start with a topic sentence, include details and examples from the section that support the topic, and end with a summarizing sentence.

## GeoActivity  Compare Zimbabwe's Crop Production

**1.** Students' graphs should resemble the following:

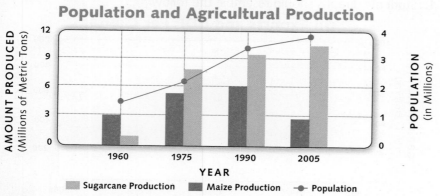

**Population and Agricultural Production**

**2.** 1961: 0.24 metric tons; 2005: 0.08 metric tons

**3.** Sugarcane production in 2005 was 11 times the amount it was in 1960. Since it is a cash crop, it probably benefited the farmers who grew it and contributed to a rise in GDP.

**4.** Maize production increased slightly and then decreased. It is possible that more farmers began growing sugarcane since it was more profitable than maize.

-----

# SECTION 2.4  IMPROVING PUBLIC HEALTH

## Reading and Note-Taking

**Problem:** Malaria is one of many chronic diseases that plague Africa.
**Obstacle 1:** Organisms and insects that cause disease thrive in Africa's tropical climates.

**Strategy 1:** Government and international agencies offer medication and vaccines.
**Obstacle 2:** Poverty contributes to the spread of disease. Poor Africans may not be able to afford preventive measures such as mosquito nets, screened. windows. Communities may not have the technology for draining breeding grounds.
**Strategy 2:** NGOs help provide simple preventive measures such as mosquito nets as well as monitor disease outbreaks and treatment.
**Obstacle 3:** Malaria became a pandemic, spreading across much of the world.
**Strategy 3:** Foundations, such as the Bill and Melinda Gates Foundation, raise funds for researching vaccines and more effective medications.
**Solution:** Governments, international agencies, NGOs, and private foundations need to keep working together to fight malaria in Africa and around the world.

## Vocabulary Practice

ACADEMIC VOCABULARY
Possible response:  Malaria is an infectious disease spread by mosquitoes and can cause flu-like symptoms.

**Definition Tree**

**epidemic**
**Definition:** when a large number of people in a place get a disease that spreads fast
**Sentence:** The county's medical teams were able to stop the spread of disease before it became an epidemic.

**pandemic**
**Definition:** when a disease spreads fast and infects people over a wide area or even globally
**Sentence:** We ready about the influenza pandemic in 1918, and we all started washing our hands more.

**vaccine**
**Definition:** a medical treatment given to people to help them avoid getting a disease, like measles
**Sentence:** Not every disease has a vaccine developed for it, but those have probably helped prevent epidemics.

## GeoActivity  Interpret a Map of Malaria Outbreaks

**1.** They are shaded in the darkest color; northwestern and northeastern Ethiopia.

**2.** The malaria outbreak is less severe in the area around Addis Ababa. Since Addis Ababa is the capital of Ethiopia, people there probably have better access to medical care than people in the northern part of the country.

**3.** so they can determine where to focus their efforts first

**4.** The epidemic is more severe in the northern part of the country, so public health officials there probably focus more on containing the disease and treating people. In the south, they probably focus more on prevention and education.

# SECTION 2.5 SUDAN AND SOMALIA

## Reading and Note-Taking

**Sudan:** Differences between the north and south have led to conflict. Northern Sudan is mostly desert. Nomadic Muslim herders of Arabic descent live there. Southern Sudan is swamp and savanna that was settled by farmers of African descent who practice mainly Christianity or indigenous religions. The Sudanese government has oppressed Christians since its independence in 1956. 400,000 people have been killed. About 2.5 million people became refugees, including the Lost Boys of Sudan.

**Both:** War, famine, disease, and starvation have plagued them. The Sahel runs through them, dividing them between northern Africa and sub-Saharan Africa.

**Somalia:** Conflict exists among five major clans. The clans have never united to form a single nation. Clan-based groups overthrew the military government in 1991. With no central government, some clans turned to piracy. Many people consider Somalia to be a failed state. Somaliland and Puntland have claimed independence but have not received international recognition.

## Vocabulary Practice

**Word:** clan
**Definition:** a large group of people who are related and are loyal to their group
**Characteristic:** fierce loyalty and clashes with outsiders
**Sentence:** In Somalia, there are conflicts between and within the five clans.

**Word:** failed state
**Definition:** a country in which government, economic institutions, and order have broken down
**Characteristic:** no stable government
**Sentence:** Somalia has no central government and many people consider the country to be a failed State.

**Word:** refugee
**Definition:** someone who has been forced to leave a country because of war or for religious or political reasons
**Characteristic:** displaced and without many possessions
**Sentence:** About 2.5 million refugees, including the Lost Boys of Sudan, left Sudan as a result of the conflicts there.

## GeoActivity Build a Time Line of Events

Students' time lines should include the following dates:

**Title: Conflicts in Sudan and Somalia**
**1955** Civil war begins in Sudan.
**1969** The military stages a coup in Somalia.
**1972** Peace is established in Sudan.
**1983** Civil war begins again in Sudan.
**1991** The Somali government collapses leading to violence.
**1992** The United States leads a force to restore order in Somalia.
**1994** Peacekeeping forces withdraw.
**2000** Unsuccessful peace talks are held in Somalia.
**2002** Civil war ends in Sudan.
**2002–2005** Peace agreements are signed in Sudan.
**2003** Violence breaks out in Darfur.
**2008** The UN takes control of a peacekeeping mission in Darfur.
**2011** Southern Sudan votes for independence and becomes the Republic of South Sudan.

1. approximately 40 years (37 years)
2. Establishing peace requires compromise between sides. In most cases, there are two sides. In Somalia, however, each clan would need to compromise with not one but four other groups.
3. The events in Sudan and Somalia seem intertwined periods of peace and war. Sometimes the two countries are experiencing opposite events at the same time. This pattern is significant because it highlights the problem of general unrest in the region after colonialism ended.

# SECTION 2.6 ENDING APARTHEID

## Reading and Note-Taking

**Foundations of Apartheid:**
**1800s:** Dutch and British lay claim to lands in South Africa. Dutch settlers, known as Boers or Afrikaners, formed their own republics. Boers enslaved Africans and imported laborers from Asia.
**1902:** After a series of wars, Boer territories became British colonies known as the Union of South Africa. The British and the Boers seized land from indigenous African groups. Many Africans were killed or forced to work for the white colonists.

**Beginning of Apartheid:** The government divided South Africa into white and black areas. Only white Africans could vote. Most of the land and all of the best land was reserved for the white minority. Cities were declared white, and black Africans could enter cities only to work.
**1948:** New laws created apartheid.
**1970:** The government made all black South Africans citizens of homelands.

**End of Apartheid:**
**1923:** Black Africans formed the African National Congress. The ANC was outlawed and its leaders, including Nelson Mandela, were imprisoned.
**1977:** Stephen Biko was arrested and beaten to death.
**1980s:** Violent resistance to apartheid spread.
**1989:** White president F.W. de Klerk began to change apartheid laws, legalized the ANC, and released its leaders.
**1994:** Voting rights were extended to all South Africans. Nelson Mandela was elected president.

## Vocabulary Practice

**Word:** apartheid
**Definition:** a former social system in South Africa in which black people and people from other racial groups did not have the same political and economic rights as white people and were forced to live separately from them
**In Your Own Words:** laws that discriminated against black South Africans and segregated them from white South Africans

**Sentence:** Apartheid was an unjust system, which, like slavery in the United States, took many years to change.

**Word:** homeland
**Definition:** a native land or area set aside where a particular group of people are allowed to live
**In Your Own Words:** an area where a group lives or is forced to live
**Sentence:** Homelands were a failed and unfair way to deal with segregation and the right of black South Africans to self-govern.

**Word:** segregation
**Definition:** the practice of keeping people of different races or religions separate from each other
**In Your Own Words:** separation by race
**Sentence:** The end of segregation is only the beginning of achieving true equality for blacks in South Africa, but the country is making progress.

## GeoActivity Analyze Primary Sources: Apartheid and Segregation

1. Mandela means that the African people were struggling to gain basic rights, but that the government's oppressive system had only gotten worse. He probably wants people to continue to demand their rights.
2. Alexander writes that African Americans were forced to live in slum areas that other groups had abandoned. In both cases, oppressed groups were restricted from or forced out of desirable areas and into miserable living conditions.
3. Guaranteed political rights would allow members of oppressed groups to change laws and get fair and equal treatment.

---

## SECTION 2 REVIEW AND ASSESSMENT

### Vocabulary
1. E
2. D
3. C
4. A
5. F
6. B

### Main Idea
7. Minerals (large deposits of gold, diamonds, and other minerals) are the most important resource for the economic future of sub-Saharan Africa. (Accept oil as another possible answer.)
8. Smuggling, political unrest, and lack of infrastructure have limited the economic progress of the Central African Republic.
9. Famine is a widespread shortage of food often caused by natural disasters, drought, floods, and armed conflicts. Constant long-term hunger is often also widespread, but in contrast to famine it is persistent; it does not go away. In contrast to famine, long-term hunger is often not widely reported.
10. Malaria can be prevented by providing vaccines, mosquito nets, screened windows, adequate sanitation, and medical treatment, and by researching more effective anti-malarial drugs.
11. A major source of funding in the battle against malaria is the Bill and Melinda Gates Foundation.
12. The Lost Boys of the Sudan were young men, refugees from Sudan, who were orphaned by the civil war. They stuck together to escape the violence.

13. The Boers were Dutch colonists who settled in South Africa. The Boers enslaved Africans and seized lands from the Zulus, Xhosa, and other Africans. They killed many Africans and forced others to work for white colonists.

### Focus Skill: Analyze Cause and Effect
14. Unstable governments often allow smuggling, corruption, and political unrest. Also, without a stable government, a country's infrastructure—so essential to economic growth—is often left underdeveloped.
15. British colonialism left Nigeria divided among three major ethnic groups as well as 250 smaller groups. When Nigeria gained independence these different groups struggled for control. Conflict and corruption in the struggle to gain control of oil and its profits have prevented most Nigerians from sharing in the oil wealth.
16. Rapid population growth coupled with a less rapid growth in food production has led to an inadequate food supply, leaving many people in sub-Saharan Africa malnourished.
17. Legumes are peas or beans. Legumes add to the food supply and release helpful nutrients into the soil.
18. Microcredit offers small loans to help poor farmers invest in land, tools, and seeds.
19. Vaccines can help prevent the spread of malaria by increasing a person's resistance to the disease.
20. As a result of Darfur's government-created Arab militia, almost 400,000 people have been killed and about 2.5 million have become refugees.
21. Possible response: People become refugees—leaving their homes and sometimes, their countries—when they face violence and danger they cannot protect themselves from.
22. The effect of clan rivalry in Somalia has been the overthrow of a crumbling military government, raging violence among rival clans, disruption of farms, the absence of any central government, and the rise of piracy.
23. Homelands were self-governing areas within South Africa. The South African government made blacks citizens of homelands, rather than citizens of South Africa. The homelands were supposed to be self-governing but, in fact, the government controlled them.

### Synthesize: Answer the Essential Question
The long-range effects of colonialism still plague sub-Saharan Africa today. On the other hand, the sub-Saharan Africa's rich resources offer hope for the future. Ethnic tension, in many cases a long-term result of colonists' remapping the borders of the region, still presents challenges to African governments. Sudan and Somalia are perhaps the most extreme examples of the devastating results of unchecked ethnic rivalries. South Africa's movement from a racist to government to a democratically elected government offers hope that Africa will one day be able to harness its many resources to benefit its people.

## SECTION 2 STANDARDIZED TEST PRACTICE

**Multiple Choice**

| | | | | |
|---|---|---|---|---|
| **1.** A | **3.** B | **5.** A | **7.** C | **9.** D |
| **2.** D | **4.** B | **6.** D | **8.** B | **10.** B |

**Constructed Response**

**11.** The kgotla is a forum for discussion of community affairs.

**12.** Before he makes a decision, the tribal chief considers the opinions of all who wish to speak.

**Extended Response**

**13.** Possible response: The kgotla helped ease Botswana into parliamentary government because the forum had already given people an experience of expressing their opinions and having someone else make decisions (or represent them) based on those opinions.

**14.** Possible response: The graph shows that although the gross domestic product of Nigeria is very high, the life expectancy rate and the gross domestic product per capita is very low by comparison. This tells me that there is a lot of money being made in Nigeria, but very little of it is going to the Nigerian people.

**15.** Possible response: When you compare the GDP with the life expectancy rate and the GDP per capita it is pretty easy to see which governments are working for and protecting their people and which governments are not. Botswana, for example, has a comparatively modest GDP, but it's life expectancy rate and GDP per capita is the highest among the countries listed.

# FORMAL ASSESSMENT

## SECTION 1 QUIZ

| | | |
|---|---|---|
| **1.** C | **3.** C | **5.** D |
| **2.** B | **4.** D | **6.** A |

**7.** Some boundaries split apart cultural groups, while other boundaries lumped rivals together. Conflict resulted.

**8.** It has beautiful scenery and interesting wildlife for tourists to see.

## SECTION 2 QUIZ

| | | |
|---|---|---|
| **1.** C | **3.** B | **5.** B |
| **2.** C | **4.** A | **6.** D |

**7.** Before colonization, villagers worked together to raise food for everyone. Afterward, people raised cashed crops for export and not enough food was produced.

**8.** All the races received the right to vote, and the first black African president was elected.

## SUB-SAHARAN AFRICA TODAY TEST A

**Part 1: Multiple Choice**

| | | | | |
|---|---|---|---|---|
| **1.** B | **3.** D | **5.** B | **7.** D | **9.** C |
| **2.** A | **4.** D | **6.** C | **8.** C | **10.** B |

**Part 2: Interpret Maps**

| | | |
|---|---|---|
| **11.** A | **12.** C | **13.** C |

**14.** The parks tend to be on plains rather than in mountains. Perhaps few animals live in the mountains.

**Part 3: Interpret Diagrams**

| | | |
|---|---|---|
| **15.** A | **16.** B | **17.** A |

**18.** Botswana would be hurt more. Even though South Africa exports more diamonds, they account for a very small part of the South African economy. Botswana earns most of its export income from diamonds, so it would be hurt badly by a drop in prices.

**Part 4: Document-Based Question**
**Constructed Response**

**19.** He means that African nations will be at peace, and African leaders will work together to solve problems.

**20.** If Africa had less political turmoil, its leaders could cooperate to protect the environment.

**21.** Their value will increase enormously.

**22.** because lions are becoming so scarce and valuable

**23.** It dropped from around 450,000 to about 20,000.

**24.** It supports the idea that lions are becoming so endangered that each one is as valuable as a gem.

**Extended Response** Possible response:

**25.** Nelson Mandela would probably ask other African leaders to work cooperatively to save Africa's environment and wildlife before it is too late. He might quote Joubert's statement "As . . . wild resources on the planet shrink, we will all be looking at them as a shared and precious commodity and with a universal responsibility to protect the last of them." He might also use the data on the graph to demonstrate that if the lions are not given better protection right away, it will be too late to save them.

## SUB-SAHARAN AFRICA TODAY TEST B

**Part 1: Multiple Choice**

| | | | | |
|---|---|---|---|---|
| **1.** C | **3.** A | **5.** A | **7.** A | **9.** C |
| **2.** D | **4.** C | **6.** D | **8.** D | **10.** C |

**Part 2: Interpret Maps**

| | | | |
|---|---|---|---|
| **11.** D | **12.** C | **13.** B | **14.** D |

**Part 3: Interpret Diagrams**

| | | | |
|---|---|---|---|
| **15.** C | **16.** D | **17.** B | **18.** D |

**Part 4: Document-Based Question**
**Constructed Response**

**19.** Africa at peace with itself and leaders working in unity

**20.** the environment

**21.** the wild resources of the planet

**22.** because it will be home to increasingly rare wildlife such as lions

**23.** about 450,000

**24.** about 20,000

**Extended Response** Possible response:

**25.** The documents address the need to protect the African environment. Specific examples include the scarcity of arable land, the loss of animal habitats, and the rapidly shrinking lion population. The problems are increasing so rapidly that Africa's valuable resources may be lost forever.Sentence: Apartheid was an unjust system, which, like slavery in the United States, took many years to change.

ACKNOWLEDGMENTS

## Text Acknowledgments

210: Excerpts from *El Libertador: Writings of Simón Bolivar* by Simón Bolívar, edited by David Bushness, translated by Fred Fornoff. Copyright © 2003 by Oxford University Press. Reprinted by permission of Oxford University Press. All rights reserved.

490: Excerpts from *The Illustrated Bhagavad Gita*, translated by Ranchor Prime. Copyright © 2003 by Godsfield Press, text © by Ranchor Prime. Reprinted by permission of Godsfield Press.

542: Excerpts from *The Analects of Confucius*, translated by Simon Leys. Copyright © 1997 by Pierre Ryckmans. Used by permission of W. W. Norton & Company, Inc.

639: Data from the International Union for Conservation of Nature (IUCN) Red List of Threatened Species by IUCN. Data copyright © 2008 by the IUCN Red List of Threatened Species. Reprinted by kind permission of IUCN.

### National Geographic School Publishing

National Geographic School Publishing gratefully acknowledges the contributions of the following National Geographic Explorers to our program and to our planet:

Greg Anderson, National Geographic Fellow
Katey Walter Anthony, 2009 National Geographic Emerging Explorer
Ken Banks, 2010 National Geographic Emerging Explorer
Katy Croff Bell, 2006 National Geographic Emerging Explorer
Christina Conlee, National Geographic Grantee
Alexandra Cousteau, 2008 National Geographic Emerging Explorer
Thomas Taha Rassam (TH) Culhane, 2009 National Geographic Emerging Explorer
Jenny Daltry, 2005 National Geographic Emerging Explorer
Wade Davis, National Geographic Explorer-in-Residence
Sylvia Earle, National Geographic Explorer-in-Residence
Grace Gobbo, 2010 National Geographic Emerging Explorer
Beverly Goodman, 2009 National Geographic Emerging Explorer
David Harrison, National Geographic Fellow
Kristofer Helgen, 2009 National Geographic Emerging Explorer
Fredrik Hiebert, National Geographic Fellow
Zeb Hogan, National Geographic Fellow
Shafqat Hussain, 2009 National Geographic Emerging Explorer
Beverly and Dereck Joubert, National Geographic Explorers-in-Residence
Albert Lin, 2010 National Geographic Emerging Explorer
Elizabeth Kapu'uwailani Lindsey, National Geographic Fellow
Sam Meacham, National Geographic Grantee
Kakenya Ntaiya, 2010 National Geographic Emerging Explorer
Johan Reinhard, National Geographic Explorer-in-Residence
Enric Sala, National Geographic Explorer-in-Residence
Kira Salak, 2005 National Geographic Emerging Explorer
Katsufumi Sato, 2009 National Geographic Emerging Explorer
Cid Simoes and Paola Segura, 2008 National Geographic Emerging Explorers
Beth Shapiro, 2010 National Geographic Emerging Explorer
José Urteaga, 2010 National Geographic Emerging Explorer
Spencer Wells, National Geographic Explorer-in-Residence

## Photographic Credits

iii (l) ©Innovative Images/National Geographic School Publishing (c) ©Mary Lynne Ashley/National Geographic School Publishing (r) ©Martin Photography/National Geographic School Publishing. iv (l) ©Aesthetic Life Studio/National Geographic School Publishing (c) ©Gary Donnelly/National Geographic School Publishing (r) ©Cliento Photography/National Geographic School Publishing. vi Top to Bottom Left Side: ©Chris Ranier ©Gemma Atwal ©Ken Banks ©Rebecca Hale/National Geographic Stock ©Christina Conlee ©The Ocean Foundation/National Geographic Stock. Top to Bottom Right Side: ©Sybille Frütel Culhane ©Kevin Krug ©Mark Theissen/National Geographic Stock ©Tyrone Turner/National Geographic Stock ©Adrian Jackson ©G. Anker ©Courtesy of the Jane Goodall Institute. vii Top to Bottom Left Side: ©Chris Ranier ©Rebecca Hale, National Geographic Stock ©Brant Allen ©Rolex Awards ©Beverly Joubert/National Geographic Stock. Top to Bottom Right Side: ©Beverly Joubert/National Geographic Stock ©Calit2, Erik Jepsen ©Ka'uila Barber ©National Geographic Society, Explorer Programs and Strategic Initiatives ©Sharon Farmer ©Mark Thiessen/ National Geographic Stock. viii Top to Bottom Left Side: ©Rebecca Hale/National Geographic Stock ©Lana Eklund ©Katsufumi Sato ©Victor Sanchez de Fuentes. Top to Bottom Right Side: ©Beth Shapiro ©Victor Sanchez de Fuentes ©Rachel Etherington ©David Evans/ National Geographic Society. ix ©Richard Barnes/ National Geographic Stock. x ©John Burcham, National Geographic Stock. xi ©Raul Touzon, National Geographic Stock. xii ©Rod Smith/National Geographic My Shot/National Geographic Stock. xiii ©Richard List, Corbis. xiv ©Photolibrary. xv ©David Alan Harvey/ National Geographic Stock. xvi ©Smar Jodha/National Geographic My Shot/National Geographic Stock. xvii ©Kenji Kondo/epa/Corbis. xvii ©Gavin Hellier/Alamy. xix ©Nigel Pavitt, Corbis. xx ©R. Wallace/Stock Photos/ Corbis. A1 ©Michael Dunning/Photographer's Choice/ Getty Images. A6 (bl) ©Mark Hamblin/Photolibrary (br) ©Thomas Marent/Minden Pictures/National Geographic Stock (c) ©Gerard Soury/Photolibrary (t) ©John Cancalosi/Photolibrary. A7 (bl) ©Adam Jones/Getty Images (br) ©Klaus Nigge/National Geographic Stock (c) ©DLILLC/Corbis (t) ©Thomas Marent/Minden Pictures/ National Geographic Stock. 1 (bkg) ©Franck Guiziou/ Hemis/Corbis (b, l, r) ©Mark Thiessen/National Geographic Society. 2 (bl) ©Sharon Farmer (br) ©Ka'uila Barber (cl) ©G. Anker (cr) ©Rolex Awards (tl) ©National Geographic Stock (tr) ©Calit2, Erik Jepsen. 3 (b) ©Mark Thiessen/National Geographic Stock (c) ©Ken Banks (tl)



©Gemma Atwal (tr) ©Tyrone Turner/National Geographic Stock. 4 (bkg) ©Suman Bajpeyi/National Geographic My Shot/National Geographic Stock (l) ©Jennifer Shaffer/National Geographic School Publishing (t) ©Fresco JLinga/National Geographic My Shot/National Geographic Stock. 5 ©Scott S. Warren/ National Geographic Stock. 6 (l) ©Susan Byrd/National Geographic My Shot/National Geographic Stock (r) ©Mitchell Funk/Photographer's Choice /Getty Images. 7 ©Nigel Pavitt, Corbis. 8 (bkg) ©Richard Barnes/National Geographic Stock (bl) ©Mitchell Funk/Photographer's Choice/Getty Images (cl) ©NASA Goddard Space Flight Center. (tl) ©David Evans/National Geographic Society. 10 ©Stephen Alvarez/National Geographic Stock. 11 ©Sunpix Travel/Alamy. 12 (bc) ©Mike Theiss/National Geographic Stock (cl) ©Blakeley/Alamy (cr) ©Michael S. Yamashita/National Geographic Stock 13 (tl) ©John Wark/Wark Photography, Inc. (tr) ©Mark Remaley/ Precision Aerial Photo. 15 (b) ©Michael S. Yamashita/ National Geographic Stock (t) ©Ma Wenxiao/ Sinopictures/Photolibrary. 16 ©Susan Byrd/National Geographic My Shot/National Geographic Stock. 20 ©Stephen Alvarez/National Geographic Stock. 23 ©PictureLake/Alamy. 26 ©Brooks Kraft/Corbis. 28 (bc) ©James Forte/National Geographic Stock (bl) ©Kenneth Garrett/National Geographic Stock (br) ©Michael Poliza/ National Geographic Stock (bkg) ©National Geographic Maps. 29 (bcl) ©N.C. Wyeth/National Geographic Stock (bcr) ©Justin Guarlglia/National Geographic Stock (bl) ©Kenneth Garrett/National Geographic Stock (br) ©Abraham Nowitz/National Geographic Stock 33 (b) ©David Trood/Getty Images (tr) ©Peter Carsten/National Geographic Stock. 34 ©Andrew Hasson/Alamy. 38 ©George H.H. Huey/Corbis. 41 (tc) ©Images & Volcans/ Photo Researchers, Inc. (tr) ©Chris Cheadle/Getty Images. 44 ©Bill Hatcher/National Geographic Stock. 46 (bc) ©Michael Doolittle/Alamy (cl) ©Daniel Dempster Photography/Alamy (tl) ©Tom Bean/Alamy. 47 (tl) ©Frank Krahmer/Corbis (tr) ©imagebroker/Alamy. 50 ©Panoramic Images/Getty Images. 52 ©Michael Nichols/ National Geographic Stock. 53 ©Russ Bishop/Alamy. 54 ©Kip Evans Photography. 55 ©NASA Goddard Space Flight Center. 56 (bc) ©Gordon Wiltsie/National Geographic Stock (bl) ©Ralph Lee Hopkins/National Geographic Stock (bkg) ©George Grall/National Geographic Stock (br) ©Paul Nicklen/National Geographic Stock 57 (bcl) ©Norbert Rosing/National Geographic Stock (bcr) ©William Albert Allard/National Geographic Stock (bl) ©Stuart Franklin/National Geographic Stock (br) ©Priit Vesilind/National Geographic Stock. 58 (b) ©David R. Frazier Photolibrary, Inc./Alamy (cl) ©Olivier Asselin/Alamy. 59 ©Greg Elms/ Lonely Planet Images. 63 ©John Stanmeyer/National Geographic Stock. 64 ©Nic Bothma/epa/Corbis. 65 ©Alain Nogues/Corbis. 67 ©Michael Dunning/ Photographer's Choice/Getty Images. 72 ©Romeo Gacad/ AFP/Getty Images. 74 (b) ©Tetra Images/Corbis (bkg) ©John Burcham, National Geographic Stock (c) ©Walter Meayers Edwards, National Geographic Stock (t) ©Beth Shapiro. 77 ©Petra Engle/National Geographic Stock. 78 (b) ©Phil Schermeister/National Geographic Stock (bkg) ©Menno Boermans/Aurora Photos/Corbis (t) ©SeBuKi/ Alamy. 80 ©Mike Grandmaison/Corbis. 82 ©Bill Hatcher/National Geographic Stock. 84 ©Daniel H. Bailey/Corbis. 86 (bkg) ©Jean-Pierre Lescourret/Corbis (cr) ©Mauricio Ramos. 88 ©Jon Arnold Images Ltd/ Alamy. 89 ©American School Private Collection/Peter Newark American Pictures/The Bridgeman Art Library Nationality. 90 ©Thomas Sbampato/Photolibrary. 91 ©The Granger Collection. 92 (l) ©The Granger Collection (r) ©photostock1/Alamy. 93 ©Visions LLC/Photolibrary. 95 ©William Manning/Corbis. 96 ©Bettmann/Corbis. 98 (l) ©Corbis (r) ©American School Private Collection/ Courtesy of Swann Auction Galleries/ The Bridgeman Art Library. 99 ©Corbis. 100 ©Bettmann/Corbis. 101 ©Lynn Johnson/National Geographic Stock. 102 ©The Art Archive/Museo Ciudad Mexico/Gianni Dagli Orti. 103 (l) ©Kenneth Garrett/National Geographic Stock (r) ©David R. Frazier Photolibrary, Inc./Alamy. 104 ©The Stapleton Collection/The Bridgeman Art Library. 105 ©The Stapleton Collection/The Bridgeman Art Library. 106 ©The Granger Collection. 107 (b) ©The Granger Collection (t) ©Look and Learn Magazine Ltd/The Bridgeman Art Library. 108 (l) ©North Wind Picture Archives/Alamy (r) ©Randy Faris/Corbis. 109 (l) ©Corbis (r) ©Charles & Josette Lenars/Corbis. 110 ©North Wind Picture Archives/Alamy. 111 ©Hulton Archive/Getty Images. 114 ©Joe McNally/National Geographic Stock. 116 ©Jennifer Shaffer/National Geographic School Publishing. 117 ©Mike Theiss/National Geographic Society Image Sales. 118 ©Jennifer Shaffer/National Geographic School Publishing/Art Institute of Chicago. 120 ©Car Culture/Corbis. 123 (c) ©James Forte/National Geographic Stock (tr) ©Michael Dunning/Photographer's Choice/Getty Images. 124 ©Marjorie Kamys Cotera/ Daemmrich Photography/The Image Works. 125 (b) ©Robb Kottmyer (t) ©Roger Meno. 126 ©Tono Labra/ Photolibrary. 127 ©Keith Dannemiller/Alamy. 128 ©STR/ Reuters/Corbis. 130 ©Alfredo Guerrero/epa/Corbis. 131 ©Blaine Harrington III/Alamy. 136 ©Corbis Premium RF/ Alamy. 138 (b) ©Georgios Kollidas/Alamy (bkg) ©Raul Touzon, National Geographic Stock (c) ©Stephen Alvarez, National Geographic Stock. 141 ©Konrad Wothe/Minden Pictures. 142 (b) ©Jon Arnold Images Ltd/ Alamy (bkg) ©Menno Boermans/Aurora Photos/Corbis (t) ©Danny Lehman/Corbis. 144 ©Dr. Richard Roscoe/ Visuals Unlimited, Inc. 147 ©Stuart Westmorland/ Corbis. 148 (b) ©Paul Hoekman (t) ©Bryan Wallace. 150 (bc) ©Roy Toft/National Geographic Stock (bl) ©Michael Nichols/National Geographic Stock (bkg) ©Paul Sutherland/National Geographic Stock (br) ©Steve Winter/National Geographic Society Image Sales. 151 (bcl) ©Michael Melford/National Geographic Stock (bcr) ©Bobby Haas/National Geographic Stock (bl) ©Christian Ziegler/National Geographic Stock (br) ©Roy Toft/ National Geographic Stock. 152 ©Steve Winter/National Geographic Stock. 155 ©The Bridgeman Art Library. 156 (br) ©Georgios Kollidas/Alamy (r) ©Hemis/Alamy. 157 ©Stuwdamdorp/Alamy. 158 (bl) ©Creativ Studio Heinemann/Westend61/Corbis (c) ©Interfoto/Alamy. 159 (br) ©Reuters/Corbis (tl) ©Bettmann/Corbis (tl) ©Creativ Studio Heinemann/Westend61/Corbis. 162 ©Walter Bibikow/JAI/Corbis. 164 ©Martin Gray/National Geographic Stock. 165 ©Danita Delimont/Alamy. 166 ©Nico Tondini/Photolibrary. 167 ©Rick Gerharter/Lonely Planet Images. 168 ©National Geographic Stock. 169 ©Frans Lanting/Corbis. 170 ©Photolibrary. 172 ©Yuan Man/Xinhua Press/Corbis. 173 ©Logan Abassi/UN Handout/Corbis. 174 ©JS Callahan/tropicalpix/Alamy. 175 ©Michael Dunning/Photographer's Choice/Getty Images. 176 ©Lonely Planet Images /Alamy. 178 (bkg) ©Christian Heeb/Aurora Photos (c) ©Roy Toft/National Geographic Stock (r) ©Micahel & Patricia Fogden/ Minden Pictures/National Geographic Stock. 179 ©Arterra Picture Library/Alamy. 183 (l) ©Jacques Marais/ Getty Images (r) ©Danny Lehman/Corbis. 184 ©Christian Zeigler/National Geographic Stock. 186 (b) ©Frans Lanting/Corbis (bkg) ©Rod Smith/National Geographic My Shot/National Geographic Stock (cl) ©David R. Frazier Photolibrary, Inc./Alamy (tl) ©Photograph by



Victor Sanchez de Fuentes. 189 ©Nick Gordon/Oxford Scientific (OSF)/Photolibrary. 190 (bkg) ©Menno Boermans/Aurora Photos/Corbis (bl) ©Colin Monteath/ Minden Pictures/National Geographic Stock (br) ©John Eastcott and Yva Momatiuk/National Geographic Stock. 192 ©Ivan Kashinsk/National Geographic Stock. 196 (bkg) ©Melissa Farlow/National Geographic Stock (br) ©Aldo Sessa/Tango Stock/Getty Images. 199 (br) ©Michael Nichols/National Geographic Stock (tr) ©Michael Dunning/Photographer's Choice/Getty Images. 200 ©Ethan Welty/Aurora Photos/Alamy. 201 ©Gnter Wamser/F1online digitale Bildagentur GmbH/Alamy. 202 ©Christina Conlee. 203 (b) ©Christina Conlee (t) ©Robert Clark/National Geographic Stock. 206 (bc) ©Maria Stenzel/National Geographic Stock (c) ©Peruvian School/Museo Arqueologia, Lima, Peru/Boltin Picture Library/The Bridgeman Art Library International (tr) ©McConnell, James Edwin/Private Collection /Look and Learn/The Bridgeman Art Library International. 207 ©Cro Magnon/Alamy. 208 (bc) ©The Art Archive/ Bibliothéque des Arts Décoratifs Paris/Gianni Dagli Orti (tr) ©The Art Archive/Bibliothéque des Arts Décoratifs Paris/Gianni Dagli Orti. 209 ©The Art Archive/ Kharbine-Tapabor. 211 ©Luis Marden/National Geographic Stock. 215 ©Florian Kopp/imagebroker/ Alamy. 216 ©Paolo Aguilar/epa/Corbis. 219 ©Corey Wise/Lonely Planet Images/Getty Images. 220 ©Mike Theiss/National Geographic Stock. 221 ©Richard Nowitz/National Geographic Stock. 223 ©Ivan Alvarado/ Reuters/Corbis. 224 ©Jeremy Hoare/Alamy. 225 (b) ©James P. Blair/National Geographic Stock (c) ©Nicolas Misculin/Reuters (t) ©Kit Houghton/Corbis. 226 ©Jennifer Shaffer/National Geographic School Publishing. 228 ©Keren Su/Corbis. 229 (t) ©Imaginechina/Corbis. 231 ©Robert Clark/National Geographic Stock. 232 ©Sebastiao Moreira/epa/Corbis. 234 (b) ©Mike Theiss/National Geographic Stock (bl) ©Charles Dharapak/Pool/Reuters. 240 ©Pete McBride/ National Geographic Stock. 242 (b) ©Bob Krist/National Geographic Stock (bkg) ©Richard List/Corbis (c) ©Anne Keiser/National Geographic Stock. 245 ©Atlantide Phototravel/Corbis. 246 (b) ©Yann Arthus-Bertrand/ Corbis (bkg) ©Menno Boermans/Aurora Photos/Corbis (t) ©Douglas Pearson/Corbis. 248 ©Owi-Diasign/ Photolibrary. 250 ©National Geographic Stock. 252 ©Octavio Aburto. 254 (bc) ©Anne Keiser/National Geographic Stock (bl) ©Agnieszka Pruszek/National Geographic My Shot/National Geographic Stock (bkg) ©Jim Richardson/National Geographic Stock (br) ©Steve Raymer/National Geographic Stock. 255 (bcl) ©Greg Dale/National Geographic Stock (bcr) ©James P. Blair/ National Geographic Stock (bl) ©Richard Nowitz/ National Geographic Stock (br) ©James L. Stanfield/ National Geographic Stock. 256 ©Panoramic Images/ National Geographic Stock. 258 (l) ©Richard Nowitz/ National Geographic Stock (r) ©The Art Gallery Collection/Alamy. 259 ©PoodlesRock/Corbis. 260 ©Jean-Pierre Lescourret/Corbis. 262 (l) ©Hoberman Collection/Corbis (r) ©The Bridgeman Art Library International. 263 ©North Wind Picture Archives/Alamy. 266 (bl) ©The Bridgeman Art Library (br) ©Underwood & Underwood/Corbis. 267 (bl) ©Doug Taylor/Alamy (br) ©The Bridgeman Art Library (t) ©The Bridgeman Art Library. 268 ©Richard Schlect/National Geographic Stock. 270 ©Paul Thompson/Corbis. 272 (l) ©The Bridgeman Art Library (r) ©The Gallery Collection/ Corbis. 273 (b) ©Peter Horree/Alamy (t) ©The Bridgeman Art Library. 274 ©The Bridgeman Art Library. 275 ©Scanfoto/X00729/Reuters/Corbis. 276 (l) ©Stefano Bianchetti/Corbis (r) ©Clynt Garnham/Alamy. 277 (l) ©Michael Nicholson/Corbis (r) ©Michael Nicholson/ Corbis. 279 ©DC Premiumstock/Alamy. 282 ©Rudy Sulgan/Corbis. 284 ©MARKA/Alamy. 286 (l) ©Leonardo da Vinci (1452-1519) Louvre, Paris, France/ Giraudon/ The Bridgeman Art Library (r) Claude Monet (1840-1926) Musee Marmottan, Paris, France/Giraudon/The Bridgeman Art Library Nationality. 287 ©Arnaud Chicurel/Hemis/Corbis. 288 ©The Gallery Collection/ Corbis. 289 ©Columbia/The Kobal Collection. 290 ©Jon Arnold/JAI/Corbis. 291 ©Sergiy Koshevarov/ StockPhotoPro. 292 ©Photolibrary. 294 ©Paul Seheult/ Eye Ubiquitous/Corbis. 295 ©Perutskyi Petro/ Shutterstock Photos. 296 ©Gregory Wrona/Alamy. 299 ©Michael Dunning/Photographer's Choice/Getty Images. 304 ©Grand Tour/Corbis. 306 (b) ©Gerd Ludwig/Corbis (bkg) ©Photolibrary (c) ©Gordon Wiltsie, National Geographic Stock (t) ©Rebecca Hale, National Geographic Stock. 309 ©Klaus Nigge/National Geographic Stock. 310 (bkg) ©Menno Boermans/Aurora Photos/Corbis (br) ©Bruno Morandi/Robert Harding World Imagery/Corbis (tl) ©Maxim Toporskiy/Alamy. 312 ©Denis Sinyakov/Reuters/Corbis. 314 ©Cary Wolinsky/ National Geographic Stock. 316 ©National Geographic Stock. 318 ©Gerd Ludwig/National Geographic Stock. 319 (tl) ©U.S. Geological Survey (tr) ©NASA. 320 (l) ©Sisse Brimberg/National Geographic Society (r) ©James L. Stanfield/National Geographic Society. 321 (l) ©Massimo Pizzotti/Getty (r) ©Dallas and John Heaton/ Photolibrary. 322 ©Richard Klune/Corbis. 323 ©imagebroker/Alamy. 324 ©The Bridgeman Art Library (r) ©Cary Wolinsky/National Geographic Society. 325 (l) ©The Bridgeman Art Library. 326 ©North Wind Picture Archives/Alamy. 328 (l) ©Bettmann/Corbis (r) ©The Art Archive. 329 (b) ©Bettmann/Corbis (t) ©Thomas Johnson/Sygma/Corbis. 332 ©Paul Harris/JAI/Corbis. 334 ©Arne Hodalic/Corbis. 335 (tc) ©Michael Runkel/Robert Harding World Imagery/Corbis (tr) ©Maria Stenzel/ National Geographic Stock (tr) ©Sean Sprague/ Photolibrary. 336 ©Olaf Meinhardt/Visum/Fotofinder. 339 ©Kristel Richard/Grand Tour/Corbis. 340 ©Shepard Sherbell/Corbis Saba. 342 ©Imagesource/Photolibrary. 344 ©Oleg Nikishin/Stringer/Getty Images. 347 (c) ©iStockphoto ©Michael Dunning/Photographer's Choice/Getty Images. 352 ©iStockphoto. 354 (b) ©Ingo Arndt/Minden Pictures/National Geographic Stock (bkg) ©David Alan Harvey/National Geographic Stock (c) ©Mitsuaki Iwago/Minden Pictures/National Geographic Stock (t) ©Kakenya Ntaiya. 357 ©Top-Pics TBK/Alamy. 358 (bkg) ©Menno Boermans/Aurora Photos/Corbis (bl) ©tbkmedia/Alamy (tr) ©Michael Poliza/National Geographic Stock. 360 ©Michael Nichols/National Geographic Stock. 362 ©Philippe Bourseiller/Getty Images. 364 ©Ian Nichols/National Geographic Stock. 366 ©Mike Hutchings/Reuters. 368 (bc) ©Beverly Joubert/National Geographic Stock (bl) ©Beverly Joubert/ National Geographic Stock. 370 ©Gerald Hoberman/ Hoberman Collection UK/Photolibrary. 372 (bl) ©The Trustees of the British Museum/Art Resource (br) ©ADB Travel/dbimages/Alamy. 373 ©HIP/Art Resource. 376 ©Private Collection/Look and Learn/The Bridgeman Art Library International. 377 (bl) ©Mary Evans Picture Library/The Image Works (br) ©Bruce Dale/National Geographic Stock. 378 (bc) ©James L. Stanfield/National Geographic Stock (bl) ©Tim Laman/National Geographic Stock (bkg) ©George Steinmetz/National Geographic Stock (br) ©Annie Griffiths/National Geographic Stock. 379 (bcl) ©Roy Toft/National Geographic Stock (bcr) ©Tino Soriano/National Geographic Stock (bl) ©Jodi Cobb/National Geographic Stock (br) ©Ed Kashi/ National Geographic Stock. 382 ©Ralph Lee Hopkins/



National Geographic Stock. 384 ©Vanessa Burger/Images of Africa Photobank Alamy. 386 ©Paul Gilham–FIFA/ FIFA via Getty Images. 387 ©David Alan Harvey/ National Geographic Stock. 388 (bc) ©Nigel Pavitt/John Warburton-Lee Photography/Alamy (bl) ©Sean Sprague/ Still Pictures/Photolibrary. 389 (cl) ©Michael Nichols/ National Geographic Stock (tr) ©Suzi Eszterhas/Minden Pictures/National Geographic Stock. 390 ©Jane Goodall Institute. 391 (bkg) ©Gerry Ellis/ Minden Pictures/ National Geographic Stock (br) ©Wade Davis/Ryan Hill. 392 ©Finbarr O'Reilly/Reuters. 394 ©George Steinmetz/ Corbis. 396 (b) ©Pascal Maitre/National Geographic Stock (tr) ©Joerg Boethling/Alamy. 398 ©Louise Gubb/ Corbis. 399 ©Michael Dunning/Photographer's Choice/ Getty Images. 400 ©Frederic Courbet/Still Pictures/ Photolibrary. 402 ©Ulrich Doering/Alamy. 403 ©Trinity Mirror/Mirrorpix/Alamy. 406 (bl) ©Chris Stenger/FN/ Minden Pictures/National Geographic Stock (br) ©Walker, Lewis W./National Geographic Stock. 407 (bkg) ©Clement Philippe/Arterra Picture Library/Alamy (bkg) ©Tim Fitzharris/Minden Pictures/National Geographic Stock (cf) ©Mattias Klum /National Geographic Stock (l) ©Tom Vezo/Minden Pictures/National Geographic Stock (rbkg) ©Ted Wood/Aurora Photos (rf) ©Thomas Lehne/ Alamy. 408 ©Anup Shah/Corbis. 410 (b) ©Martin Gray/ National Geographic Stock (bkg) ©Smar Jodha/National Geographic My Shot/National Geographic Stock (c) ©David Boyer/National Geographic Stock (t) ©Thomas Culhane. 413 ©Vanessa Lefort/National Geographic My Shot/National Geographic Stock. 414 (bkg) ©Menno Boermans/Aurora Photos/Corbis (cl) ©Gary Cook/Alamy (cr) ©Peter Adams/Getty Images. 416 ©Ed Kashi/National Geographic Stock. 418 ©Fischer Gunter/WoodyStock/ Alamy. 420 ©Chris Bradley/Axiom/photolibrary. 422 (bl) ©Victor R. Boswell, Jr/National Geographic Stock (br) ©Scala/Art Resource 423 (bl) ©Erich Lessing/Art Resource (br) ©Corbis. 424 ©Richard Nowitz/National Geographic Stock. 425 ©Oliver Weiken/epa/Corbis. 426 ©Bachmann Bachmann/F1 Online/photolibrary. 427 (bl) ©James Brunker/Alamy (tr) ©Kordcom Kordcom/age fotostock/photolibrary. 428 ©Yann Arthus-Bertrand/ Corbis. 429 ©The Art Archive/Topkapi Museum Istanbul/Dagli Orti. 430 ©Gwill Owen/Sylvia Cordaiy Photo Library Ltd /Alamy. 431 ©NASA/JSC/Gateway to Astronaut Photography of Earth. 432 (bl) ©Paul Sutcliffe/ Alamy. (br) ©Erich Lessing/Art Resource. 433 (bc) ©Mary Jelliffe/Ancient Art & Architecture Collection Ltd./ Alamy (tr) ©Kenneth Garrett/National Geographic Stock. 434 ©Kenneth Garrett/National Geographic Stock. 438 ©Keren Su/Corbis. 440 ©Alberto Arzoz/Axiom/Aurora Photos. 441 ©Walter Bibikow/Jon Arnold Images Ltd./ Alamy. 442 ©Gavin Hellier/Alamy. 443 ©David Bathgate/ Corbis. 444 (b) ©Radius Images/Corbis (bl) ©G. Anker. 445 ©Hanan Isachar/Corbis. 446 ©NASA/Science Faction/Corbis. 447 ©Matthias Seifert/Reuters/Corbis. 449 (tr) ©Umit Bektas/Reuters/Corbis ©Felipe Trueba/ epa european pressphoto agency. 450 ©Mohammad Berno/Document Iran/Corbis. 452 ©David Rubinger/ Time & Life Pictures/Getty Images. 454 ©Sabah Arar/ AFP/Getty Images. 457 ©Tim Gurney/Alamy. 459 ©Shehzad Noorani/Stillpictures/Aurora Photos. 463 ©Mark Thiessen/National Geographic Stock. 464 ©Bildarchiv Preussischer Kulturbesitz/Art Resource. 466 (b) ©Peter Adams/Corbis (bkg) ©Tibor Bognar/ agefotostock (c) ©Kenji Kondo/epa/Corbis (t) ©Hussain RAE photos. 469 ©Lynn M. Stone/Nature Picture Library. 470 (bkg) ©Menno Boermans/Aurora Photos/Corbis (bl) ©Tiziana and Gianni Baldizzone/Corbis (l) ©Dinodia Images/Alamy (tc) ©Stephen Sharnoff/National Geographic Stock. 472 (bkg) ©Bobby Model/National Geographic Stock (l) ©James L. Stanfield/National Geographic Stock. 474 ©Frederic Soltan/Sygma/Corbis. 476 ©Lynsey Addario/National Geographic Image Collection. 478 ©Prakash Singh/AFP/Getty Image. 479 ©Blue Legacy International. 481 ©Michael Dunning/ Photographer's Choice/Getty Images. 482 ©Luca Tettoni/ Corbis. 483 (b) ©The Schoyen Collection (t) ©The Schoyen Collection. 484 (l) ©Silvio Fiore/SuperStock (r) ©The Trustees of the British Museum. 485 ©Thomas Retterath/Getty Images. 488 ©Jeremy Horner/Corbis. 489 ©Lineair/Photolibrary. 490 ©Bettmann/Corbis. 491 ©Art Directors & TRIP/Alamy. 494 ©Harish Tyagi/epa/Corbis. 496 ©Louise Batalla Duran/Alamy. 497 ©Bruce Dale/ National Geographic Stock. 498 (bkg) ©Ed Kashi/ National Geographic Stock (l) ©Jodi Cobb/National Geographic Stock. 500 ©Ajay Verma/Reuters/Corbis. 501 (b) ©Foodfolio–StockFood Munich (t) ©Abraham Nowitz/National Geographic Stock. 502 (bkg) ©David Cumming/Eye Ubiquitous/Corbis (bl) ©Robert Wallis/ Corbis (bc) ©Stephen Romilly/Alamy. 503 (b) ©Dharma Productions/The Kobal Collection (t) ©Frazer Harrison/ Getty Images. 504 ©Eric Feferberg/Pool/Reuters. 506 ©Fredrik Renander/Alamy. 507 (t1) ©Ed Kashi/National Geographic Stock (t2) ©Ed Kashi/National Geographic Stock (t2) ©Fridmar Damm/Corbis (t3) ©Akhtar Soomro/ Deanpictures/The Image Works (t4) ©Akhtar Soomro/ Deanpictures/The Image Works (t5) ©Andrew Holbrooke/ Corbis (t7) ©National Geographic Maps (t8) ©National Geographic Maps. 508 ©Ed Kashi/National Geographic Image Collection. 510 ©Sajjad Hussain/AFP/Getty Images. 511 ©Dinodia Photo Library. 512 ©Akhtar Soomro/Deanpictures/The Image Works. 514 ©Andrew Holbrooke/Corbis. 522 (b) ©Michael Nichols/National Geographic Stock (bkg) ©George Steinmetz/National Geographic Stock (c) ©Gavin Hellier/Alamy (t) ©Albert Lin. 525 ©Mitsuaki Iwago/Minden Pictures/National Geographic Stock. 526 (b) ©Chun Ki Leung/National Geographic My Shot /National Geographic Stock (bkg) ©Menno Boermans/Aurora Photos/Corbis (t) ©Wang Jianjun/TAO Images Limited/Alamy. 528 ©Fritz Hoffmann/National Geographic Stock. 530 ©Reuters/ Mainichi Shimbun. 532 ©Toby Adamson/Axiom Photographic Agency/Getty Images. 534 ©Alison Wright/ National Geographic Stock. 536 (b) ©Unterthiner, Stefano/National Geographic Stock (cl) ©Katsufumi Sato/National Geographic Society. 538 (bl) ©Richard Swiecki/Royal Ontario Museum/Corbis (br) ©Ira Block/ National Geographic Stock. 539 (bc) ©O. Louis Mazzatenta/National Geographic Stock (tc) ©Atlantide Phototravel/Corbis. 540 (bc) ©Michael S. Yamashita/ National Geographic Stock (bl) ©Justin Guariglia/ National Geographic Stock (bkg) ©O. Louis Mazzatenta/ National Geographic Stock (br) ©Michael S. Yamashita/ National Geographic Stock. 541 (bcl) ©Kenneth Ginn/ National Geographic Stock (bcr) ©Kate Staszczak/ National Geographic My Shot/National Geographic Stock (bl) ©Michael S. Yamashita/National Geographic Stock (br) ©Ira Block/National Geographic Stock. 542 ©Shiwei/ Best View Stock/photolibrary. 544 ©Redlink/Corbis. 546 (bkg) ©Gregory A. Harlin/National Geographic Stock (b) ©National Geographic Maps. 548 ©Wendy Connett/ Alamy. 549 ©Rob Howard/Corbis. 550 ©Ira Block/ National Geographic Stock. 551 ©Ira Block/National Geographic Stock. 552 ©Asian Art & Archaeology, Inc./ Corbis. 553 (b) ©Private Collection/Peter Newark Military Pictures/The Bridgeman Art Library International. 554 (bl) ©H. Edward Kim/National Geographic Stock (br) ©Korea News Service/Reuters/ Corbis. 555 (bl) ©John Van Hasselt/Sygma/Corbis ©(br) ©The Trustees of The British Museum/Art Resource. 556

# ACKNOWLEDGMENTS | TEACHER'S EDITION

## Photographic Credits

## Map Credits

## Illustrator Credit

## Front Cover: